ENGINEERING
ANALYSIS

PRENTICE-HALL ENGINEERING SCIENCE SERIES

Hall and Ibele, *Engineering Thermodynamics*
Li, *Engineering Analysis*
Shames, *Engineering Mechanics: Statics*
Shames, *Engineering Mechanics: Dynamics*
Shames, *Engineering Mechanics: Statics and Dynamics*

ENGINEERING ANALYSIS

WEN-HSIUNG LI

Professor of Civil Engineering
Syracuse University

1960

PRENTICE-HALL, INC.,
Englewood Cliffs, N.J.

Library of Congress Catalog Card Number : 60-12245

PRINTED IN THE UNITED STATES OF AMERICA

27723—C

PREFACE

The material covered in this book has been the basis of a course taught by the author at The Johns Hopkins University. Its purpose is to present mathematics, as a technical language and a practical tool, to engineering undergraduates. Examples of this application of mathematics are drawn from various branches of engineering and physics. The student is trained to formulate problems mathematically and to arrive at their solutions.

The student will need only an elementary knowledge of the Calculus as a prerequisite. In fact, the material covered in the first three chapters has been so arranged that it can be taught to students who are taking Integral Calculus concurrently. Chapter 4 is self-contained and can be used as a text for an introductory course of ordinary differential equations.

WEN-HSIUNG LI

CONTENTS

CHAPTER 4. ORDINARY DIFFERENTIAL EQUATIONS 197

CHAPTER 5. FOURIER SERIES 339

INDEX 357

ENGINEERING
ANALYSIS

CHAPTER 1

APPLICATIONS OF DIFFERENTIAL CALCULUS

1–1. Introduction

Engineering analysis is the process of arriving at an answer to an engineering problem. As the factors influencing an engineering problem may be social or economic, as well as physical, a working knowledge of the fundamental principles governing these factors is necessary for successful engineering analysis. Many engineering problems are quantitative in nature. In the analysis of these problems, it is desirable, and very often necessary, to employ mathematical principles. The application of mathematical principles in engineering analysis forms the subject matter of this book.

Mathematics has a dual role in engineering analysis. First, it is a language for describing concisely and precisely the basic principles of physical and other phenomena. For example, physical laws can be described with mathematical formulas. Secondly, mathematics is a tool for obtaining a quantitative answer from the basic formulas. The engineering student should learn to speak in this language and to use this tool with ease.

Although this book deals with the language and the use of mathematics, it is not a book in mathematics. Mathematics deals with concise and rigorous proof of theorems, while the aim of engineering application is to obtain a quantitative answer. Thus, in engineering analysis, certain assumptions and approximations may be made, through necessity or for economy of time and effort of computation, as long as the result remains accurate enough for the intended purpose. However, this does not mean that rigor has no place in engineering analysis. On the contrary, without a rigorous mathematical basis, each step in the analysis will be uncertain; and, when approximations are made, the degree of accuracy of the result will be difficult to ascertain. As the student grows in his ability to apply his mathematical knowledge, he will increasingly feel the need of further study of mathematical theories.

1–2. Functions

In analysis, the engineer must deal with the relationship existing between different quantities. When the value of one quantity varies with the values of other quantities, the former is said to be a *function* of the latter, and these quantities are also said to have a functional relationship among them. For instance, if the power consumption C of a community depends on the population P, the temperature T, and so on, then we can write

$$C = f(P, T, \ldots)$$

Here, f stands for "function of," and is identically equal to C. A shorter method of expression is often used: $C(P, T, \ldots)$ which reads "C is a function of P, T, etc."

In the expression above, C is usually referred to as the *dependent variable*, and P, T, ... as the *independent variables*. By this, we imply that, if a set of values of P, T, ... is known, the corresponding value of C is determined. Since C, P, T, ... are related to one another, we can also write $P(C, T, \ldots)$, instead of $C(P, T, \ldots)$. The same relationship should enable one to compute the population P of the community, if its power consumption C, etc. are known, and vice versa. Thus, which quantity is the dependent variable depends on the point of view. Perhaps a more general expression is

$$F(C, P, T, \ldots) = 0$$

which may be read as "C, P, T, ... are functionally related." In this form, any one of the variables is said to be an *implicit function* of the other variables. For example, the following expressions indicate the same relationship among the variables x, y, and z:

$$x(y, z) = \frac{z^2}{2 + 3y}$$

$$y(x, z) = \frac{1}{3}\left(\frac{z^2}{x} - 2\right)$$

$$z(x, y) = \pm\sqrt{2x + 3xy}$$

$$F(x, y, z) = 2x + 3xy - z^2 = 0$$

Note that $x(y, z)$ and $y(x, z)$ are single-valued, while $z(x, y)$ is multi-valued. In the latter case, the analyst has to decide whether all the values are valid in a given problem.

In a particular problem, the engineer has to know the purpose of the investigation, in order to decide how many variables are to be included in the analysis. Very often, it is impossible to include, or even realize, all the factors involved. Some of the factors involved may not be important for a particular problem, and therefore can be neglected. Sometimes, one or more variables may have constant values in a particular problem, and are no longer variables in the analysis. For example, if the problem is to find the influence of weather on power consumption of a particular community, P may be considered to be constant, and therefore is not a variable in $C(T, \ldots)$. Thus, even for the same phenomenon, the number of factors to be taken into account depends on the purpose of the investigation and the desired accuracy of the result.

A functional relationship may be expressed in words, with tables of corresponding values of the variables, with graphs, or with formulas. While other ways of expression may be suitable for particular purposes, the use of formulas or equations is the most, and sometimes the only, suitable way for analysis. When equations are utilized, the symbols and units used for the variables must first be defined. When coordinate axes are used, their directions and the position of the origin must be clearly indicated.

Very often, a formula holds only within certain limits of the variables, and yields erroneous results outside these limits of validity. In using a formula, especially an empirical one, it is therefore extremely important to know its limits of validity. On the other hand, by limiting the validity of formulas within finite ranges of the variables, one can often describe a function with two or more simple formulas instead of a complicated one. See Example 1–1 below.

Example 1–1. The number of a certain article in stock in a store is shown graphically in Fig. 1–1. Starting with 1000 units, the stock decreases linearly with time to 200 in 20 days. The stock is then immediately replenished to 1000 units and the process repeats. Find an expression for the stock as a function of time.

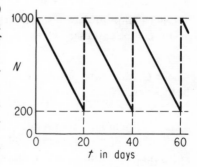

Fig. 1–1

Let t=time in days, and $N(t)$=number of units in stock at any time. In this case, it is convenient to use separate equations for the function $N(t)$, each valid for a different range of t.

For $0 < t < 20$, since N is known to vary linearly with t, we have

$$N = b_1 + m_1 t \qquad \text{(for } 0 < t < 20)$$

where b_1 and m_1 are constants whose values are to be determined. Since $N(0) = 1000$ and $N(20) = 200$ (here, $N(20)$ reads "the value of N at $t = 20$"), the values of b_1 and m_1 must be such that

$$1000 = b_1 + 0$$
$$200 = b_1 + 20m_1$$

giving $b_1 = 1000$ and $m_1 = -40$. Thus

$$N = 1000 - 40t \qquad \text{(for } 0 < t < 20)$$

Similarly, for $20 < t < 2 \times 20$, we have $N = b_2 + m_2 t$. With $N(20) = 1000$ and $N(40) = 200$, we must have $b_2 = 1800$ and $m_2 = -40$. Thus

$$N = 1800 - 40t$$

or

$$N = 1000 - 40(t - 20) \qquad \text{(for } 20 < t < 2 \times 20)$$

Note the similarity between this equation and that for the first cycle. It can be easily seen that, in general, for $20n < t < 20(n+1)$,

$$N = 1000 - 40(t - 20n)$$

Thus the function $N(t)$ is described with separate equations with n taking the values 0, 1, 2, 3, ..., one value for each cycle.

Example 1–2. The observed weight of a decomposing mass of radioactive material is shown in the table. See if the weight can be expressed by an exponential decay formula.

Time	Weight W in grams	$\log_{10} W$
Jan. 1, 1900	2.00	0.301
1910	1.78	0.250
1920	1.59	0.204
1930	1.41	0.149
1940	1.26	0.100
1950	1.12	0.049
1960	1.00	0.000

Let $t =$ time in decades, with $t = 0$ on Jan. 1, 1900. If the weight $W(t)$ in grams can be expressed by the exponential decay formula

$$W = Ce^{-kt}$$

where C and k are positive constants, we have, by taking the logarithms of both sides,

$$\log W = \log C - (k \log e)t$$

This is a linear equation relating the variables $\log W$ and t. If this equation is correct, the plot of the observed $\log W$ vs t should form a straight line. This is found to be the case, as shown in Fig. 1–2. To determine the values of $\log C$ and $k \log e$ in the linear equation, use the values of $\log W$ and t of any two points on the line (not necessarily the observed points), such as A and B:

$$0.301 = \log C - 0$$
$$0.000 = \log C - (k \log e)6$$

giving $\log C = 0.301$ or $C = 2.00$, and $k = \log C/6 \log e = 0.116$. Thus

$$W = 2.00e^{-0.116t}$$

Note that three significant figures are used in the values of C and k because the known values involved in the multiplication and division in their determination are accurate to three figures. Also note that, on the right-hand side of Fig. 1–2, a logarithmic scale of W is shown. It can be seen that the same plot is obtained either by plotting log W on natural scale, or by plotting W on logarithmic scale. To save the work of looking up logarithms of numbers, coordinate papers with one or both coordinates in logarithmic scale are made available commercially. They are known as semi-log and log-log papers, respectively.

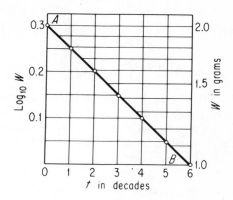

Fig. 1–2

Problems

1–1. The temperature T in °C varies along a 2-cm long hot filament. Let x be the distance in cm from one end of the filament. Find an empirical expression for $T(x)$ to describe the following observation: $T(0) = 50$, $T(1) = 500$, $T(2) = 50$, and the temperature varies linearly from the midpoint to the ends of the filament.

Ans. $T = 50 + 450x$, for $0 < x < 1$; etc.

1–2. The population of a certain city has been observed to vary with time. From the given data, see if the relationship can be expressed as $P = Ae^{ct}$, where A and c are constants. If so, determine A and c.

Time	Population P in millions
Jan. 1, 1900	0.50
1920	0.75
1940	1.11
1960	1.66

1–3. The discharge Q of water over the spillway of a reservoir is observed to be related to the head H above the crest of the spillway as shown in Fig. 1–3. From the observed data, see if the relationship can be expressed as $Q = KH^n$, where K and n are constants. If so, find the values of K and n.

H in ft	Q in cu ft per sec
1.00	100
2.00	284
3.00	519
4.00	801

Ans. $Q = 100H^{1.50}$

Fig. 1–3   Fig. 1–4

1–4. Express the volume $V(h, H, W, D)$ enclosed in the building shown in Fig. 1–4. If all buildings under consideration are so proportioned that $H=0.6W$ and $h=0.4W$, express V with the least possible number of variables.

Ans. $V=0.8W^2D$

1–5. A car starts from rest and its speed v (in mph) increases linearly with time t (in sec) to 40 mph in 10 sec. The speed then remains constant for an hour, after which it decreases linearly with time, to come to rest in 5 sec. Express $v(t)$.

1–6. Given $f(x)=x^3+2x-5$, find $f(0)$ and $f(1)$. With $f(xy)$ denoting the result of substituting xy for x in the formula for $f(x)$, find $f(xy)$ and $f(x)\cdot f(y)$. Are the results equal?

1–3. Checking equations

When equations are used to express the relationship among variables, it is obviously desirable to check the correctness of the expression. Two obvious ways of checking are (1) checking the limiting cases, and (2) dimensional checking.

An expression $f(x)$ should yield a correct value or values of f for any given value of x within the range of validity. In many cases, the values of $f(x)$ are known for some particular values of x. To be correct, the expression $f(x)$ must at least yield these known values of $f(x)$ at the corresponding values of x. For example, let it be given that the amount R of a mass of disintegrating radium at any time t is

$$R = R_0 e^{-kt} \tag{1–1}$$

where R_0 and k are positive constants for a particular case. We know that, as time goes on indefinitely, the amount of radium is supposed to be reduced to zero. Also, we know that we have a certain amount of radium to start with. To be correct, Eq. (1–1) must therefore give a positive value of R at $t=0$, and give $R=0$ at $t=+\infty$. These conditions are satisfied by the equation. However, this does not mean that the expression is correct for other values of t. In other words, these conditions are *necessary* conditions for the expression to be correct, but are not *sufficient* conditions. (The terms necessary condition and sufficient condition are encountered very often in the study of mathematics. To get a simple meaning of these terms, consider the following statements: "To pay for the annual tuition fee here, it is necessary, but not sufficient, to have one dollar. For the same purpose, it is sufficient, but not necessary, to have one million dollars. It is necessary and sufficient to have an amount equal to the tuition fee. To be admitted to this school, it is not necessary and not sufficient to be a good athlete.") If a formula does not satisfy these necessary conditions, one can be sure that the formula cannot be valid in a range including these limiting cases. This information, though negative in nature, is useful for detection of some mistakes in analysis.

Another check is performed by examining the dimensions of the terms in an equation. All quantities can be expressed in terms of some quantities regarded as "fundamental" quantities. For example, in the study of kinematics, all quantities involved can be expressed in terms of length $[L]$ and time $[T]$. For instance, speed is expressed in terms of length per unit time, such as mph, ft per sec, cm per sec, etc. In this case, length and time are called the fundamental quantities, and the *dimensions* of speed are $[L/T]$ or $[L^1 T^{-1}]$. All correct equations should be dimensionally homogeneous; i.e., all terms in an equation should be of the same dimensions. For example, for a particle travelling linearly away from the origin at a constant speed v, its distance from the origin at any time t is

$$S = S_0 + vt \qquad (1-2)$$

where S_0 is the value of S at $t = 0$. This equation is dimensionally homogeneous, because the dimension of each term is $[L]$. It is thus possible to detect some mistakes in analysis by checking the dimensional homogeneity of the equations.

Note that the validity of a dimensionally homogeneous equation is independent of the units used, as long as the same units for the fundamental quantities are used in all quantities involved. Equation (1-2) is valid when the unit of length is the mile and the unit of time is the hour (S and S_0 in miles, t in hours, and v in mph). It is equally valid when S and S_0 are in feet, t in seconds, and v in ft per sec. For another example, take Eq. (1-1). Since the term R is a weight, the other term $R_0 e^{-kt}$ must also be a weight. Since e is a number, and therefore dimensionless, R_0 must be a weight, and k must have the dimension $[T^{-1}]$ so that kt is dimensionless. The validity of Eq. (1-1) is independent of the units used for weight and time.

It should be mentioned that not all equations encountered in engineering practice are dimensionally homogeneous in appearance. Many empirical formulas are being used which are valid only with a particular set of units under some specified conditions. For example, for a particular case with $v = 30$ mph and $S_0 = 0$ at $t = 0$, Eq. (1-2) becomes $S = 30t$. This formula is not dimensionally homogeneous in appearance. It is valid only for these particular values of v and S_0, and S must be expressed in miles and t in hours. Actually, the number 30 represents a quantity with the dimensions $[L/T]$. To facilitate dimensional checking in analysis, it is therefore wise, whenever convenient, to represent all the quantities with symbols and substitute their numerical values in the particular problem at the end of the analysis.

Although these checks do not prove the correctness of the analysis, they help to reveal some of the mistakes that may have been made in the analysis. The student should develop the habit of checking his equations frequently. If it is more convenient to use numerical values for some of the quantities in the analysis, the units used must be clearly stated. These units should be consistent with the units of the other quantities in the equation.

Example 1–3. Three marks, A, B, and C, are established along a straight line on the shore. A boat is sailing along a line through C, perpendicular to the line ABC. The distance S from the point C to the boat varies with the angle γ, as shown in Fig. 1–5. Given that B is $\frac{1}{6}$ mile from C and A is $\frac{1}{2}$ mile from C, see if it is feasible to determine S in feet from an observed value of γ.

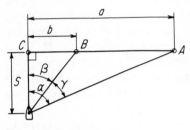

Fig. 1–5

Let a and b represent the distances AC and BC, respectively. The problem is to find S as a function of γ. Since $\gamma = \alpha - \beta$, and S can easily be related to α and β through cot $\alpha = S/a$ and cot $\beta = S/b$, we have

$$\cot \gamma = \cot (\alpha - \beta) = \frac{1 + \cot \alpha \cdot \cot \beta}{\cot \beta - \cot \alpha} = \frac{1}{a-b}\left(S + \frac{ab}{S}\right)$$

From this, one can solve for $S(\gamma)$, if necessary.

This result can be checked for the limiting cases when $S=0$ and $S=\infty$, since one knows by inspection that $\gamma = 0$ in both cases. When $S=0$ or $S=\infty$, the equation yields cot $\gamma = \infty$ or $\gamma = 0$.

An angle, being the ratio of the length of the subtending arc to the radius of a circle, has no dimension. Dimensionally, it may be represented by $[L^0]$ or $[1]$. Similarly, a trigonometric function of an angle is also dimensionless. The result above is dimensionally correct, since dimensionally S is $[L]$. So are ab/S and $a-b$. Thus both sides of the equation are dimensionless.

In this equation, all lengths must be expressed in the same unit. Let S be expressed in feet. Then $a=2640$ ft ($\frac{1}{2}$ mile), and $b=880$ ft ($\frac{1}{6}$ mile). Thus, in this particular case,

$$\cot \gamma = \frac{1}{1760}\left(S + \frac{2{,}323{,}200}{S}\right)$$

This equation is plotted as Fig. 1–6. For a given value of γ, there are generally two values of S. In order to determine which of the two values should be used, the variation of γ with S should also be observed. The distance S

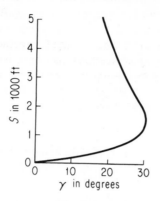

Fig. 1–6

cannot be accurately determined when γ is near 30°. More accurate results are obtained when S is less than about 1000 ft.

Example 1–4. A piston is connected to a crank through a connecting rod, as shown in Fig. 1–7. The crank rotates about point B. Point A is the extreme position of the piston, and S is the dis-placement of the piston from point A. Find the position of the piston as a function of the position of the crank; i.e., $S(\theta)$.

Since point A is the position of the piston when the angle θ is zero, the dis-tance AB must be $(L+R+h)$. At any angle θ,

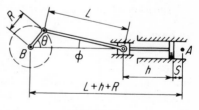

Fig. 1–7

$$S = (L+R+h)-h-L \cos \phi - R \cos \theta = L(1-\cos \phi)+R(1-\cos \theta)$$

In this expression, S, ϕ, and θ are variables. However, the value of $\cos \phi$ is related to the angle θ:

$$L \sin \phi = R \sin \theta$$

or

$$\cos \phi = \sqrt{1-\sin^2 \phi} = \sqrt{1-\left(\frac{R}{L} \sin \theta\right)^2}$$

Therefore

$$S = L\left[1-\sqrt{1-\left(\frac{R}{L} \sin \theta\right)^2}\right] + R(1-\cos \theta)$$

This expression is dimensionally correct. For the limiting cases when $\theta=0$ and $\theta=2\pi$, we know by inspection that $S=0$. Also, when $\theta=\pi$, we must have $S=2R$. These conditions are satisfied by this equation.

Problems

1–7. An unstretched elastic string 2 in. in length is attached to a pair of scissors, as shown in Fig. 1–8. The maximum value of the angle θ between the two blades is 120°. Express the length L of the stretched string as a function of θ. State the limits of validity of the expression. Knowing that L is $5\sqrt{2}$ in. when $\theta=90°$, check your answer with this case.

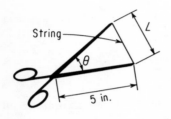

Fig. 1–8

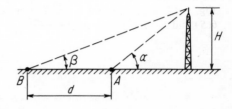

Fig. 1–9

1–8. The elevation of the top of an antenna is located with an angle α at a fixed point A, as shown in Fig. 1–9. The angle β observed at another point B depends on its distance d from A. Given the height of the tower H, find angle β as a function of d. Check your result with limiting cases when $d=0$ and $d=\infty$.

$$Ans. \quad \beta=\cot^{-1}\left(\cot\alpha+\frac{d}{H}\right)$$

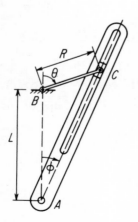

Fig. 1–10

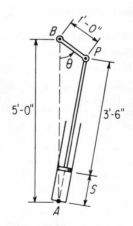

Fig. 1–11

1–9. A crank of length R with a sliding block C is rotating about point B, as shown in Fig. 1–10. The block C is sliding in the slot of a slotted lever which is hinged at point A at a distance L from B. Find the position of the lever as a function of the position of the crank; i.e., $\phi(\theta)$. Check your result with the limiting cases when $\theta = 0$, π, and 2π.

$$Ans. \quad \phi = \tan^{-1} \frac{R \sin \theta}{R \cos \theta + L}$$

1–10. A cylinder is hinged at its bottom A, as shown in Fig. 1–11. The piston is connected to a crank at the pin P. The crank rotates about point B. The dimensions of the system are shown in the sketch. Find the distance S as a function of the angle θ. Check your result with $\theta = 0$, π, and 2π.

$$Ans. \quad S \text{ in ft} = \sqrt{26 - 10 \cos \theta} - 3.5$$

1–11. In laying out a circular arc of radius R for the centerline of a highway, a point on the curve is located with a chord L and a deflection angle θ, as shown in Fig. 1–12. The values of θ and L depend on the length S of the curve. Find $\theta(S)$ and $L(S)$. Check your result with $\theta = \pi/2$.

$$Ans. \quad \theta = \frac{S}{2R}, \quad L = 2R \sin \left(\frac{S}{2R} \right)$$

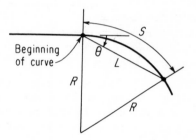

Fig. 1–12

1–4. The limit of a function

When a functional relationship is expressed with an equation, the value of the function for certain values of the variable may not be readily determined. For example, $f(x) = (\sin x)/x$ gives $f(0) = 0/0$, which is indeterminate. However, as the value of x becomes closer and closer to zero, the value of the function f becomes closer and closer to unity, as shown in the table and Fig. 1–13.

x	$\dfrac{\sin x}{x}$
$+0.5$	0.9589
$+0.1$	0.9983
$+0.01$	0.999998
$\cdots$	$\cdots$
-0.01	0.999998
-0.1	0.9983
-0.5	0.9589

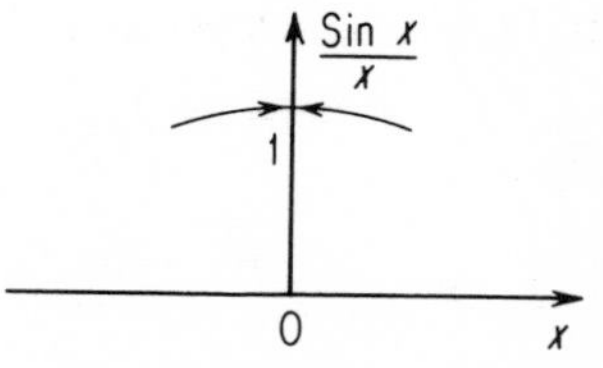

Fig. 1–13

For another example:

$$F(x) = \left| \sin \cdot x + \frac{\sin 2x}{2} + \frac{\sin 3x}{3} + \ldots + \frac{\sin nx}{n} \right|, \quad n \gg 1$$

Here, the symbol $|\ \ |$ signifies the absolute value of the quantity inside the bars, and the expression $n \gg 1$ means that n is a very large number. $F(x)$ is

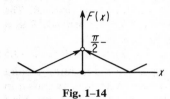

Fig. 1-14

shown graphically in Fig. 1–14. When x gets very close to zero, F becomes very close to $\pi/2$. Yet $F(0)=0$. These values of 1 and about $\pi/2$ for $f(x)$ and $F(x)$, respectively, are called the *limits* of these functions as the variable x approaches, but is not equal to, a certain value, zero in these particular cases. In engineering analysis, these limits are of greater interest than the actual value of the function, if any, at exactly these particular points. The reason for this is that the mathematical expression is only a model or representation of the actual phenomenon. It is the limit of a function that is the better representation. Furthermore, one seldom encounters in reality the variable assuming exactly a certain value.

It should be mentioned that a function may not approach a limit at some of these points of irregular behavior. For example,

$$G(x) = \cos x \cdot \cos \left(\frac{1}{x} \right)$$

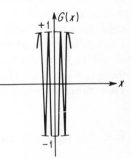

Fig. 1-15

Here $G(0)$ is not defined, and $G(x)$ fluctuates between $+1$ and -1 when x approaches zero, as shown in Fig. 1–15. There is no limit for $G(x)$ as x approaches zero.

In the first example, with $f(x)=(\sin x)/x$, we have seen that we can reduce the difference between $f(x)$ and the limit of the function, 1, to a value as small as desired by bringing the value of x sufficiently close to the value zero. For example, if we want this difference reduced to 0.000,002 or less, we can accomplish this by using $|x-0| \leqslant 0.01$. This fact is used to form a definition of the limit of a function: if, for any positive number ϵ, however small (such as 0.000,002), there exists a positive number δ (such as 0.01) such that

$$|f(x)-A| < \epsilon \quad \text{when} \quad |x-a| \leqslant \delta$$

then

$$\lim_{x \to a} f(x) = A \tag{1-3}$$

Here, the symbol $\lim_{x \to a} f(x)$ reads "the limit of $f(x)$ as the value of x approaches the value of a." Note that $f(a)$ may or may not exist, and, if $f(a)$ exists, it may or may not be equal to the limit A.

Many quantities are defined as the limit of a function. For example, the average speed v of a car during a period τ, beginning at $t=t_1$, is the ratio of the distance L travelled during τ, to τ. Since L varies with τ, we have the average speed as a function of τ: $v(\tau)=L(\tau)/\tau$. The instantaneous speed at $t=t_1$ is defined as the average speed with $\tau \to 0$ ($\tau \neq 0$; with $\tau=0$, we would have $L(0)=0$ and $v(0)=0/0$). In other words, the instantaneous speed is defined as $\lim\limits_{\tau \to 0} \dfrac{L(\tau)}{\tau}$. As another example, take the density at a point of a "continuous" material. The density is defined as $\lim\limits_{V \to 0} \dfrac{M(V)}{V}$, where V is a volume of the material enclosing the point in question, and M is the mass of the material enclosed in V. (Physically, this problem is complicated by the fact that materials are not continuous, but consist of separate molecules. Thus in reality, the size of the volume V should be small compared with the least significant size in the problem, but cannot be so small that the number of molecules inside V is not large enough to give a stable value of M/V. In most engineering problems,

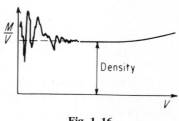

Fig. 1–16

there is a range of V where the value of M/V is stable, as shown in Fig. 1–16. This stable value is taken to be the density of the material.)

Problems

1–12. The constant e is defined as $\lim\limits_{x \to 0} (1+x)^{1/x}$. Estimate its value by computing the values of the function for x very close to zero. (Suggested values of x for computation: 0.01, 0.001, -0.001 and -0.01.)

1–13. The sum A of the principal and compound interest at the end of n years is related to the principal P deposited at the beginning, the yearly rate of interest r, and the number of times k compounded each year (e.g., $k=2$ if compounded semiannually):

$$A = P\left(1+\frac{r}{k}\right)^{kn}$$

If $r=1$ (100 per cent yearly!), compute the interest earned in the first year per dollar of principal (a) if compounded annually, (b) if compounded semiannually, and (c) if compounded continuously; i.e., $k \to \infty$.

Ans. (c) \$1.72

1–5. Continuity of functions

The elevation H of the roof along the centerline of a building is a function of the distance x from one end of the building. From Fig. 1–17, we see that the roof consists of three parts, each of which is continuous. The roof is discontinuous at the edge of the dome. By the word "discontinuous," we indicate the condition where the elevation changes suddenly. By the word "continuous," we mean the condition where no sudden change is experienced when moving toward the point from any direction. Expressing this statement in the language of mathematics, we have the following definition of continuity: the function $H(x)$ is said to be *continuous* at $x=a$ if

$$\lim_{x \to a} |H(x) - H(a)| = 0$$

or

$$\lim_{x \to a} H(x) = H(a)$$

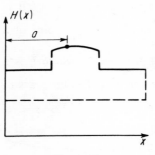

Fig. 1–17

We are interested in the continuity of functions because many mathematical steps cannot be taken across a discontinuity of a function. As these same steps cannot be taken across a point where the function becomes infinite, a function $y(x)$ is also said to be discontinuous at the point $x=b$ if $\lim_{x \to b} y(x) = \pm \infty$.

1–6. The first derivative of a function

Many problems involve the rate of change of the function with respect to the independent variable. For instance, the speed of a car is the rate of change, with respect to time t, of the distance $s(t)$ travelled. For the interval $\Delta t = t_2 - t_1$ (Δt reads "delta t" and means the change in t), the average speed is

$$\frac{s(t_2) - s(t_1)}{t_2 - t_1} \quad \text{or} \quad \frac{s(t_1 + \Delta t) - s(t_1)}{\Delta t}$$

The value of Δt may be hours or seconds. With a smaller value of Δt, we obtain the average speed during a shorter interval. To know the instantaneous speed at the instant t_1, we must make Δt infinitesimally small (i.e., smaller than any small value), since an instant has no duration, as a geometric line has no width. Thus, the instantaneous speed v at t_1 is

$$v(t_1) = \lim_{\Delta t \to 0} \frac{s(t_1 + \Delta t) - s(t_1)}{\Delta t}$$

This limiting value is called the *derivative* of the function $s(t)$ at $t=t_1$. Since the value t_1 has been chosen arbitrarily, the same is true for other values of t. Thus in general,

$$s'(t) \equiv \frac{d}{dt} s(t) \equiv \lim_{\Delta t \to 0} \frac{s(t + \Delta t) - s(t)}{\Delta t} \qquad (1\text{-}4)$$

This is the definition of the derivative $s'(t)$ of the function $s(t)$. The derivative is in general a function of t; e.g., speed $v(t)$ or $s'(t)$ varying with time. The symbol d/dt indicates the operation defined on the right-hand side of Eq. (1-4). Very often, $\frac{d}{dt} s(t)$ is written as $\frac{ds}{dt}$.

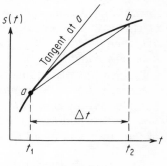

If $s(t)$ is plotted against t as shown in Fig. 1–18, the average speed during Δt is proportional to the slope of the straight line ab, the constant of proportionality depending on the units and the scales used in the graph. As Δt approaches zero, the line ab approaches the line tangent to point a. The instantaneous speed $v(t_1)$ or $s'(t_1)$ at $t = t_1$ is therefore proportional to the slope of this tangent line.

Fig. 1–18

To *differentiate* function $s(t)$ is to find its derivative $s'(t)$, as defined by Eq. (1-4). From this definition, many rules of differentiation can be derived.

Problems

1–14. Are $f'(x_0)$ and $\frac{d}{dx} f(x_0)$ the same? Find their value or values for $f(x) = x^2$ and $x_0 = 1$.

1–15. (a) If H is the elevation of a highway above sea level, and x is the distance along the highway from a fixed point, what does $\frac{d}{dx} H(x)$ represent? (b) The instantaneous rate of increase of population is said to be proportional to the population at that instant. Express this statement with a formula.

1–16. Given the graphs of several functions in Fig. 1–19, sketch the graphs of their first derivatives. Indicate the discontinuities of these functions and derivatives.

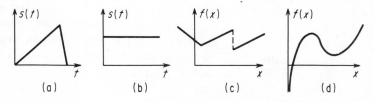

Fig. 1–19

If, in (a) and (b), $s(t)$ represents the distance traveled and t is the time, describe the motions in words.

1-7. Problems involving related time rates

In some problems, a quantity x is related to another quantity y, while x and y are varying with another variable t; i.e., we have $x(y)$, where $x=x(t)$ and $y=y(t)$. The equations $x=x(t)$ and $y=y(t)$ are called the *parametric equations* of the function $x(y)$ or the function $y(x)$. When the equation $x(y)$ or $y(x)$ is known, one can find the relationship between the rates of change dx/dt and dy/dt by differentiating $x(y)$ or $y(x)$ with respect to t, remembering that both x and y are functions of t.

Problems involving relative motions are often encountered in engineering practice. Usually, the motion of one body is known and the problem is to find the motion of another body connected to it. To solve these problems, one can first find the position x of one body as a function of the position y of the other, and then find dx/dt in terms of dy/dt.

Example 1–5. Blocks A and B in Fig. 1–20 are hinged at the two ends of a rod of length L. Block A slides in a vertical slot, while block B is moved in a horizontal slot such that $x=a \sin (2\pi t/p)$, where constant a is the amplitude of the oscillation of B, and is known to be smaller than L. The constant p is the period taken in each cycle of oscillation. Find the speed of block A as a function of time.

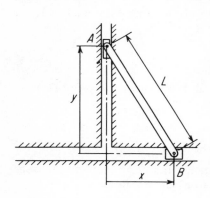

Let $y(t)$ be the distance of A from the intersection of the slots. The problem is to find dy/dt while dx/dt is known to be $(2\pi a/p) \cos (2\pi t/p)$. We can first find $y(x)$ from the fact that, at any time, we always have

Fig. 1–20

$$x^2+y^2 = L^2$$

Differentiate with respect to t, remembering that both x and y are functions of t.

$$2x \frac{dx}{dt}+2y \frac{dy}{dt} = 0$$

$$\frac{dy}{dt} = -\frac{x}{y}\frac{dx}{dt} = -\frac{x}{\sqrt{L^2-x^2}}\frac{dx}{dt}$$

$$= -\frac{2\pi a^2}{p} \sin \left(\frac{2\pi t}{p}\right) \cos \left(\frac{2\pi t}{p}\right) \Big/ \sqrt{L^2-a^2 \sin^2 \left(\frac{2\pi t}{p}\right)}$$

This expression can be easily seen to be dimensionally correct, with L and a being lengths, t and p being time, and dy/dt being length per unit time. As a check on limiting cases, we have the following known conditions: when $x=0$ at $t=0$, $p/2$, p, ..., block A is at its highest position with zero speed. Also, when $x=\pm a$ at $t=p/4$, $3p/4$, ..., block A is at its lowest position with zero speed. The solution satisfies all these limiting cases.

Example 1–6. Find the motion of the piston in Example 1–4 when the crank rotates about point B at the speed of 2 revolutions per minute. Given $R=3$ ft and $L=6$ ft.

Here, both S and θ vary with time t. The angular speed $d\theta/dt$ being given, the problem is to find dS/dt. We can first find the function $S(\theta)$. This has been shown in Example 1–4 to be

$$S = L\left[1 - \sqrt{1 - \left(\frac{R}{L}\sin\theta\right)^2}\right] + R(1 - \cos\theta)$$

To obtain dS/dt, differentiate with respect to t, remembering that both S and θ are functions of t.

$$\frac{dS}{dt} = R\sin\theta\left[\frac{R}{L} \cdot \frac{\cos\theta}{\sqrt{1 - \left(\frac{R}{L}\sin\theta\right)^2}} + 1\right]\frac{d\theta}{dt}$$

The unit of angle should be the radian. If the foot is used as the unit of length and the second as the unit of time, we have

$$\frac{d\theta}{dt} \text{ in radians per sec} = \frac{2\pi \times 2 \text{ rpm}}{60} = \frac{\pi}{15}$$

$$\frac{dS}{dt} \text{ in fps} = \frac{\pi}{5}\sin\theta\left[\frac{\cos\theta}{2\sqrt{1 - \frac{1}{4}\sin^2\theta}} + 1\right]$$

A check with limiting cases can be performed, since it can be seen by inspection that, when $\theta=0$, π, or 2π, the piston is at its extreme position with zero speed. This solution does give zero speed at these values of θ.

We can also write dS/dt as a function of time. Let $t=0$ when $\theta=0$ in a certain cycle. Then $\theta=t\pi/15$ radians.

$$\frac{dS}{dt} = \frac{\pi}{5}\sin\left(\frac{\pi t}{15}\right)\left[\frac{\cos\left(\frac{\pi t}{15}\right)}{2\sqrt{1 - \frac{1}{4}\sin^2\left(\frac{\pi t}{15}\right)}} + 1\right] \text{ fps}$$

Example 1–7. The sides of a rectangle x and y are increasing at the rates of 2 in. per min and 3 in. per min, respectively. Find the rate of increase of its area at the instant when x is 4 in. and y is 6 in.

Let $A =$ area xy. Here A, x, and y are functions of time t. Therefore

$$\frac{dA}{dt} = x\frac{dy}{dt} + y\frac{dx}{dt}$$

With lengths in in. and t in min, $dy/dt = 3$ and $dx/dt = 2$. Thus, at any t,

$$\frac{dA}{dt} = 3x + 2y \text{ sq in. per min}$$

At the particular instant when $x = 4$ and $y = 6$,

$$\frac{dA}{dt} = 3 \times 4 + 2 \times 6 = 24 \text{ sq in. per min}$$

Problems

1–17. The area of an equilateral triangle is decreasing at the rate of 3 sq in. per sec. Find the rate of change of a side at the instant (a) when the side is 10 in. long, and (b) when the area is 20 sq in.   *Ans.* -0.346 and -0.509 in. per sec

1–18. Find the rate of change of the surface of a sphere (a) with respect to its diameter, and (b) with respect to its volume.   *Ans.* $2\pi D$; $\left(\frac{32\pi}{3V}\right)^{1/3}$

1–19. Wheat is dumped from a hopper onto a level floor at a rate of 10 cu ft per min, forming a cone. While the size of the cone is continuously changing, its height is always equal to $\frac{1}{3}$ of the diameter of its base. Find the rate of change of its height as a function of time.

1–20. A ladder 30 ft long is leaning against a wall. The foot of the ladder is moving away at the rate of 0.2 fps. (a) Find the rate at which the top of the ladder is moving when the foot is 15 ft from the wall. (b) At what position is the top of the ladder when the two ends are moving at the same rate?

Ans. 0.115 fps; 21.2 ft

1–21. In the mechanism shown in Fig. 1–21, the crank is rotating at a speed of 3 rpm. Find an expression for the speed of the piston. Check your answer with one or more limiting cases.

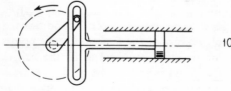

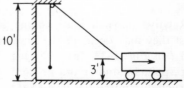

Fig. 1–21   **Fig. 1–22**

1–22. A weight is attached to a car through a cable and a pulley, as shown in Fig. 1–22. If the car is travelling at the rate of 10 mph, what is the rate at which the weight ascends when it is 2 ft off the ground. The cable is 20 ft long.

Ans. 11.9 fps

1–23. A man 6 ft tall is walking along a straight line away from a lamp at a speed of 240 ft per min. The lamp is 10 ft above the level ground. Find the rate at which the length of the shadow is changing.   *Ans.* 360 ft per min

1–24. If the crank in Problem 1–10 is rotating at an angular speed of 30 rpm, find the speed of the piston when $\theta = 0$, $\pi/2$, and π.   *Ans.* 0, $5\pi/\sqrt{26}$, 0 fps

1–25. Show that in Problem 1–9 the angular speed $d\phi/dt$ of the slotted lever is related to the angular speed $d\theta/dt$ of the crank by

$$\frac{d\phi}{dt} = \frac{R^2 + RL \cos \theta}{R^2 + L^2 + 2RL \cos \theta} \cdot \frac{d\theta}{dt}$$

1–8. Maxima and minima

Since engineering may be defined as the performance of a job to obtain maximum result with minimum expenditure, the maximum and minimum values of functions are naturally of great interest in engineering analysis. Let us first define the terms relative maximum and minimum. By *relative maximum*, we mean the value of the function $f(x)$ at a point x_0 about which a range of the variable x can be found within which $f(x)$ is nowhere greater than $f(x_0)$. Thus, all the dots in Fig. 1–23 represent relative maxima. Similarly, all the circles indicate relative minima.

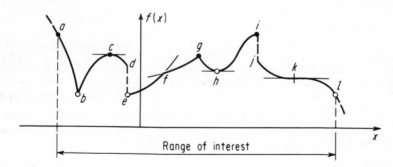

Fig. 1–23

Relative maxima and minima may occur under several conditions. (a) First they may occur at the limits of interest of the function; e.g., points *a* and *l* in Fig. 1–23. (b) They may occur at discontinuities of the function (e.g., points *e* and *i*) and its derivative (e.g., points *b* and *g*). However, not all such discontinuities give relative maxima or minima (e.g., points *d*, *f*, and *j*). (c) Thirdly, relative maxima and minima may occur where $f(x)$ and

$f'(x)$ are continuous. When $f(x)$ is continuous at x_0, we can reason that the derivative must change in sign at x_0, from positive values to negative values for a maximum, and from negative to positive for a minimum. If, furthermore, $f'(x)$ is continuous at x_0, $f'(x_0)$ must have zero value. Thus, if $f(x)$ and $f'(x)$ are continuous, $f'(x)=0$, and $f'(x)$ changes in sign at $x=x_0$, then $f(x_0)$ is either a relative maximum or minimum. Further test is necessary to determine which is the case, as will be discussed in Art. 1–10. A computation of the values of $f(x)$ or $f'(x)$ for x slightly different from x_0 will usually indicate which the case may be. Note that $f'(x)=0$ is only a necessary but not a sufficient condition for the occurrence of relative maxima or minima under this category. We can have $f'(x)=0$ where the function is neither a relative maximum nor a minimum; e.g., point k in Fig. 1–23, where $f'(x)$ does not change in sign.

While the condition $f'(x)=0$ is very useful in locating relative maxima and minima, one should not forget the other possibilities mentioned above. Furthermore, the graph of the function near $f'(x)=0$ is often very flat. A slight change of the independent variable there may not change the value of the function significantly. As engineering problems are influenced by many other factors, one must not be dogmatic in using the solution according to $f'(x)=0$. However, these relative maximum and minimum values serve as a guide for engineering decisions.

Example 1–8. Find the dimensions of a rectangular fenced-in area of 15,000 sq ft with a partitioning fence parallel to a side for minimum length of fence required.

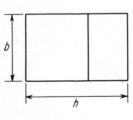

Fig. 1–24

Let b and h be the sides of the area, as shown in Fig. 1–24. The required length L of fence is then $L=3b+2h$. Since the enclosed area $A=bh$ is given as 15,000 sq ft, b and h cannot vary independently. The length L is therefore a function of one variable only, b or h. Using b as the independent variable, we have $h=A/b$ and

$$L(b) = 3b+\frac{2A}{b}$$

This equation gives the required length L for any b that may be chosen as shown in Fig. 1–25. At the point of minimum L,

$$\frac{dL}{db} = 3-\frac{2A}{b^2} = 0$$

giving $b=\pm\sqrt{2A/3}$. The negative value has no physical meaning. With the foot as the unit of length, we have $A=15,000$, b for minimum $L=\sqrt{2\times 15,000/3}=100$ ft, $h=A/b=150$ ft, and the minimum $L=600$ ft.

We can easily test whether this solution is the maximum or minimum, without constructing the graph in Fig. 1–25. For $b = 100-$, $dL/db = 3-(3+) < 0$; and for $b = 100+$, $dL/db = 3-(3-) > 0$. Therefore, 600 ft is the minimum possible length for the purpose.

If for other reasons it seems desirable to have $b = 120$ ft, the required length is then 610 ft. To arrive at a decision, the engineer has to compare the benefit thus derived and the cost of ten additional feet of fence.

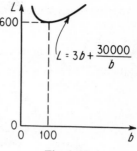

Fig. 1–25

Example 1–9. The number of a certain article that can be sold yearly varies inversely as the second power of the sale price. If the cost of manufacture is \$10 each, find the sale price for maximum yearly profit.

Let N = number of articles sold yearly, and s = sale price in dollars per article. Then yearly profit P in dollars is

$$P = N(s-10)$$

But N = constant k/s^2. Thus, P can be expressed as a function of s:

$$P(s) = \frac{k(s-10)}{s^2}$$

The yearly profit P is maximum when

$$\frac{dP}{ds} = -\frac{k}{s^2} + \frac{20k}{s^3} = 0$$

giving $s = \$20$ for maximum annual profit.

At low values of N or s, the relationship between N and s is better described by the dashed line in Fig. 1–26(a) than by the empirical relation given above.

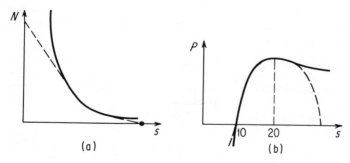

Fig. 1–26

Corresponding to this dashed curve, there is the dashed line in Fig. 1–26(b). Our analysis has been based on the empirical formula $N = k/s^2$. The answer is still valid, because this formula describes the $N-s$ relationship very well near $s=20$.

Example 1–10. The safe spacing from center to center of automobiles is experimentally found on a certain highway to be

$$L \text{ in ft} = 20 + 0.06V^{3/2} \qquad (\text{for } 20 \leqslant V \leqslant 70)$$

where V is the car speed in mph. Speeds higher than 70 mph are considered dangerous. Find the safe speed for maximum capacity of the highway.

The number of cars passing a station depends on the speed and spacing of cars. Since the safe spacing depends on the speed, the number of cars passing is determined by the speed. Let $v=$ safe speed of cars in ft per hr, $T=$ interval in hrs between the passing of two successive cars, and $N=$ number of cars passing a station per hr per lane. Since $v=5280V$, $T=L/v$, and $N=1/T$,

$$N(V) = \frac{5280V}{20 + 0.06V^{3/2}}$$

Maximum N is obtained by setting $dN/dV=0$, which gives

$$V = \left(\frac{2 \times 20}{0.06}\right)^{2/3} = 76 \text{ mph}$$

This value is not acceptable, as any speed higher than 70 mph is considered dangerous. The answer is therefore 70 mph. This is an example where the maximum occurs at a limit of interest. Note that, according to the expression $N(V)$, $N=6710$ and 6700 for $V=76$ and 70, respectively. The difference in N between the two speeds is only 10 cars per hr per lane.

Example 1–11. For a bridge crossing a wide stream with level bedrock, as shown in Fig. 1–27, the cost of each pier is the same. It is found that, within

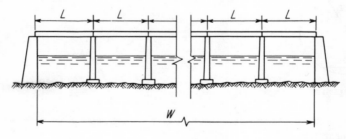

Fig. 1–27

wide limits of span lengths, the cost of each pier and abutment is independent of the span length L. The cost per span of superstructure is cL^2, where c is a known constant. Find the most economical span length for the bridge.

Let $W=$ the known total length of bridge. The number of spans is then W/L and the number of piers is $(W/L)-1$. Let $A=$ cost of each abutment and $B=$ cost of each pier. The total cost T of the bridge is

$$T(L) = 2A+\frac{W}{L}\,cL^2+\left(\frac{W}{L}-1\right)B$$

Minimum T is obtained with $dT/dL=0$, which gives the most economical L as

$$cL^2 = B$$

However, the value of L must be such that the number of spans, W/L, is an integer. The answer for the most economical span length L is to make the cost cL^2 of each span as close as possible to the cost B of each pier. This value of L is not necessarily equal to, but is very close to, $\sqrt{B/c}$.

Problems

1–26. Show that the rectangle of maximum area that can be inscribed in a semicircle is half of a square.

1–27. Find the maximum volume of an open-top rectangular box made from a 4 ft by 8 ft cardboard, with squares cut from the corners as shown in Fig. 1–28.

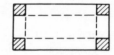

Ans. 12.3 cu ft

Fig. 1–28

1–28. To be acceptable for parcel post, a package should be such that its combined length and girth is not more than 100 inches. Design a cylindrical package with maximum volume for parcel post.   *Ans.* 11,750 cu in.

1–29. Find the section of a rectangular beam that can be cut from a cylindrical log of radius R to get maximum stiffness. The stiffness of a rectangular beam is proportional to bh^3. See Fig. 1–29.
                    Ans. $b=R$

1–30. Each page of a book is to contain 28 sq in. of printed area, with a $\frac{3}{4}$ in. margin at the sides and a 1 in. margin at the top and bottom. Find the dimensions of the page for minimum weight of the book.
                    Ans. 6.08 in. by 8.11 in.

Fig. 1–29

1–31. The yearly demand for a certain article is estimated to be 400,000 if the sale price is $1.00, and none if the price is $3.00. The variation between these two limits can be assumed to be linear. The cost of manufacture consists of two parts: an overhead expense of $2500 per year, and a labor, material and sales cost of $1.25 per article. Find the maximum possible yearly profit.   *Ans.* $150,500

1–32. The amount of dirt r in lb per sec that can be removed by a washer is found to be $r=\sqrt{Q}-1$ (for $Q>1$), where Q is the rate of flow through the machine in cu ft per sec. (a) Find the rate of flow for minimum volume of water used in a given job, with R lb of dirt to-be removed. (b) If the water supply is only 3 cfs, what is the percentage of volume of water required in addition to the minimum possible? *Ans.* 4 cfs; 2.5 per cent

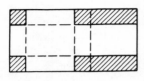

Fig. 1–30

1–33. The hourly fuel cost for a steamer varies as the cubic of the speed, and is $30 per hour for a speed of 10 mph. If other expenses are $100 per hour, find the most economical speed for a given voyage. *Ans.* 11.86 mph

1–34. Find the maximum volume of a rectangular box, with a top cover, made from a 4 ft by 8 ft cardboard, as shown in Fig. 1–30. *Ans.* 6.16 cu ft

1–9. Differentials

In the derivative $\dfrac{d}{dx} y(x)$, the symbol d/dx indicates an operation as specified in Eq. (1–4):

$$\frac{d}{dx} y = \lim_{\Delta x \to 0} \frac{\Delta y}{\Delta x}$$

Very often, $(d/dx)y$ is written as dy/dx. Since dy/dx represents the limit, as Δx approaches zero, of the ratio of Δy to Δx, it is very tempting to consider dy and dx as two quantities. However, they must not be taken as the limits of Δy and Δx, respectively, since these limits are equal to zero as Δx approaches zero. If we want dx and dy to designate some quantities, they must be so defined that

$$\frac{(dy)}{(dx)} = \frac{d}{dx} y$$

The quantities dy and dx so defined are called *differentials*. Differential dx is defined as an increment of the variable x, not necessarily small. Differential dy must then be defined as

$$dy = \left(\frac{d}{dx} y\right) \cdot dx = y'(x)\, dx \qquad (1–5)$$

By this definition, dy is not the increment Δy as shown in Fig. 1–31. However, it can be shown that dy approaches Δy if the increment Δx becomes infinitesimal: since

$$y'(x) = \lim_{\Delta x \to 0} \frac{\Delta y}{\Delta x}$$

the ratio $\Delta y/\Delta x$ is in general not quite equal to $y'(x)$. Therefore

$$\frac{\Delta y}{\Delta x} = y'(x) + k$$

where

$$\lim_{\Delta x \to 0} k = 0 \qquad (1–6)$$

Thus

$$\Delta y = y'(x)\,\Delta x + k\,\Delta x \qquad (1\text{–}7)$$

Since the increments Δx and dx can be chosen to be equal, we have from Eqs. (1–5) and (1–7):

$$\Delta y = dy + k\,\Delta x \qquad (1\text{–}8)$$

Now, as Δx and dx become infinitesimal on approaching zero, dy and Δy also become infinitesimal, according to Eqs. (1–5) and (1–7), respectively. So does the value of k, according to Eq. (1–6). In Eq. (1–8), the term $k\,\Delta x$ is a product of two infinitesimal quantities, and is therefore very small in comparison with dy and Δy. Such smaller terms are called higher-order terms

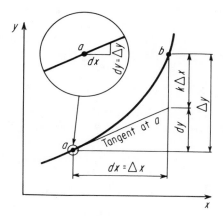

Fig. 1–31

and can be dropped in analysis. The quantities dy and Δy, though infinitesimal, are the largest in order of magnitude in Eq. (1–8), and therefore must be retained. In other words, as $\Delta x \to 0$, the difference between Δy and dy approaches zero even faster than Δy and dy. Thus

$$\lim_{\Delta x \to 0} \Delta y = dy \qquad (1\text{–}9)$$

This proof can be interpreted geometrically as follows. As Δx approaches zero, point b in Fig. 1–31 will move into the proximity of point a, indicated by the small circle around the point. According to Eq. (1–9), the length $k\,\Delta x$ in Eq. (1–8) is negligible in comparison with Δy or dy. Geometrically, this means that, inside the circle around point a, the curve ab coincides with the tangent, and therefore appears as a straight line as shown in the inserted enlargement in Fig. 1–31. The use of an enlargement of an infinitesimal area will be found helpful in many other problems.

In analysis, the increment dx is usually taken to be an infinitesimal. Only then is dy equal to the corresponding increment Δy of the function. However, if Δx is small, though not infinitesimal, the differential dy can be used as an approximation of the actual increment Δy. In this way, Δy can often be quickly estimated without prolonged computation, as shown in the following examples.

Example 1–12. The possible error in the length of the side of a 30-in. cube is 0.05 in. Estimate the maximum possible error of its volume.

Let us first compute the error in the usual manner, and compare the result with the computation involved in using differentials. The maximum possible error occurs when all the sides are either too long or too short. When all sides are too long, the error is $30.05^3 - 30.00^3$, or 135 cu in. When all sides are too short, the error is $29.95^3 - 30.00^3$, or -135 cu in.

We can estimate these errors by using differentials as follows. Let $V=$ volume in cu in., and $x=$ length of each side in in. When all sides are of equal length, $V=x^3$ and $dV=3x^2\,dx$. Since $dx=\pm 0.05$, which is small compared with the side of 30 in., the increment ΔV due to dx is very close to dV. Thus

$$\Delta V \doteq dV = 3 \times 30^2 \times (\pm 0.05) = \pm 135 \text{ cu in.}$$

This value is a good representation of the values of ΔV because dx is small. The amount of computation involved is much less when differentials are used.

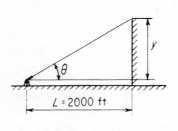

Fig. 1–32

Example 1–13. The height of a building is determined with a transit, as shown in Fig. 1–32. The angle measurement is 30° with a possible error of 0.1°. Estimate the possible error in the computed height of the building due to the error of the angle measurement.

Let $y=$ elevation of roof above transit in ft. Then $y=2000 \tan \theta$ and $dy=2000 \sec^2 \theta\, d\theta$. For small increment $d\theta=0.00174$ radian (or 0.1°),

$$\Delta y \doteq dy = 2000 \times \sec^2 30° \times (\pm 0.00174) = \pm 4.65 \text{ ft}$$

Example 1–14. Find $\sqrt[5]{33}$ approximately.

Let $y=\sqrt[5]{x}$. We know that, for $y=2$, $x=32$. Now $x=33$; i.e., $dx=1$, which is small compared with 32. We have the change Δy from 2:

$$\Delta y \doteq dy = \frac{1}{5}x^{-4/5}\,dx = \frac{1}{5} \times 32^{-4/5} \times 1 = \frac{1}{5 \times 2^4} = \frac{1}{80}$$

Thus

$$\sqrt[5]{33} = 2 + \Delta y \doteq 2\frac{1}{80}$$

Problems

1–35. Using differentials, find approximately the error in the calculated value of the density of a spherical mass of 250 grams, if the diameter is measured as 4 cm, with a possible error of 0.03 cm. *Ans.* 0.17 g/cu cm

1–36. Using differentials, show that, for an increase of 1 per cent in the diameter of a sphere, the area of its surface increases approximately 2 per cent, and the volume approximately 3 per cent.

1–37. Using differentials, find the approximate values of (a) $\sqrt{101}$, and (b) $\sqrt[6]{66}$. *Ans.* 10.05, 2.01

1–10. Higher derivatives

The derivative of the function $y(x)$ is the rate of change of y with respect to the variable x, as defined in Eq. (1–4). The derivative y' is, in general, a function of the variable x. The derivative of the first derivative $y'(x)$ is called the *second derivative*, and is usually denoted by $y''(x)$ or d^2y/dx^2, which is a contraction of $\dfrac{d}{dx}\left(\dfrac{d}{dx}y\right)$. The second derivative $y''(x)$ is the rate of change of $y'(x)$ with respect to the variable x. A simple example is the case of $s(t)$, representing the distance travelled as a function of time t. The first derivative $s'(t)$ is the rate of change of the distance s with time, and is therefore the speed. The second derivative $s''(t)$ is the derivative of s' with respect to time, and is the rate of change of speed with time. Similarly, the derivative of the second derivative is called the *third derivative*, and so on for higher derivatives. The dimensions of the nth derivative $d^n s/dt^n$ are equal to the dimensions of s divided by n times those of t. For example, when s is a length and t is time, d^2s/dt^2 has the dimensions $[L/T^2]$ and is expressed in units such as ft per sec^2, cm per sec^2, etc.

When $y(x)$ is plotted against x, $y'(x)$ is indicated by the slope of the graph. A positive value of $y'(x)$ indicates an increasing value of $y(x)$ with increase of x. Since $y''(x)$ is the derivative of $y'(x)$, a positive value of $y''(x)$ indicates an increasing slope with increase of x. Thus, a positive value of $y''(x)$ corresponds to a curve concave upward in the $y(x)$ graph with y as ordinates. Similarly, a negative value of $y''(x)$ corresponds to a curve concave downward in the $y(x)$ graph. The condition $y''(x_0)=0$ indicates zero curvature in the curve at $x=x_0$.

We have seen in Art. 1–8 that, if $y(x)$ and $y'(x)$ are continuous and $y'(x)$ changes sign at $x=x_0$ (and therefore $y'(x_0)=0$), $y(x_0)$ is either a relative maximum or a minimum. Now, if $y''(x_0)$ is positive, $y(x)$ is concave upward at $x=x_0$. Therefore, $y(x_0)$ must be a relative minimum, e.g., point h in Fig. 1–23. Similarly, if $y''(x_0)$ is negative, $y(x_0)$ must be a relative maximum, e.g., point c. If $y''(x_0)=0$, $y(x_0)$ is neither a maximum nor a minimum, e.g., point k.

Example 1–15. In Example 1–8, the required length L of fence is found to be

$$L(b) = 3b + \frac{2A}{b}$$

$$\frac{dL}{db} = 3 - \frac{2A}{b^2}$$

By putting $dL/db=0$, we obtain $b=100$ ft and $L=600$ ft. Test by $L''(b)$ to de termine whether 600 ft is the minimum required length.

For any b, $d^2L/db^2 = 4A/b^3$. When $b=100$, d^2L/db^2 is positive. Therefore, 600 ft is the minimum value for L.

Problems

1–38. Sketch the graph of $f''(x)$ vs x for the function shown in Fig. 1–19(d).

1–39. Test, by using the second derivatives of the functions, to determine whether your answers to Problems 1–27 and 1–28 are maxima or minima.

1–11. Indeterminate forms

At some values of the independent variable, some functions assume a form which is indeterminate; e.g., $0/0$, ∞/∞, $0 \cdot \infty$, 1^∞, 0^0, ∞^0, and $(\infty - \infty)$. Consider the case of $f(x)/\phi(x)$ at $x=a$, with $f(a)=0$ and $\phi(a)=0$. Take for example the function $(\sin x)/x$ at $x=0$. This function has the form $0/0$. We have seen in Art. 1–4 that this function approaches 1 as a limit as x approaches 0. Take for another example the function $(x^2+4x+4)/(x^2-4)$ at $x=-2$. Again, this function has the form $0/0$. By computing the function with x very close to the value of -2, we can show that this function approaches the limit 0 as x approaches -2. Thus, the form $0/0$ has no definite value. How-ever, we are actually interested in the value of $\lim\limits_{x \to a} \dfrac{f(x)}{\phi(x)}$ instead of $f(a)/\phi(a)$. This limit can be estimated by computing $f(x)/\phi(x)$ with values of x very close to a, but can be more easily ascertained by using *de l'Hospital's rule*: if $f(a)=0$ and $\phi(a)=0$, and $f(x)$ and $\phi(x)$ are differentiable and continuous near $x=a$,

$$\lim_{x \to a} \frac{f(x)}{\phi(x)} = \frac{f'(a)}{\phi'(a)} \tag{1–10}$$

There is a simple geometrical interpretation of this equation. In Fig. 1–33, we have a case with $f(a)=0$ and $\phi(a)=0$. As x approaches a, we have $f(x)= f'(a) \cdot (x-a)$ and $\phi(x)=\phi'(a) \cdot (x-a)$, as shown in the enlargement of the area near $x=a$, in which the two curves appear as straight lines. Thus, we have Eq. (1–10).

For the case of $f(x)/\phi(x)$ at $x=a$, with $f(a)=\infty$ and $\phi(a)=\infty$, we also have de l'Hospital's rule:

$$\lim_{x\to a}\frac{f(x)}{\phi(x)}=\frac{f'(a)}{\phi'(a)} \qquad (1\text{–}11)$$

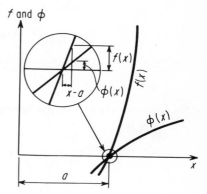

f and ϕ

The geometrical interpretation of this equation is more complicated and is not given here.

By using Eqs. (1–10) and (1–11), many other indeterminate forms can be evaluated:

(a) If $f(a)=0$ and $\phi(a)=\infty$,

$$\lim_{x\to a} f(x)\cdot\phi(x) = \lim_{x\to a}\frac{f(x)}{1/\phi(x)}$$

which can be evaluated by using Eq. (1–10).

Fig. 1–33

(b) If $f(a)=\infty$ and $\phi(a)=\infty$,

$$\lim_{x\to a}[f(x)-\phi(x)] = \lim_{x\to a} f(x)\left[1-\frac{\phi(x)}{f(x)}\right]$$

in which $\lim\limits_{x\to a}\dfrac{\phi(x)}{f(x)}$ can be first evaluated by using Eq. (1–11).

(c) If $f(a)=\infty$ and $\phi(a)=0$, f^ϕ at $x=a$ can be evaluated as follows:

$$\lim_{x\to a}\log[f(x)^{\phi(x)}] = \lim_{x\to a}\frac{\log f(x)}{1/\phi(x)}$$

which can be evaluated by using Eq. (1–11).

Example 1–16. Find $\lim\limits_{x\to 0}\dfrac{e^x+e^{-x}-2}{x^2}$.

Let $f(x) = e^x+e^{-x}-2$, and $\phi(x) = x^2$. We have $f(0) = 0$ and $\phi(0) = 0$, and $f(0)/\phi(0)$ takes the indeterminate form $0/0$. In using Eq. (1–10), we have $f'(x)=e^x-e^{-x}$ and $\phi'(x)=2x$. However, $f'(0)/\phi'(0)$ has the form $0/0$. De l'Hospital's rule must be used again, as follows:

$$\lim_{x\to 0}\frac{e^x+e^{-x}-2}{x^2} = \lim_{x\to 0}\frac{e^x-e^{-x}}{2x} = \lim_{x\to 0}\frac{e^x+e^{-x}}{2} = 1$$

Problems

1–40. By using de l'Hospital's rule, show that $\lim\limits_{x\to 0}\dfrac{\sin x}{x} = 1$.

1–41. When a uniform bar of cross-sectional area A and length L is stretched by a pair of forces of P each, the bar is elongated by the amount PL/AE, where E is a constant depending upon the material of the bar. For a nonuniform bar with sectional area A_1 at one end and varying in a certain manner to A_2 at the other end, the elongation is

$$\frac{PL}{A_1E}\left[\sqrt{\frac{A_1}{A_2-A_1}}\ \tan^{-1}\sqrt{\frac{A_2-A_1}{A_1}}\right]$$

Show that, as A_2 approaches the value A_1, this formula is reduced to that for a uniform bar.

1–12. Taylor's expansion of a function

Suppose that the City of Baltimore is completely isolated. It is required to estimate the temperature along a line directed to Washington, D.C., by making temperature observations *in Baltimore*. With one observation of the temperature in Baltimore, the best estimate is made with the assumption that the temperature is the same from Baltimore to Washington. If two observations are made, one at the north side and the other at the south side of Baltimore, and it is found that the temperature is increasing towards the south, a better estimate can be made with the assumption that the rate of increase of temperature is the same from Baltimore to Washington. With more data of the distribution of temperature in Baltimore, a greater refinement of the estimate can be made. This is an example of the fact that the values of a function can often be determined from the characteristics of the function at a particular value of the independent variable.

In analysis, it is often desirable to express a function $f(x)$ in terms of its characteristics at a particular value of the variable x, such as $f(a)$, $f'(a)$, $f''(a)$, etc., at $x=a$. In the physical example cited above, let x be the distance measured from, say, New York, $f(x)$ be the temperature, and $x=a$ at Baltimore. Then the temperature and its rate of change at Baltimore are $f(a)$ and $f'(a)$, respectively. According to the scheme outlined above, we put

$$f(x) = f(a)+f'(a)\cdot(x-a)+ \ldots$$

A complete form of this formula is furnished by Taylor's series, which gives $f(x)$ in terms of $f(a), f'(a), f''(a)$, etc. The following is a simple derivation of Taylor's series.

Assume that it is possible to express $f(x)$ with a power series:

$$f(x) = \sum_{n=0}^{\infty} c_n(x-a)^n = c_0+c_1(x-a)+c_2(x-a)^2+ \ldots +c_n(x-a)^n+ \ldots$$

The validity of this assumption will be discussed in the next article. Here, the symbol $\sum$ (capital sigma) indicates the sum of all the terms, with n taking all the values of integers between and including the limits, 0 and ∞ in this case. When one or both of the limits of n go to $\pm\infty$, the series will contain an infinite number of terms and is called an *infinite series*. In the power series, the coefficients are constants. To be useful in analysis, the series must not only represent $f(x)$ faithfully, but must also give the same values of derivatives as the derivatives of $f(x)$. The constants c are to be determined so as to satisfy this requirement:

$$f(x) = c_0 + c_1(x-a) + c_2(x-a)^2 + \quad c_3(x-a)^3 + \quad\quad c_4(x-a)^4 + \ldots$$
$$f'(x) = \quad\quad c_1 \quad\quad + 2c_2(x-a) + \quad 3c_3(x-a)^2 + \quad 4c_4(x-a)^3 + \ldots$$
$$f''(x) = \quad\quad\quad\quad 2c_2 \quad\quad + 3\cdot2c_3(x-a) + \quad 4\cdot3c_4(x-a)^2 + \ldots$$
$$f'''(x) = \quad\quad\quad\quad\quad\quad\quad 3\cdot2c_3 \quad\quad + 4\cdot3\cdot2c_4(x-a) + \ldots$$
$$\cdots$$

$$f^n(x) = n!\, c_n + (n+1)!\, c_{n+1}(x-a) + \ldots$$

All these equations should hold for all values of x where the expansion is valid, including the particular value $x=a$. The values of the coefficients can be determined by letting variable x take the value a: $c_0 = f(a)$, $c_1 = f'(a)$, $c_2 = f''(a)/2!$, $c_3 = f'''(a)/3!$, and in general $c_n = f^n(a)/n!$ Thus

$$f(x) = f(a) + f'(a)\cdot(x-a) + \frac{f''(a)}{2!}(x-a)^2 + \frac{f'''(a)}{3!}(x-a)^3 + \ldots$$

$$+ \frac{f^n(a)}{n!}(x-a)^n + \ldots \qquad (1\text{–}12)$$

This is *Taylor's expansion* of $f(x)$ about $x=a$.

In Fig. 1–34 is shown a function $f(x)$. If only the first term of Taylor's series is used, line I is obtained. Line II is obtained by using two terms of the series, and so on for the other lines. We expect that, *if* the expansion is possible, only a finite number of terms is necessary for practical analysis, and a better representation of $f(x)$ is obtained with a larger number of terms of the series. Also we expect that, the required accuracy being equal, the smaller the difference $(x-a)$, the less number of terms in the series is necessary. If this is the case, we can in analysis replace $f(x)$, which may be rather difficult to handle, with

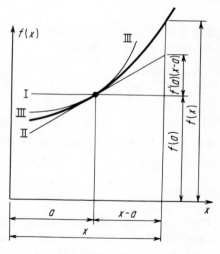

Fig. 1–34

a few terms of a Taylor's series. In doing this, we choose the value a such that $f(a)$, $f'(a)$, etc. are known or can be computed, and the values $(x-a)$ are small within the range of interest.

Very often, we find that zero is a good value for a. When $a=0$,

$$f(x) = f(0) + f'(0)\,x + \frac{f''(0)}{2!}\,x^2 + \frac{f'''(0)}{3!}\,x^3 + \ldots + \frac{f^n(0)}{n!}\,x^n + \ldots \qquad (1\text{--}13)$$

This is called *Maclaurin's series*. It is a special case of Taylor's series.

Example 1–17. Expand $f(x) = 1/(1+x)$ about $x=0$, and compute $f(0.1)$ and $f(0.5)$ with increasing number of terms of Taylor's series. (This example is given to demonstrate the characteristics of Taylor's series, and should not be taken as a recommended way of computing simple functions such as $1/(1+x)$.)

First, from $f(x)$, $f'(x)$, etc., compute $f(0)$, $f'(0)$, etc.:

$$
\begin{aligned}
f(x) &= (1+x)^{-1} & f(0) &= 1 \\
f'(x) &= -(1+x)^{-2} & f'(0) &= -1 \\
f''(x) &= 2(1+x)^{-3} & f''(0) &= 2 \\
f'''(x) &= -3{\cdot}2(1+x)^{-4} & f'''(0) &= -3!
\end{aligned}
$$

$$\ldots \qquad\qquad \ldots$$

$$f^n(x) = (-1)^n\, n!\,(1+x)^{-(n+1)} \qquad f^n(0) = (-1)^n\, n!$$

Substituting into Eq. (1–13), we have the expansion:

$$\frac{1}{1+x} = 1 - x + x^2 - x^3 + x^4 - \ldots + (-1)^n\, x^n + \ldots$$

For $x=0.5$, we know that $f(0.5) = \tfrac{2}{3}$ from the left-hand side of the equation. From the series, we have

Value of 1st term =	1		1 term = 1	Error =	−0.333
2nd	−0.5	Sum of 2 terms	0.5		0.167
3rd	0.25	3	0.75		−0.083
4th	−0.125	4	0.625		0.042

For $x=0.1$, we know that $f(0.1) = 0.909$. From the series, we have

Value of 1st term =	1		1 term = 1	Error =	−0.091
2nd	−0.1	Sum of 2 terms	0.9		0.009
3rd	0.01	3	0.91		−0.001

Note that the error becomes smaller with increasing number of terms in each case, and that the error is smaller when x is closer to the value a about which the function is expanded ($a=0$ in this case).

Example 1–18. Compute sin 10°, i.e., sin $(\pi/18)$.

Let $f(x) = \sin x$. Since $\pi/18$ is closer to 0 than any other value of x for which the values of sin x and its derivatives are known, expand $f(x)$ about $x=0$.

We have

$$
\begin{array}{llll}
f(x) & = & \sin x & \qquad f(0) & = & 0 \\
f'(x) & = & \cos x & \qquad f'(0) & = & 1 \\
f''(x) & = & -\sin x & \qquad f''(0) & = & 0 \\
f'''(x) & = & -\cos x & \qquad f'''(0) & = & -1 \\
f^{iv}(x) & = & \sin x & \qquad f^{iv}(0) & = & 0 \\
& \cdots & & \qquad & \cdots &
\end{array}
$$

$$
f^n(x) = \sin\left(x + \frac{n\pi}{2}\right) \qquad f^n(0) = \sin\left(\frac{n\pi}{2}\right)
$$

Substituting into Eq. (1–13), we have the expansion:

$$
\sin x = x - \frac{x^3}{3!} + \frac{x^5}{5!} - \frac{x^7}{7!} + \frac{x^9}{9!} - \cdots \tag{1–14}
$$

With $x = \pi/18$,

$$
\sin\left(\frac{\pi}{18}\right) = \frac{\pi}{18} - \frac{1}{3!}\left(\frac{\pi}{18}\right)^3 + \frac{1}{5!}\left(\frac{\pi}{18}\right)^5 - \cdots
$$

Value of 1st term =	0.17453	1 term =	0.17453
2nd	−0.00089	Sum of 2 terms	0.17364
3rd	0.000001	3	0.17364

It seems that the value is 0.17364. However, it is necessary to find out whether the infinite number of terms following the third term would add up to something substantial. This question will be taken up in the next article.

Example 1–19. Compute sin 40°, i.e., sin (2π/9).

Let $f(x) = \sin x$, and expand $f(x)$ about $x = \pi/4$. This value is chosen because $f(x)$ and its derivatives are known at this value, and it is close to the value $2\pi/9$. With $a = \pi/4$, we have

$$
\begin{array}{llll}
f(x) = & \sin x & \qquad f(a) = & 1/\sqrt{2} \\
f'(x) = & \cos x & \qquad f'(a) = & 1/\sqrt{2} \\
f''(x) = & -\sin x & \qquad f''(a) = & -1/\sqrt{2} \\
f'''(x) = & -\cos x & \qquad f'''(a) = & -1/\sqrt{2} \\
f^{iv}(x) = & \sin x & \qquad f^{iv}(a) = & 1/\sqrt{2} \\
& \cdots & \qquad & \cdots
\end{array}
$$

Substituting into Eq. (1–12), we have

$$
\sin x = \frac{1}{\sqrt{2}}\left[1 + \left(x - \frac{\pi}{4}\right) - \frac{1}{2!}\left(x - \frac{\pi}{4}\right)^2 - \frac{1}{3!}\left(x - \frac{\pi}{4}\right)^3 + \frac{1}{4!}\left(x - \frac{\pi}{4}\right)^4 + \cdots\right]
$$

With $x = 2\pi/9$, we have $\left(x - \dfrac{\pi}{4}\right) = -\pi/36$.

Value of 1st term =	0.70711		
2nd	−0.06171	Sum of 2 terms =	0.64540
3rd	−0.00269	3	0.64271
4th	0.00008	4	0.64279
5th	0.000002		

If an expansion about $x=0$ (see Eq. (1–14)) is used, terms up to the ninth power of x must be used to obtain the value 0.64279.

Problems

1–42. Show that

$$e^x = 1+x+\frac{x^2}{2!}+\frac{x^3}{3!}+ \ldots +\frac{x^n}{n!}+ \ldots \qquad (1\text{–}15)$$

1–43. Show that

$$\cos x = 1-\frac{x^2}{2!}+\frac{x^4}{4!}-\frac{x^6}{6!}+\frac{x^8}{8!}- \ldots \qquad (1\text{–}16)$$

and compute cos 5° with terms up to x^2.   *Ans.* 0.9962

1–44. By using Taylor's series, compute $\log_e 1.2$ with three terms of the series.

Ans. 0.18

1–13. Remainder in Taylor's series

In the example given at the beginning of the last article, the temperature of Washington, D.C., is estimated from Baltimore, first with the assumption that the temperature is uniform between the two cities, and then, for a better estimate, with the assumption that the rate of change of temperature with distance is uniform between the two cities, and so on. Taylor's series, Eq. (1–12), confirms the logic of this process. However, this method will fail in estimating the temperature in a house from an adjoining house in winter. The reason for this is that, because of the difference in living habits of the two families, the two houses may be vastly different in temperature. In other words, we find that this method does not work when there is a temperature discontinuity at the common wall, or better still, when there are discontinuities of temperature gradient at the interfaces of the common wall. Similarly, this method will also fail if there is a temperature discontinuity between Baltimore and Washington, such as a cold front.

In deriving Taylor's series in the previous article, we have assumed that such an expansion of a function $f(x)$ is possible. In view of these facts, we expect that such an expansion is not possible if there is a discontinuity in $f(x)$ or $f'(x)$. We can even speculate that the expansion should be limited if there is a discontinuity in $f''(x)$ or the higher derivatives. This speculation is correct, and is stated as *Taylor's theorem*: any function $f(x)$ that possesses a continuous derivative $f^n(x)$ in the interval $[a, b]$ from $x=a$ to $x=b$ inclusive, can be expanded in the following form for all values of x in the interval $[a, b]$:

$$f(x) = f(a)+f'(a)\cdot(x-a)+\frac{f''(a)}{2!}(x-a)^2+ \ldots +\frac{f^{n-1}(a)}{(n-1)!}(x-a)^{n-1}+R_n$$

where

$$R_n = \frac{f^n(\xi)}{n!}(x-a)^n \qquad (\xi \text{ between } x \text{ and } a) \qquad (1\text{–}17)$$

Here, R_n is called the *remainder* after n terms, and represents the error of using the sum of terms up to the $(n-1)$ power of $(x-a)$. In Eq. (1–17), only the range of the possible values of ξ (pronounced Xi) is known. Thus, Eq. (1–17) does not enable us to compute R_n exactly, but we can estimate the maximum possible value of R_n (see examples below). The knowledge of the maximum possible error of a result should be very comforting to the analyst.

According to this theorem, it is impossible to use Taylor's series to represent $f(x)$ across a discontinuity of $f(x)$ or $f'(x)$, n in Eq. (1–17) being zero in the latter case. These conditions are shown in Fig. 1–35, where lines I, II,

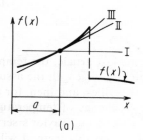

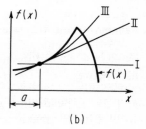

Fig. 1–35

and III represent the sum of one, two, and three terms of the series respectively. If $f'(x)$ is continuous and $f''(x)$ is discontinuous in $[a, b]$; i.e., $n=1$ in Eq. (1–17), we have

$$f(x) = f(a)+f'(\xi)\cdot(x-a) \qquad (\xi \text{ between } x \text{ and } a)$$

The geometrical representation of this expression is shown in Fig. 1–36, where the slope of chord AB is equal to that of the tangent to the curve of $f(x)$ at a certain point ξ between a at A and x at B. This expression gives very little information, except that $f(x)$ is probably different from $f(a)$. If $f''(x)$ or a higher derivative is continuous in $[a, b]$, $f(x)$ can be expanded into a larger number of terms, and more information can be obtained from the series. Functions with all the derivatives continuous can be expanded into infinite series, if so desired; e.g., $\sin x$, $\cos x$, e^x and e^{-x}.

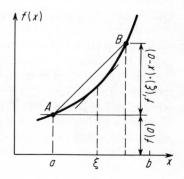

Fig. 1–36

Example 1–20. Expand $f(x)=1/(1+x)$ about $x=0$ and compute $f(0.5)$ with four terms of the series. Find the maximum possible error of the result.

The first part of this problem is the same as in Example 1–17, where we have

$$f(x) = (1+x)^{-1}$$
$$f^n(x) = (-1)^n n!(1+x)^{-(n+1)}$$

(and, in particular, $\qquad f^{iv}(x) = 4!/(1+x)^5$)

and the series expansion about $a = 0$:

$$f(x) = 1-x+x^2-x^3+R_4$$

where, according to Eq. (1–17), with $n=4$,

$$R_4 = \frac{1}{4!}f^{iv}(\xi)\cdot(x-0)^4 = \frac{x^4}{(1+\xi)^5} \qquad (\xi \text{ between 0 and } x)$$

This expansion is valid for all values of x, as long as $f^{iv}(x)$ is continuous in the interval $[0, x]$. In this case, $f^{iv}(x)$ is continuous in the interval $[0, 0.5]$. Therefore, we can compute $f(0.5)$ with this expansion. With $x=0.5$, the value of ξ lies between 0 and 0.5. The maximum possible value of R_4 (if $\xi=0$) is $0.5^4=0.0625$. The minimum possible value of R_4 (if $\xi=0.5$) is $0.5^4/(1+0.5)^5$ $=0.0082$. Since the sum of the first four terms is 0.625, the value of $f(0.5)$ is somewhere between 0.63 ($=0.625+0.0082$) and 0.69 ($=0.625+0.0625$).

Example 1–21. Expand $\sin x$ about $x=0$, and compute $\sin(\pi/18)$ with terms up to x^4. Find the maximum possible error of the result.

The first part of this problem is the same as in Example 1–18, where we have

$$f(x) = \sin x$$
$$f^n(x) = \sin\left(x+\frac{n\pi}{2}\right)$$

(in particular, $f^v(x)=\cos x$) and

$$\sin x = 0+x+0-\frac{x^3}{3!}+0+R_5$$

where, according to Eq. (1–17),

$$R_5 = \frac{f^v(\xi)}{5!}(x-0)^5 = \frac{\cos \xi}{5!}x^5 \qquad (\xi \text{ between 0 and } x)$$

This expansion is valid for all values of x, since $f^v(x)$ is continuous in any interval $[0, x]$. With $x=\pi/18$, the sum of the terms up to x^4 (three of these five terms being zero) has been shown to be 0.17364 in Example 1–18. The maximum possible error of this sum is equal to the maximum possible value of R_5 with ξ assumed to be zero. Thus

$$R_5 < \frac{1}{5!}\left(\frac{\pi}{18}\right)^5 = 0.000,001$$

Therefore, $\sin(\pi/18)=0.17364$, accurate to five places.

Problems

1–45. Expand e^x about zero to four terms with a remainder. If $e^{1.1}$ is computed with four terms, what is the maximum possible error of the result? *Ans.* 0.18

1–46. By using the remainder of Taylor's series, find the number of terms in Eq. (1–16) that must be included so as to compute $\cos 5°$ accurate to five places.

Ans. Include $x^2/2$

1–14. Convergence of Taylor's series

We have seen examples of Taylor's series in which the magnitude of the remainder R_n after n terms becomes smaller as n increases. However, this is not always the case. Sometimes, an expansion of a function according to Taylor's theorem may have a remainder R_n which does not decrease in magnitude as n increases. In fact, $|R_n|$ may increase indefinitely with n. In such a case, a greater error will result by using more terms of the series, and therefore the Taylor's expansion has no value in analysis.

Take for example the function $f(x) = 1/(1+x)$. Since

$$^n(x) = (-1)^n \frac{n!}{(1+x)^{n+1}}$$

all the derivatives of $f(x)$ are continuous for all values of x, except at $x = -1$. The expansion of $f(x)$ about zero has been shown in Examples 1–17 and 1–20 to be

$$f(x) = \frac{1}{1+x} = 1 - x + x^2 - x^3 + \ldots + (-1)^{n-1}x^{n-1} + R_n$$

According to Taylor's theorem, this expansion with R_n is supposed to be applicable for all values of x larger than -1. According to Eq. (1–17), the remainder R_n is

$$R_n = \frac{f^n(\xi)}{n!} x^n = (-1)^n \frac{x^n}{(1+\xi)^{n+1}} \qquad (\xi \text{ between 0 and } x)$$

For the purpose of instruction, let us examine $|R_n|$ for $x > 0$. Since $0 < \xi < x$,

$$|R_n| < x^n \qquad (x > 0) \tag{1–18}$$

Using this expression of $|R_n|$, consider the following three cases:

(a) For $0 < x < 1$, the value of $|R_n|$ is less than x^n, which decreases as n increases. Thus, $|R_n|$ cannot, if it increases at all, increase indefinitely with n. (We have seen in Example 1–17 that $f(x)$ can be computed to a desired accuracy with a finite number of terms of the series, for $0 < x < 1$.)

(b) When $x = 1$, Eq. (1–18) gives $|R_n| < 1$. There is no indication that $|R_n|$ will decrease or increase with increase of n. (With $x = 1$, the series becomes

$$f(1) = \tfrac{1}{2} = 1 - 1 + 1 - \ldots + R_n$$

$|R_n|$ is therefore equal to 1/2, for any value of n.)

(c) When $x > 1$, x^n increases indefinitely with n. Thus R_n can also increase indefinitely with n. (The series and the function are plotted in Fig. 1–37.

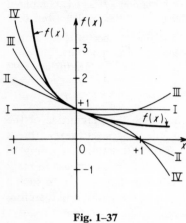

It can be seen that, the more terms are included in the series, the larger the error, when $x > 1$.)

Thus, according to Taylor's theorem as represented by Eq. (1–18), the expansion for $1/(1 + x)$ shown above is useful for $0 < x < 1$, and is of doubtful use for $x \geqslant 1$.

This phenomenon is directly connected to the convergence and divergence of infinite series. If, at certain x, the sum of the series approaches $f(x)$ as a limit as the number of terms increases, the series is said to be *convergent* to the value of the function at this x. If the series does not approach a limit, it is said to be

Fig. 1–37

divergent at this x, and has no practical use in analysis. For an infinite Taylor's series to converge to the value of the function in the interval $[a, b]$, it is necessary and sufficient that in this interval

$$\lim_{n \to \infty} R_n = 0$$

The series

$$f(x) = 1 - x + x^2 - x^3 + \ldots + (-1)^n x^n + \ldots$$

converges to $f(x)$ for $-1 < x < 1$, and is divergent for $|x| \geqq 1$.

In order to represent a function $f(x)$ within certain allowable error with a finite number of the functions of the series, the series must not only converge to $f(x)$, but must also converge equally rapidly for all values of x in the interval. In other words, the series must be such that, by taking say N terms or more, we can reduce the error below the allowable for all x in the interval. Such a series is said to be *uniformly convergent* to the function in the interval. In the case of a series of continuous functions converging to a continuous function $f(x)$, it can be shown that the series is uniformly convergent if and only if, in the interval,

$$\lim_{n \to \infty} \max |R_n| = 0$$

Thus, the series above is uniformly convergent for $-1 < x < 1$.

In engineering analysis, other infinite series of functions will be encountered. It is extremely important to know whether the series is uniformly convergent. For example, if $f(x)$ is represented by a uniformly convergent series in an interval $[a, b]$, and the derivative of the series, term by term, is also a uniformly convergent series, it can be proved that this second series converges to $f'(x)$ in this interval. The student is advised to study the Weierstrass M-test for uniform convergence in texts of the Calculus. Using this test, one can show that the derivative of a uniformly convergent power series is always uniformly convergent in the same interval. Thus, a uniformly convergent Taylor's series can be differentiated term by term.

When a Taylor's expansion about a particular value of the independent variable gives a divergent series in the range of interest, an expansion about another value of the variable may give a uniformly convergent series in this range. For example, while the expansion of $f(x)=1/(1+x)$ about zero is divergent in the range $2<x<3$, an expansion of $f(x)$ about 2 can be shown to be uniformly convergent in this range (see Problem 1–47).

Problem

1–47. Expand $f(x)=1/(1+x)$ about $x=2$ into a Taylor's series with a remainder R_n. According to Taylor's theorem, within what range of x is this expansion permissible? Show that $|R_n|$ of this series decreases with increase of n in the interval $1<x<3$.

1–15. Approximating functions by means of series

Justifiable approximations are invaluable in engineering analysis. Not only are the time and effort of computation greatly reduced, but also mistakes are less likely to occur, because of the simplification of the mathematical processes. Very often, it is permissible to reduce an unsolvable nonlinear equation to a linear equation by approximation. The process of such a reduction is called linearization, which is a commonly used technique in analysis. On the other hand, the accuracy of the result will be compromised by approximation. Unless there is a worthwhile gain in simplicity, approximation should not be used. It is therefore good practice to try to analyse a problem by exact methods and use approximation only when it is profitable to do so.

Approximations can be made in many ways. Taylor's expansion furnishes one of the most elegant methods of approximation. With Taylor's expansion, the following common approximations can be derived:

(a) For $x<k$,

$$(k\pm x)^n = k^n \left[1\pm n\left(\frac{x}{k}\right)+\frac{n(n-1)}{2!}\left(\frac{x}{k}\right)^2 \pm \cdots\right] \qquad (1\text{--}19)$$

e.g.,

$$\sqrt[3]{1+x} = 1+\frac{x}{3}-\frac{x^2}{9}+ \cdots = 1+\frac{x}{3}- \cdots$$

$$\frac{1}{(1+x)^2} = 1-2x+3x^2- \cdots = 1-2x+ \cdots$$

(b) For small θ,

$$\sin \theta = \theta - \frac{\theta^3}{3!} + \ldots = \theta - \ldots$$

$$\cos \theta = 1 - \frac{\theta^2}{2!} + \ldots = 1 - \ldots$$

$$\tan \theta = \theta + \frac{\theta^3}{3} + \ldots = \theta + \ldots$$

In general, the aim is to express a function as a uniformly convergent series with ascending power of a small quantity, such as x/k and θ above, so that the higher-order terms can be neglected, if desired. The number of terms to be retained in the approximation depends on the purpose of the analysis and the magnitude of error that can be tolerated. In linearization, only the first power of the variable can be retained.

When an approximation is made, it is useful to know the error involved. When Taylor's series is utilized, the error in using only n terms is

$$R_n = \frac{f^n(\xi)}{n!}(x-a)^n \qquad (\xi \text{ between } a \text{ and } x)$$

It is interesting to note that the first term after n terms is $\frac{f^n(a)}{n!}(x-a)^n$, which differs from R_n only in the factor $f^n(a)$. Thus, the error has the same order of magnitude as the first term neglected in the series.

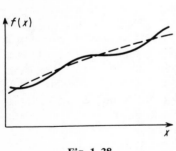

Fig. 1–38

As mentioned in the previous article, a uniformly convergent power series can be differentiated term by term. Thus, when Taylor's series is used as an approximation of $f(x)$, the series can be differentiated to yield an approximation of $f'(x)$. However, one should realize that the percentage error of this approximation of $f'(x)$ is expected to be much higher than that of the approximation of $f(x)$. That this is true of all approximations, obtained by means of Taylor's series or not, can be seen in Fig. 1–38. While the dashed line is a good representation of the solid line as far as their ordinates are concerned, the two lines may have vastly different slopes.

Example 1–22. It has been shown that, for the direct-acting engine in Example 1–4,

$$S = L\left[1 - \sqrt{1 - \left(\frac{R}{L}\sin \theta\right)^2}\right] + R(1 - \cos \theta)$$

and therefore

$$S' = \frac{dS}{dt} = R \sin\theta \left[1 + \frac{R}{L} \cdot \frac{\cos\theta}{\sqrt{1-\left(\frac{R}{L}\sin\theta\right)^2}}\right] \frac{d\theta}{dt}$$

For a particular case, R is much smaller than L. Investigate the possibility of approximations for S and S'.

When $R/L \ll 1$, we have a good approximation with just a few terms of the following power series of R/L. Using Eq. (1–19),

$$\sqrt{1-\left(\frac{R}{L}\sin\theta\right)^2} = 1 - \frac{\sin^2\theta}{2}\left(\frac{R}{L}\right)^2 - \frac{\sin^4\theta}{8}\left(\frac{R}{L}\right)^4 - \cdots$$

Thus

$$S = R\left[1 - \cos\theta + \frac{\sin^2\theta}{2}\left(\frac{R}{L}\right) + \frac{\sin^4\theta}{8}\left(\frac{R}{L}\right)^3 + \cdots\right]$$

Note that, by moving R out, we reduce each term in the bracket to a number, thus facilitating comparison of magnitude. The number of terms to be retained depends on the degree of accuracy required. Since $R/L \ll 1$ and $\sin\theta \leq 1$, the fourth term in the parentheses is always much smaller than the third term, and can therefore be dropped, if desired. Also, it can be verified that $(\sin^2\theta)/2$ is not greater than $(1 - \cos\theta)$ for any value of θ. The third term is therefore always much smaller than the algebraic sum of the first two terms. The third term can, therefore, also be dropped if desired. If only two terms are used, the error of the approximation is of the order of $\dfrac{\sin^2\theta}{2} \cdot \dfrac{R^2}{L}$ and the result is

$$S \doteq R(1 - \cos\theta)$$

No more terms can be neglected in this equation, since $\cos\theta$ can be as large as one. One might ask whether it would be profitable to expand $\cos\theta$ into a series and retain only a few terms. The answer is *No*, because a large number of terms in this series must be retained to give a reasonable approximation of $\cos\theta$ when the value of θ is large. Thus, further simplification is not feasible.

An approximation for S' can be obtained by differentiating the series expansion of S:

$$S' = R \sin\theta \left[1 + \frac{R}{L}\cos\theta + \frac{1}{2}\left(\frac{R}{L}\right)^3 \sin^2\theta \cdot \cos\theta + \cdots\right] \frac{d\theta}{dt}$$

When $R/L \ll 1$, the simplest approximation of S', corresponding to $S \doteq R(1-\cos\theta)$, is

$$S' \doteq R \sin\theta \frac{d\theta}{dt}$$

These approximate expressions for S' can also be obtained by expanding the exact formula for S' into Taylor's series directly. See Problem 1–48.

Example 1–23. An elliptical cam is rotating at a constant angular speed $d\theta/dt$. Find the velocity dh/dt of the cam follower as shown in Fig. 1–39. Investigate the possibility of an approximation for dh/dt when the major axis

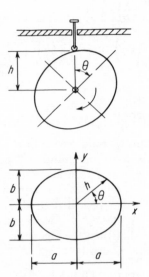

Fig. 1–39

of the elliptical cam is longer than its minor axis by a very small amount; i.e., $e \ll b$ where $e = a - b$.

To relate dh/dt to the known value of $d\theta/dt$, we can first find the relationship between $h(t)$ and $\theta(t)$. For an ellipse,

$$\frac{x^2}{a^2} + \frac{y^2}{b^2} = 1$$

With $x = h \cos \theta$ and $y = h \sin \theta$, this equation yields

$$h = \frac{ab}{\sqrt{b^2 \cos^2 \theta + a^2 \sin^2 \theta}}$$

Thus

$$h' = \frac{dh}{dt} = \frac{-ab\,(a^2 - b^2)\sin 2\theta}{2(b^2 \cos^2 \theta + a^2 \sin^2 \theta)^{3/2}} \cdot \frac{d\theta}{dt}$$

When $e \ll b$, good approximations of h and h' can be found from power series of e/b. With $a = b + e$,

$$b^2 \cos^2 \theta + a^2 \sin^2 \theta = b^2 \left[1 + \frac{e}{b} \left(2 + \frac{e}{b} \right) \sin^2 \theta \right]$$

$$h = \frac{ab}{b \sqrt{1 + \frac{e}{b} \left(2 + \frac{e}{b} \right) \sin^2 \theta}}$$

$$= a \left[1 - \frac{e}{2b} \left(2 + \frac{e}{b} \right) \sin^2 \theta + \frac{3}{8} \left(\frac{e}{b} \right)^2 \left(2 + \frac{e}{b} \right)^2 \sin^4 \theta \right.$$
$$\left. - \frac{5}{16} \left(\frac{e}{b} \right)^3 \left(2 + \frac{e}{b} \right)^3 \sin^6 \theta + \ldots \right]$$

$$= a \left[1 - \sin^2 \theta \left(\frac{e}{b} \right) - \frac{1}{2} \sin^2 \theta \, (1 - 3 \sin^2 \theta) \left(\frac{e}{b} \right)^2 \right.$$
$$\left. + \frac{1}{2} \sin^4 \theta \, (3 - 5 \sin^2 \theta) \left(\frac{e}{b} \right)^3 + \ldots \right]$$

Here, we have collected terms of like powers of e/b. This step is necessary because, when small terms are dropped, we must be consistent in keeping or dropping either all or none of the terms of like order of magnitude. In this example, the order of magnitude is indicated by the power of e/b.

We can, if we so desire, neglect terms of order of $(e/b)^2$ or higher, because they are small compared with the term $(e/b) \sin^2 \theta$, for any value of θ. The latter is retained so that h remains a function of θ.

$$h \doteq a \left(1 - \frac{e}{b} \sin^2 \theta \right)$$

By differentiation,

$$h' = \frac{dh}{dt} \doteq -\frac{ae}{b} 2 \sin \theta \cdot \cos \theta \frac{d\theta}{dt} = -\frac{ae}{b} \sin 2\theta \frac{d\theta}{dt}$$

This approximation can also be obtained directly by approximating the exact formula of h'.

Example 1–24. A liquid is flowing in a semicircular flume, as shown in Fig. 1–40. Find an expression for the ratio of the cross-sectional area A of the flow to the product of the surface width b and the depth of flow h. Find a simple approximation for A/bh, if possible. Limit attention to cases with small θ, if necessary.

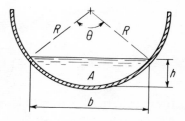

Fig. 1–40

Here, we want to find A/bh as a function of θ. We have

$$A = (\pi R^2)\frac{\theta}{2\pi} - \left(R \sin\frac{\theta}{2}\right)\left(R \cos\frac{\theta}{2}\right) = \frac{R^2}{2}(\theta - \sin\theta)$$

$$b = 2R \sin\frac{\theta}{2}$$

and

$$h = R\left(1 - \cos\frac{\theta}{2}\right)$$

Therefore

$$bh = R^2\left(2\sin\frac{\theta}{2} - 2\sin\frac{\theta}{2}\cdot\cos\frac{\theta}{2}\right) = R^2\left(2\sin\frac{\theta}{2} - \sin\theta\right)$$

and

$$\frac{A}{bh} = \frac{\theta - \sin\theta}{2\left(2\sin\frac{\theta}{2} - \sin\theta\right)}$$

To obtain an approximation for this expression, we try to expand it into a power series of θ. A simple way to do this is to expand $\sin\theta$ and $\sin(\theta/2)$ separately:

$$\frac{A}{bh} = \frac{\theta - \left(\theta - \frac{\theta^3}{6} + \frac{\theta^5}{120} - \cdots\right)}{2\left[2\left(\frac{\theta}{2} - \frac{\theta^3}{48} + \frac{\theta^5}{3840} - \cdots\right) - \left(\theta - \frac{\theta^3}{6} + \frac{\theta^5}{120} - \cdots\right)\right]}$$

$$= \frac{\frac{\theta^3}{6} - \frac{\theta^5}{120} + \cdots}{\frac{\theta^3}{4} - \frac{\theta^5}{64} + \cdots} = \frac{2}{3}\left(\frac{1 - \frac{\theta^2}{20} + \cdots}{1 - \frac{\theta^2}{16} + \cdots}\right)$$

If we limit our attention to cases with $(\theta^2/16 + \cdots)$ less than one, we can write, by using Eq. (1-19),

$$\frac{A}{bh} = \frac{2}{3}\left(1 - \frac{\theta^2}{20} + \cdots\right)\left(1 + \frac{\theta^2}{16} - \cdots\right)$$

$$= \frac{2}{3}\left(1 + \frac{\theta^2}{80} + \cdots\right)$$

It can be verified that, with two terms in the parentheses, the error is less than five per cent, even when $\theta = \pi$. For smaller values of θ, $A/bh = 2/3$, with an error of about $100\theta^2/80$ per cent (θ in radians).

Problems

1–48. In Example 1–22, an exact formula for S' is given. Show that, when $R \ll L$, this expression can be reduced to

$$S' = R \sin \theta \frac{d\theta}{dt} \left(1 + \frac{R}{L} \cos \theta + \ldots \right)$$

1–49. In Example 1–23, an exact formula for h' is given. Show that, when $e \ll b$, where $e = a - b$, this expression can be reduced to

$$h' \doteq -\frac{ae}{b} \sin 2\theta \frac{d\theta}{dt}$$

1–50. A rectangular channel of width B is delivering water at a depth h, as shown in Fig. 1–41. In the study of open-channel flow, a quantity called the hydraulic radius R is used, which is defined as the ratio of the cross-sectional area A ($= Bh$, in this case) to the wetted perimeter p ($= B + 2h$, in this case). Show that, when $h \ll B$, R is approximately equal to h, with an error of the order of $2h^2/B$.

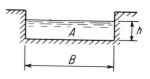

Fig. 1–41

1–51. A follower is in contact with a circular cylinder of radius R, as shown in Fig. 1–42. The cylinder has a reciprocating motion such that

$$S = 0.1 \, R \sin \omega t$$

where ω is a constant, and t is the time. Find an expression for dh/dt in terms of S and dS/dt. Show that, since S is small compared with R, this expression can be simplified to

$$\frac{dh}{dt} \doteq \frac{-R\omega}{200} \sin (2\omega t)$$

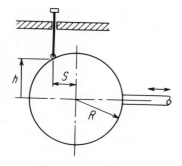

Fig. 1–42

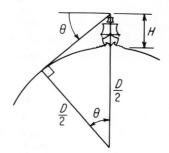

Fig. 1–43

1–52. The lookout of a boat is H above sea level, as shown in Fig. 1–43. The earth, assumed to be spherical, has a diameter D. H is much less than D. Show that the small angle θ under which the lookout sees the horizon is given by $\theta \doteq \sqrt{4H/D}$.

1-53. In laying out a railroad curve, as shown in Fig. 1–44, it is necessary to know the difference in length $(s-c)$ between the circular arc s along the centerline

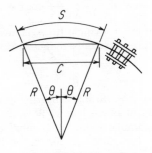

Fig. 1–44

of the track and the chord c, the distance actually measured with a tape. Show that $(s-c) \doteq R\theta^3/3$, with an error about $R\theta^5/60$.

1-16. Numerical differentiation

Very often, it is necessary to find the derivatives of a function from discrete values of the function. For example, it may be desired that the speed $s'(t)$ and the rate of change of speed $s''(t)$ of an automobile be computed from discrete observed values of the distance of travel $s(t)$. One way to do this is to plot $s(t)$ against the time t and determine $s'(t)$ from the slope of the curve. The values of $s''(t)$ can then be obtained in similar manner from a plot of $s'(t)$ against time t. For data of low accuracy, this graphical method is suitable. However, for data of higher accuracy, computation directly from the observed values of $s(t)$ may yield more accurate results.

There are several ways of computing the derivatives from discrete values of the function. One can assume that, for the case of $(N+1)$ known values of $f(x)$,

$$f(x) \doteq C_0 + C_1 x + C_2 x^2 + \ldots + C_N x^N \tag{1-20}$$

where the coefficients are unknown constants. With each known value of $f(x)$ and the corresponding value of x, one equation is obtained involving the $(N+1)$ unknown constants. Thus, from the resultant $(N+1)$ equations, these unknowns can be determined. The coefficients being known, the derivatives can then be obtained by differentiating Eq. (1–20). However, this method is tedious, and the data are seldom accurate enough to warrant the time and effort required. Another method is the method of finite differences, and is part of a larger subject in Mathematics known as Calculus of Finite Differences. However, formulas for numerical differentiation can be derived from Taylor's series without introducing this subject.

In Fig. 1–45, the known values of $f(x)$ at equal intervals of $\Delta x = b$ are shown by dots. This discussion will be confined to cases with equal intervals

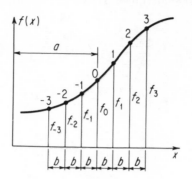

Fig. 1–45

of the variable x. (It is believed that cases with unequal intervals can be handled by the student without further instruction. See Problem 1–57.) It is assumed that the unknown function $f(x)$ can be approximated with a smooth line passing the known values. There are cases where this condition is not satisfied; e.g., $\phi(t)$ and $\psi(t)$ in Fig. 1–46, where the actual

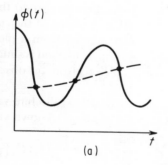

Fig. 1–46

functions are shown as full lines which cannot be approximated by the smooth dashed lines. The derivatives determined according to the dashed lines will be vastly different from the actual derivatives of the functions $\phi(t)$ and $\psi(t)$.

In Fig. 1–45, let 0 denote the point where the derivatives are to be computed. Other numbers $(\ldots, -2, -1, 1, 2, \ldots)$ are used to denote other points, as shown. For simplicity, let $f_0, f_1, \ldots, f_n, \ldots$ denote the values of $f(x)$ at points $0, 1, \ldots, n, \ldots$ respectively; i.e., $f_0 = f(a), f_1 = f(a+b), \ldots, f_n = f(a+nb)$, where a is the value of x at point 0. Our aim is to find $f_0', f_0'', \ldots$ from the known values $f_0, f_1, f_2, \ldots$ Since the actual function can be approximated by a smooth function, we can expand this function about point 0. In this way, we have expressions relating the unknown $f_0', f_0'', \ldots$ to the known values $f_0, f_1, f_2, \ldots$:

$$f_n = f_0 + nb \cdot f_0' + \frac{(nb)^2}{2} \cdot f_0'' + \frac{(nb)^3}{6} \cdot f_0''' + \frac{(nb)^4}{24} \cdot f_0^{iv} + \frac{(nb)^5}{120} \cdot f_0^{v} + \cdots$$

$$\cdots \cdots \cdots \cdots \cdots \cdots \cdots \cdots$$

$$f_3 = f_0 + 3b \cdot f_0' + \frac{9b^2}{2} \cdot f_0'' + \frac{9b^3}{2} \cdot f_0''' + \frac{27b^4}{8} \cdot f_0^{iv} + \frac{81b^5}{40} \cdot f_0^{v} + \cdots$$

$$f_2 = f_0 + 2b \cdot f_0' + 2b^2 \cdot f_0'' + \frac{4b^3}{3} \cdot f_0''' + \frac{2b^4}{3} \cdot f_0^{iv} + \frac{4b^5}{15} \cdot f_0^{v} + \cdots$$

$$f_1 = f_0 + b \cdot f_0' + \frac{b^2}{2} \cdot f_0'' + \frac{b^3}{6} \cdot f_0''' + \frac{b^4}{24} \cdot f_0^{iv} + \frac{b^5}{120} \cdot f_0^{v} + \cdots$$

$$f_{-1} = f_0 - b \cdot f_0' + \frac{b^2}{2} \cdot f_0'' - \frac{b^3}{6} \cdot f_0''' + \frac{b^4}{24} \cdot f_0^{iv} - \frac{b^5}{120} \cdot f_0^{v} + \cdots \qquad (1\text{--}21)$$

$$f_{-2} = f_0 - 2b \cdot f_0' + 2b^2 \cdot f_0'' - \frac{4b^3}{3} \cdot f_0''' + \frac{2b^4}{3} \cdot f_0^{iv} - \frac{4b^5}{15} \cdot f_0^{v} + \cdots$$

$$f_{-3} = f_0 - 3b \cdot f_0' + \frac{9b^2}{2} \cdot f_0'' - \frac{9b^3}{2} \cdot f_0''' + \frac{27b^4}{8} \cdot f_0^{iv} - \frac{81b^5}{40} \cdot f_0^{v} + \cdots$$

$$\cdots \cdots \cdots \cdots \cdots \cdots \cdots \cdots$$

$$f_{-n} = f_0 - nb \cdot f_0' + \frac{(nb)^2}{2} \cdot f_0'' - \frac{(nb)^3}{6} \cdot f_0''' + \frac{(nb)^4}{24} \cdot f_0^{iv} - \frac{(nb)^5}{120} \cdot f_0^{v} + \cdots$$

For example, we have for point 2, $x = a + 2b$, $x - a = 2b$. Expanding about point 0, where $x = a$,

$$f_2 = f(a+2b) = f(a) + \frac{f'(a)}{1!} \cdot 2b + \frac{f''(a)}{2!} \cdot (2b)^2 + \frac{f'''(a)}{3!} \cdot (2b)^3 + \frac{f^{iv}(a)}{4!} \cdot (2b)^4 + \cdots$$

$$= f_0 + 2b \cdot f_0' + 2b^2 \cdot f_0'' + \frac{4b^3}{3} \cdot f_0''' + \frac{2b^4}{3} \cdot f_0^{iv} + \cdots$$

which is the equation for f_2 in Eqs. (1–21). In Eqs. (1–21), the unknowns are the derivatives f_0', f_0'', etc. When there are $(N+1)$ known values of f, N such equations can be written, from which the first N derivatives at point 0 ($f_0', f_0'', \ldots, f_0^N$) can be determined. This method is equivalent to that of using Eq. (1–20). As with Eq. (1–20), this process is tedious, and, more often than not, the known values of the function are not accurate enough to warrant the time and effort of computation by this process. However, by taking into consideration only a limited number of equations, each with a limited number of terms, simple approximate formulas can be derived for the derivatives f_0', f_0'', etc. Although these formulas are not theoretically exact, the accuracy of the result can be made consistent with that of the data by using a proper number of equations in the derivation of the formulas.

To derive a formula for the first approximation of f_0', one can use the equation of f_1 in Eq. (1–21), with two terms on the right-hand side:

$$f_1 = f_0 + b \cdot f_0' \left(+ \frac{b^2}{2} \cdot f_0'' + \ldots \right)$$

where the terms in the parentheses have been neglected. From this equation

$$f_0' \doteq \frac{f_1 - f_0}{b} \qquad (1\text{–}22)$$

with an error of the order of $b f_0''/2$. Equation (1–22) is the first approximation of f_0' obtained by using the forward difference. Similarly, one can use the equation of f_{-1} with two terms on the right-hand side:

$$f_{-1} = f_0 - b \cdot f_0' \left(+ \frac{b^2}{2} \cdot f_0'' - \ldots \right)$$

from which

$$f_0' \doteq \frac{f_0 - f_{-1}}{b} \qquad (1\text{–}23)$$

with an error of the order of $b f_0''/2$. Equation (1–23) is the first approximation of f_0' obtained by using the backward difference. For internal points with known values of the function for larger as well as smaller values of the variable, one can utilize the central difference. Using the two equations of f_1 and f_{-1} with three terms on the right-hand side, we have

$$f_1 = f_0 + b \cdot f_0' + \frac{b^2}{2} \cdot f_0'' \left(+ \frac{b^3}{6} \cdot f_0''' + \ldots \right)$$

$$f_{-1} = f_0 - b \cdot f_0' + \frac{b^2}{2} \cdot f_0'' \left(- \frac{b^3}{6} \cdot f_0''' + \ldots \right)$$

Here, we have two equations with two unknowns, f_0' and f_0''. Eliminating f_0'' by subtracting one equation from the other, we have

$$f_1 - f_{-1} = 2b \cdot f_0' \left(+ \frac{b^3}{3} \cdot f_0''' - \ldots \right)$$

from which

$$f_0' \doteq \frac{f_1 - f_{-1}}{2b} \qquad (1\text{–}24)$$

with an error of the order of $b^2 f_0'''/6$. This is the first approximation of f_0' obtained by using the central difference. Since the term with a higher power of b is always smaller in a convergent Taylor's series, a closer approximation is obtained with the central difference. However, at the beginning of the range of the variable, the forward difference must be used; and at the end of the range of the variable, the backward difference must be used.

A second approximation of f_0' can be obtained with central differences by taking four equations from Eqs. (1–21), namely, the equations of f_1 and f_2 on one side of point 0, and f_{-1} and f_{-2} on the other side of point 0. In these four equations, take five terms on the right-hand side so as to include four unknowns, f_0', f_0'', f_0''' and f_0^{iv}.

$$
\left.
\begin{aligned}
f_2 &= f_0 + 2b \cdot f_0' + 2b^2 \cdot f_0'' + \frac{4b^3}{3} \cdot f_0''' + \frac{2b^4}{3} \cdot f_0^{iv} \left(+ \frac{4b^5}{15} \cdot f_0^{v} + \dots \right) \\
f_1 &= f_0 + b \cdot f_0' + \frac{b^2}{2} \cdot f_0'' + \frac{b^3}{6} \cdot f_0''' + \frac{b^4}{24} \cdot f_0^{iv} \left(+ \frac{b^5}{120} \cdot f_0^{v} + \dots \right) \\
f_{-1} &= f_0 - b \cdot f_0' + \frac{b^2}{2} \cdot f_0'' - \frac{b^3}{6} \cdot f_0''' + \frac{b^4}{24} \cdot f_0^{iv} \left(- \frac{b^5}{120} \cdot f_0^{v} + \dots \right) \\
f_{-2} &= f_0 - 2b \cdot f_0' + 2b^2 \cdot f_0'' - \frac{4b^3}{3} \cdot f_0''' + \frac{2b^4}{3} \cdot f_0^{iv} \left(- \frac{4b^5}{15} \cdot f_0^{v} + \dots \right)
\end{aligned}
\right\} \quad (1\text{–}25)
$$

To solve for f_0', eliminate the other three unknowns, as follows: subtracting f_{-2} from f_2 and subtracting f_{-1} from f_1, we have

$$
f_1 - f_{-1} = 2b \cdot f_0' + \frac{b^3}{3} \cdot f_0''' \left(+ \frac{b^5}{60} \cdot f_0^{v} + \dots \right)
$$

$$
f_2 - f_{-2} = 4b \cdot f_0' + \frac{8b^3}{3} \cdot f_0''' \left(+ \frac{8b^5}{15} \cdot f_0^{v} + \dots \right)
$$

Eliminating f_0''', we obtain

$$
f_0' \doteq \frac{8(f_1 - f_{-1}) - (f_2 - f_{-2})}{12b} \tag{1–26}
$$

with an error of the order of $b^4 f_0^{v}/30$. Note that the values of f_1 and f_{-1} have much greater influence than f_2 and f_{-2} on the computed values of f_0'. Values of f for points further away from point 0 have less influence on the computed f_0'. This shows that a good approximation of f_0' can be obtained by considering only a few known values of f near point 0.

Equation (1–26) is the second approximation of f_0' with central differences. Formulas for the second approximation of f_0' with forward or backward differences can be derived by the same principle. Successive approximations can also be obtained by taking into consideration a larger number of equations with enough terms to include an equal number of unknown derivatives.

Example 1–25. The observed distance of travel $s(t)$ of a car is given in the list below. Find the speed $s'(t)$ of the car at $t = 4$ seconds.

t in sec:	0	2	4	6	8
s in ft:	0	30	72	108	160

The first approximation with backward difference, according to Eq (1–23), is:

$$s'(4) \doteq \frac{72 - 30}{2} = 21 \text{ ft/sec}$$

The first approximation with central difference, according to Eq. (1–24), is:

$$s'(4) \doteq \frac{108 - 30}{2 \times 2} = 19\tfrac{1}{2} \text{ ft/sec}$$

The second approximation with central differences, according to Eq. (1–26), is:

$$s'(4) \doteq \frac{8(108 - 30) - (160 - 0)}{12 \times 2} = 19\tfrac{1}{3} \text{ ft/sec}$$

Problems

1–54. By using equations from Eqs. (1–21), derive a formula for the second approximation of f_0' with forward differences. The interval b of the variable is constant. Also show that the error of this formula is of the order of $b^2 f_0'''/3$.

$$\textit{Ans. } f_0' = \frac{4f_1 - f_2 - 3f_0}{2b} + \frac{b^2 f_0'''}{3} + \ldots$$

1–55. Estimate dy/dx at $x = 0.50$ from the given values of x and y, using (a) the first approximation with forward difference, (b) the first approximation with central difference, and (c) the second approximation with central differences.

x	y
0.40	0.625,000
0.45	0.555,556
0.50	0.500,000
0.55	0.454,545
0.60	0.416,667

The given values of y have been computed from $y = 1/(4x)$ to six decimal places. Evaluate dy/dx at $x = 0.50$ by differentiation and substitution. Compute the error and list the methods (a), (b) and (c) in order of accuracy.

$$\textit{Ans. } -0.90910; \; -1.01011; \; -0.99959; \; -1; \text{ c, b, a.}$$

1–56. Round off the values of y listed in Problem 1–55 to four places, and, for each of the five values of y, introduce a random error ranging in value between -0.0099 and $+0.0099$. (This can be done by opening a telephone book at random five times, and reading off each time the value of the last two digits in the page number. Flip a coin to determine whether the "error" is positive or negative. List your new set of values of y. These now have "built in" errors somewhat similar to those which naturally occur in taking physical measurements.) Repeat Problem 1–55 with your new set of values of y, and list the methods (a), (b) and (c) in order of accuracy. (Note that, since random errors have been introduced, no conclusions can be drawn from a single trial. The results of the class as a whole will be compiled.)

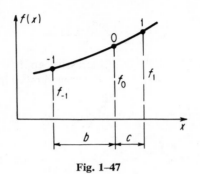

Fig. 1–47

1–57. With known values of f_1, f_0, and f_{-1} spaced at different intervals b and c, as in Fig. 1–47, show that, as a first approximation with central difference,

$$f_0' = \frac{b^2 f_1 - c^2 f_{-1} - (b^2 - c^2) f_0}{bc\,(b+c)}$$

1–17. Numerical differentiation (continued)

In Art. 1–16, formulas have been derived for the successive approximations of f_0' with forward, backward or central differences. By the same method, formulas for higher derivatives can be derived. For example, to derive a formula for the first approximation of f_0'' with central differences, use the two equations of f_1 and f_{-1} from Eqs. (1–21), and include in them two unknowns f_0' and f_0'':

$$f_1 = f_0 + b \cdot f_0' + \frac{b^2}{2} \cdot f_0'' \left(+ \frac{b^3}{6} \cdot f_0''' + \frac{b^4}{24} \cdot f_0^{iv} + \ldots \right)$$

$$f_{-1} = f_0 - b \cdot f_0' + \frac{b^2}{2} \cdot f_0'' \left(- \frac{b^3}{6} \cdot f_0''' + \frac{b^4}{24} \cdot f_0^{iv} - \ldots \right)$$

To eliminate f_0', add f_1 to f_{-1}:

$$f_1 + f_{-1} = 2f_0 + b^2 \cdot f_0'' \left(+ \frac{b^4}{12} \cdot f_0^{iv} + \ldots \right)$$

from which

$$f_0'' \doteq \frac{f_1 - 2f_0 + f_{-1}}{b^2} \tag{1–27}$$

with an error of the order of $b^2 f_0^{iv}/12$. In a similar manner, the formulas for the first approximation of f_0'' with forward differences can be shown to be

$$f_0'' \doteq \frac{f_2 - 2f_1 + f_0}{b^2} \qquad (1\text{–}28)$$

with an error of the order of $b \cdot f_0'''$. The formula for the first approximation of f_0'' with backward differences can be shown to be

$$f_0'' \doteq \frac{f_0 - 2f_{-1} + f_{-2}}{b^2} \qquad (1\text{–}29)$$

with an error of the order of $b \cdot f_0'''$. Successive approximations can also be obtained by taking into consideration a larger number of equations.

It can be seen from the errors of Eqs. (1–22) to (1–29) that, when the known values of the function f_0, f_1, etc. are exact, the higher the approximation and the shorter the interval, the better the computed values of the derivatives. However, observed values are never exact. There are always some random errors, large or small, in the observed data. With random errors in the data, a higher approximation does not necessarily give a better result. This can be illustrated graphically in Fig. 1–48. Let the full line represent the actual function which is unknown to the observer. His observed values of the function are shown as large dots. In computing f_0' to the first approximation with central difference according to Eq. (1–24), in which the observed values of f_{-1} and f_1 are utilized, he obtains the slope at point 0 of the dashed line which passes through the three points -1, 0 and 1. In computing the value of f' to the second approximation with central differences according to Eq. (1–26), in which the observed values of f_{-2}, f_{-1}, f_0, f_1 and f_2 are utilized, he obtains the slope at 0 of the dotted line which passes through the five points from -2 to 2. The slope of the dotted line is not necessarily a better approximation of the slope of the full line (the actual function) at point 0 (see Example 1–26). However, when the random errors are small, the second approximation usually gives a better result.

It can also be seen that, with random errors in the data, the accuracy of the computed values of the derivatives is not necessarily increased by decreasing the interval of the variable. In fact, the results very often become worse. In Fig. 1–49, the dashed line and the observed values are the same as those in Fig. 1–48. This dashed line gives the first approximations of f_0' and f_0''. If, in addition, there are two more observed values as shown by the circles, the first approximations of f_0' and f_0'' will be given by the dotted line. It can be seen that, in this particular case, there is no definite improvement in the computed value of f_0', and f_0'' is becoming farther away from the true value as represented by the full line.

When an approximation is used for a function, such as a truncated series, the higher the order of its derivative, the poorer will be the approximate representation. This is especially true when there are random errors in the observed values of the function. This can be illustrated graphically in Fig. 1–49. The dashed line passing through the points -1, 0 and 1, gives the first approximations of f_0' and f_0'' according to Eqs. (1–24) and (1–27), respectively. While the slope of the dashed line is a fair approximation of the slope of the full line (the actual function), these two lines give vastly different values of f_0'' in this particular case. While the full line is concave downward (negative f_0''), the dashed line is concave upward (positive f_0''). Therefore, derivatives of high order can only be obtained from data of high accuracy.

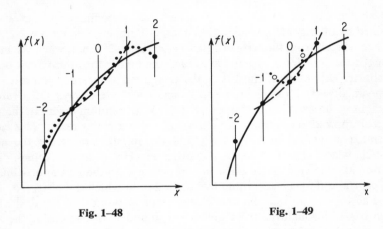

Fig. 1–48   Fig. 1–49

In summary, the method of numerical differentiation should be applied only to cases where a smooth curve passing the plotted values of observation does represent the actual function fairly well. Although it is theoretically desirable to have small intervals of observation (see definition of derivatives in Eq. (1–4)), they must be consistent with the accuracy of the observations. Unless the data are very accurate, it usually does not pay to use the more complicated approximations, especially in the case of high derivatives. However, the labor of deriving the formulas in these two articles is not a complete loss. These formulas will be found useful for other purposes; e.g., in a method of numerical solution of differential equations.

Example 1–26. The observed values of a function $f(x)$ are given:

$$x \quad 0 \quad 1 \quad 2 \quad 3 \quad 4$$
$$\text{observed } f(x) \quad 0.2 \quad 1.0 \quad 1.3 \quad 1.9 \quad 1.8$$

Compute f' at $x=2$ with central differences to the first and second approximations. Also compute f'' at $x=2$ to the first approximation with central differences. If the actual function is $f(x)=\sqrt{x}$, is the second approximation of $f'(2)$ a better result than the first approximation in this case? What is the actual value of $f''(2)$?

Here $b = \Delta x = 1$. The first approximation of $f'(2)$ according to Eq. (1–24) is:

$$f'(2) \doteq \frac{1.9 - 1.0}{2} = 0.45$$

The second approximation according to Eq. (1–26) is: .

$$f'(2) \doteq \frac{8(1.9 - 1.0) - (1.8 - 0.2)}{12} = 0.47$$

The actual value is:

$$f'(x) = \frac{1}{2\sqrt{x}}, \qquad f'(2) = \frac{1}{2\sqrt{2}} = 0.35$$

Therefore, the second approximation of $f'(2)$ is not better than the first approximation in this case.

The first approximation of $f''(2)$ according to Eq. (1–27) is:

$$f''(2) \doteq \frac{1.9 - 2 \times 1.3 + 1.0}{1^2} = 0.30$$

The actual value is:

$$f''(x) = \frac{-1}{4x\sqrt{x}}, \qquad f''(2) = \frac{-1}{4 \times 2\sqrt{2}} = -0.09$$

Problems

1–58. Using your data of x and $y(x)$ (with random errors) in Problem 1–56, estimate the value of y'' at $x = 0.5$ to the first approximation with central differences. (The actual value of y'' at $x = 0.5$ is 4.)

1–59. Suppose that the values of y at $x = 0.45$ and $x = 0.55$ are not available. Repeat Problem 1–58 with only the values of y at $x = 0.4, 0.5$ and 0.6. This has the effect of doubling the value of Δx. Does this help your answer? (Since the errors in the data are random, individual results are not conclusive. The experience of the class as a whole will be compiled.) Do you think it might in principle further improve your answers if Δx were again increased? Explain in a few words.

1–18. Functions of several variables

Previous examples and problems in this chapter have been so chosen that only functions of one independent variable are involved. In many engineering problems, functions of several variables are encountered. In this section, previous discussions are extended to cover these functions.

In the case of a function of two variables, there is a simple geometrical representation, as shown in Fig. 1–50. If $f(x, y)$ is single-valued, the function is represented by a surface. The function is said to be continuous at (a, b) if, in moving towards this point from any direction, the same value of $f(a, b)$ is attained; i.e.,

$$\lim_{\substack{x \to a \\ y \to b}} f(x, y) = f(a, b)$$

Thus $f(x, y)$ is continuous at point A, and discontinuous at point B in Fig. 1–50. In the case of functions of more than two variables, such simple geo-

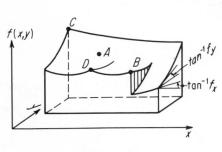

Fig. 1–50

metrical interpretation is not available. However, it is not difficult to understand the definition of continuity in these cases; e.g., for continuity of $f(x, y, z)$ at (a, b, c),

$$\lim_{\substack{x \to a \\ y \to b \\ z \to c}} f(x, y, z) = f(a, b, c)$$

The derivative $F'(x)$ of $F(x)$ is the rate of change of $F(x)$ with respect to x. In the case of a function of more than one variable, e.g., $f(x, y)$, it is necessary to specify the variable with respect to which the rate of change is under consideration. The rate of change of $f(x, y)$ with respect to x (with x changing while y remains constant) is denoted by $\partial f/\partial x$ or $f_x(x, y)$, and is called the *partial derivative* of $f(x, y)$ with respect to x. At any arbitrary point (x_0, y_0), this partial derivative is defined as

$$f_x(x_0, y_0) \equiv \lim_{\Delta x \to 0} \frac{f(x_0 + \Delta x, y_0) - f(x_0, y_0)}{\Delta x} \tag{1–30}$$

where y is kept at y_0 while x makes a change Δx. This definition is analogous to Eq. (1–4) for a function of one variable. (Since the point (x_0, y_0) is arbitrary, the subscript $_0$ in Eq. (1–30) can be dropped.) In the case of a function of two variables, this partial derivative is represented in Fig. 1–50 by the slope of the line on the surface directed in the x direction. Similarly, we have $\partial f/\partial y$ or $f_y(x, y)$ being represented by the slope of the line on the surface directed in the y direction. In finding the partial derivative of a given function with respect to a variable, other variables are considered as constants. For example, for $f(x, y) = x^2 y$, we have $f_x(x, y) = 2xy$ and $f_y(x, y) = x^2$.

Higher partial derivatives are defined in a similar manner; e.g.,

$$f_{yx} = \frac{\partial^2 f}{\partial y \partial x} = \frac{\partial}{\partial y} \left(\frac{\partial f}{\partial x} \right)$$

$$f_{xx} = \frac{\partial^2 f}{\partial x^2} = \frac{\partial}{\partial x} \left(\frac{\partial f}{\partial x} \right)$$

For $f_x = 2xy$, we have $f_{yx} = 2x$ and $f_{xx} = 2y$. It can be proved that, if f_{xy} and

f_{xy} are both continuous in a region, then $f_{xy}=f_{yx}$; i.e., the order of differentiation is immaterial (for the proof, consult textbooks on the Calculus).

Between the points (x_0, y_0) and $(x_0+\Delta x, y_0+\Delta y)$, there is a difference Δf of the function $f(x, y)$. In the case of functions of one variable, the change of the function can be represented by the differential as the change of the variable approaches zero (see Eq. (1–9)). We are going to find an expression for the total differential df of function $f(x, y)$ to represent Δf when the changes of both variables approach zero. For any Δx and Δy,

$$\Delta f = f(x_0+\Delta x, y_0+\Delta y)-f(x_0, y_0)$$

This can be rewritten as

$$\Delta f = \frac{f(x_0+\Delta x, y_0+\Delta y)-f(x_0, y_0+\Delta y)}{\Delta x} \Delta x + \frac{f(x_0, y_0+\Delta y)-f(x_0, y_0)}{\Delta y} \Delta y$$

where Δx and Δy may be replaced by the differentials dx and dy which, as in Eq. (1–9), represent any (finite or infinitesimal) change of the independent variables. As Δx and Δy approach zero, we have, according to Eq. (1–31),

$$\lim_{\Delta y \to 0}\left[\lim_{\Delta x \to 0} \frac{f(x_0+\Delta x, y_0+\Delta y)-f(x_0, y_0+\Delta y)}{\Delta x} dx\right]$$
$$= \lim_{\Delta y \to 0} f_x(x_0, y_0+\Delta y)dx = f_x(x_0, y_0)dx$$

and

$$\lim_{\Delta y \to 0} \frac{f(x_0, y_0+\Delta y)-f(x_0, y_0)}{\Delta y} dy = f_y(x_0, y_0)dy$$

Thus we have for $f(x, y)$

$$df = \lim_{\substack{\Delta x \to 0 \\ \Delta y \to 0}} \Delta f = f_x \, dx + f_y \, dy \qquad (1\text{–}31)$$

For this case of a function of two variables, there is a geometrical interpretation of these terms, as shown in Fig. 1–51, where Δf is given by the surface of $f(x, y)$, while df is given by a plane tangential to this surface. As dx and dy approach zero, the difference $(\Delta f - df)$ approaches zero (compare Fig. 1–51 with Fig. 1–31).

In general, the total differential of $f(x, y, z, \ldots)$ is

$$df = f_x \, dx + f_y \, dy + f_z \, dz + \ldots$$
$$(1\text{–}32)$$

When the changes of the variables are

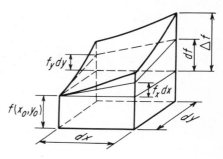

Fig. 1–51

small, df can be used as an approximation of Δf (see Example 1–27). If the variables x, y, z, $\ldots$ are in turn functions of a variable t, then f is completely determined by t. For the rate of change of f with respect to t, we have, from Eq. (1–32),

$$\frac{df}{dt} = \frac{\partial f}{\partial x}\frac{dx}{dt} + \frac{\partial f}{\partial y}\frac{dy}{dt} + \frac{\partial f}{\partial z}\frac{dz}{dt} + \cdots \qquad (1\text{–}33)$$

which is called the *total derivative* (see Example 1–28).

A function of several variables $f(x, y, \ldots)$ is said to be a relative maximum at $(x_0, y_0, \ldots)$ if, in varying all the variables by some sufficiently small amount from $(x_0, y_0, \ldots)$, no greater value of f is encountered. A relative minimum is defined in an analogous manner. As in the case of a function of one variable, the relative maxima and minima can occur at the boundary of the region of interest (such as point C in Fig. 1–50), or at discontinuities of the function or its partial derivatives (such as points B and D in the same figure), or at a point where the function and its first partial derivatives are continuous. In the latter case, the necessary condition for a relative maximum or minimum to occur is that all the first partial derivatives of the function be zero; e.g., for $f(x, y)$, $f_x = 0$ and $f_y = 0$ simultaneously. Note that these are not sufficient conditions. For example, if the surface $f(x, y)$ has the shape of a saddle, these conditions are satisfied at the middle of the saddle, but this point is neither a maximum nor a minimum. However, by physical consideration, one can usually tell whether one has obtained a maximum or a minimum in using these conditions. (There is an analytical method of determining whether the result is a maximum or a minimum or neither, analogous to the method of using the second derivative of a function of one variable. Consult textbooks on the Calculus.) For an example of finding a maximum of a function of several variables, see Example 1–29.

Corresponding to the Taylor's expansion in Eq. (1–12) of a function of one variable, a Taylor's expansion can be written for a function of several variables under suitable conditions. Take for example $f(x, y)$. When the function can be expanded about (a, b), we have

$$f(x, y) = c_0 + [c_1(x-a) + c_2(y-b)]$$
$$+ [c_3(x-a)^2 + c_4(x-a)(y-b) + c_5(y-b)^2] + \cdots$$

where the constants are to be determined. In a manner completely analogous to the derivation of Eq. (1–12), we require that $f(a, b)$ and the partial derivatives $f_x(a, b)$, $f_y(a, b)$, $f_{xx}(a, b)$, $f_{xy}(a, b)$, $f_{yy}(a, b)$, $\ldots$ at the point (a, b) can be obtained from the series. This requirement gives $c_0 = f(a, b)$, $c_1 = f_x(a, b)$, $c_2 = f_y(a, b)$, $2c_3 = f_{xx}(a, b)$, $c_4 = f_{xy}(a, b)$, $2c_5 = f_{yy}(a, b)$, $\ldots$ Thus, we have the Taylor's expansion of $f(x, y)$ about (a, b):

$$f(x, y) = f(a, b) + [f_x(a, b)\cdot(x-a) + f_y(a, b)\cdot(y-b)]$$
$$+ \frac{1}{2!}\,[f_{xx}(a, b)\cdot(x-a)^2 + 2f_{xy}(a, b)\cdot(x-a)(y-b)$$
$$+ f_{yy}(a, b)\cdot(y-b)^2]$$
$$+ \cdots \qquad (1\text{–}34)$$

As in the case of functions of one variable, the Taylor's expansion can be used in computing the function, in obtaining approximations, and in deriving formulas for numerical differentiation.

Example 1–27. The height of a building is determined with a transit, as shown in Fig. 1–32. The angle measurement is 30°, with a maximum error of 0.1°, and the distance measurement is 2000 ft, with a maximum error of 2 ft. Estimate the maximum possible error in the computed height of the building.

For $y(L, \theta) = L \tan \theta$, Eq. (1–31) gives

$$dy = \frac{\partial y}{\partial L} dL + \frac{\partial y}{\partial \theta} d\theta = \tan \theta \, dL + L \sec^2 \theta \, d\theta$$

For small changes of the variables, $\Delta y \doteq dy$. Here, maximum $dL = \pm 2$ ft and $d\theta = \pm 0.00174$ radian. Maximum Δy is obtained with dL and $d\theta$ contributing errors of the same sign. In this case, this occurs when dL and $d\theta$ have the same sign. Thus

maximum $\Delta y = \pm \tan 30° \times 2 \pm 2000 \sec^2 30° \times 0.00174 = \pm 5.80$ ft.

Example 1–28. The market price of used cars of a certain model is found to be increasing by 2 cents per mile toward the west from Detroit. Due to depreciation, the price decreases generally at a rate of two dollars per day. If a person is driving a car of this model towards the west at a rate of 400 miles per day, is the value of the car increasing or decreasing?

This problem can be solved with simple arithmetic. However, it is instructive to consider the price as a function of time and space, as follows. Let x be the distance of a place from Detroit in miles, t be the time in days, and $P(x, t)$ be the market price of this model, in dollars. It is given that

$$P(x, t) = P(0, 0) + 0.02x - 2.00t$$

If the variable x is also used to indicate the position of the car in question, then

$$x(t) = 400t$$

Thus, the value P of this particular car during this trip becomes a function of time. We want to see if dP/dt is positive or negative. From Eq. (1–33),

$$\frac{dP}{dt} = \frac{\partial P}{\partial x} \cdot \frac{dx}{dt} + \frac{\partial P}{\partial t} \cdot \frac{dt}{dt}$$

$$= 0.02 \times 400 - 2.00 \times 1 = 8.00 - 2.00 = 6.00 \text{ dollars per day.}$$

Thus, this man is gaining six dollars a day during this trip. Note that, if $\partial P/\partial t = 0$ (no depreciation), there would be a gain of eight dollars per day due to the change of location of the car. This change due to change of location alone is called a convective change. If $dx/dt = 0$ (not moving), there would be a loss of two dollars per day due to depreciation. This change due to change of time alone is called a local change.

Example 1–29. The mean velocity in a long straight channel increases with, among other things, the hydraulic radius A/p, where A is the cross-sectional area and p the wetted perimeter of the section of the flow. A canal of trapezoidal section with $A = 200$ sq ft is to be constructed. Find y, B, and θ in Fig. 1–52, so that the carrying capacity is maximum.

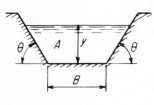

Fig. 1–52

Since A is given, the maximum capacity is obtained with maximum mean velocity and, therefore, with minimum p. First find $p(y, B, \theta)$:

$$p = B + 2y \csc \theta$$

However, the variables are not free to vary independently, but must be so related that $A = 200$ sq ft:

$$yB + y^2 \cot \theta = A$$

With this, one of the variables, say B, can be eliminated in $p(y, B, \theta)$. Thus

$$p(y, \theta) = \frac{A}{y} - y \cot \theta + 2y \csc \theta$$

Minimum p occurs when $\partial p/\partial y = 0$ and $\partial p/\partial \theta = 0$ simultaneously:

$$\frac{\partial p}{\partial y} = -\frac{A}{y^2} - \cot \theta + 2 \csc \theta = 0$$

$$\frac{\partial p}{\partial \theta} = y \csc^2 \theta - 2y \csc \theta \cot \theta = 0$$

The second equation gives $\theta = \pi/3$, or 60°. Substituting into the first equation, we have $y = 10.7$ ft. Also, for $A = 200$ sq ft, $B = 12.4$ ft. This section is half of a hexagon.

Problems

1–60. Suppose that the elevation $h(x, y)$ of a hill above the horizontal $x - y$ plane is given by

$$h = 5000 - 0.02x^2 - 0.01y^2$$

all measurements being in feet. Sketch the contours for $h = 5000$, 4750 and 4700 ft and estimate from your graph the rate of change of h in the x direction and in the y direction at (100, 100). Check your result with derivatives of $h(x, y)$.

Ans. -4, -2

1–61. The outside dimensions of a rectangular metal box are 2 ft by 3 ft by 4 ft. The walls are $\frac{1}{2}$ in. thick. By using differentials, estimate the amount of metal in the walls. *Ans.* 2.17 cu ft

1–62. The unit weight of a brick of metal is to be determined. Its weight is 20.00 lb with a maximum error of ± 0.02 lb, and its dimensions are 2 in. by 4 in. by 8 in. with a maximum error of ± 0.003 in. in each measurement. By using differentials, estimate the maximum possible error of the computed unit weight.

Ans. 0.0011 lb/cu in.

1–63. The temperature $T(x, t)$ in a long tunnel (x being the distance from the entrance) is given as

$$T = A - Be^{-x} \sin (2\pi t)$$

where t is the time in days. What is the temperature $T(t)$ at the entrance, and what do the constants A and B represent? What is approximately the temperature $T(t)$ at a point far away from the entrance? If a person walks into the tunnel at a constant speed v, what is the temperature $T(t)$ he experiences? Find the rate of temperature change $T'(t)$ he experiences. Can you obtain the same result by using Eq. (1–33)?

1–64. The two identical cranks shown in Fig. 1–53 are rotating at known speeds ω_1 and ω_2. Find the angular speed $d\theta/dt$ of the slotted bar in terms of α and β.

$$\textit{Ans.} \quad \frac{9(\omega_1 \sin \alpha - \omega_2 \sin \beta)}{9 + (\cos \beta - \cos \alpha)^2}$$

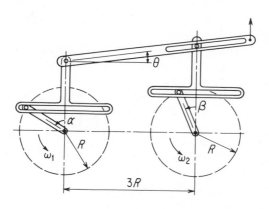

Fig. 1–53

1–65. To be acceptable for parcel post, a package should be such that its combined length and girth is not more than a specified length L. Show that, for maximum volume, a rectangular package should have a square cross section and a length of $L/3$.

CHAPTER 2

VECTOR ALGEBRA

2–1. Vectors and vector analysis

There are physical quantities that can be described adequately for analytical purposes with a magnitude, such as temperature and density. These quantities are called *scalars*. There are other physical quantities that must be described with a direction as well as a magnitude, such as force, rectilinear displacement and velocity (the magnitude of which is called speed). We have seen systems of mathematics for the analysis of problems involving scalar quantities. Naturally, it is desirable to have an equivalent unified system of analysis for directed quantities. Just as the scalar addition $2+3=5$ is true in the counting of apples or of hours, an equivalent system of rules of operation (addition, multiplication, differentiation, etc.) should be made available in handling most, if not all, of the directed quantities, be they forces or velocities. Such a system has been developed and is known as *Vector Analysis*. Directed quantities are usually referred to as *vectors*. In this chapter, some of the algebraic rules of Vector Analysis are introduced.

It should be clear that not all directed physical quantities must necessarily follow these man-made rules. Although these rules have been defined with most of these directed quantities in mind, there is no guarantee that all of them will follow these rules to yield meaningful results. A parallel can be drawn from the case of forming a social club. Although the constitution of the club has been written with many of the prospective members in mind, there is no guarantee that all qualified persons in the world will support the constitution. We shall see later an example of these directed quantities which do not follow the rules of Vector Analysis. In dealing with a directed quantity, it is therefore important to find out whether it follows these rules.

A vector can be represented graphically by a segment of a straight line with an arrowhead. The length of the segment is proportional to the magnitude of the vector. The orientation of the segment and the arrowhead indicate the direction of the vector. In a formula, a vector is usually represented by a boldface type, such as *A*, or a letter with an arrowhead, such as $\overrightarrow{A}$. Its magnitude, which is a scalar, is represented by $|A|$, or $|\overrightarrow{A}|$, or simply *A*.

For the purpose of analysis, a vector is completely described by its direction and magnitude, but not its location. Thus, by *A* = *B*, we mean that the two vectors *A* and *B* are in the same direction, as well as equal in magnitude. However, they may or may not be located at the same place. See Fig. 2–1(*a*). By *C* = *mD*, where *m* is a positive scalar quantity, we mean that vector *C* is

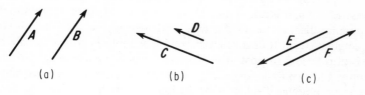

(a)   (b)   (c)

Fig. 2–1

in the same direction as vector *D*, and is *m* times vector *D* in magnitude, as shown in Fig. 2–1(b). By *E* = −*F*, we mean that the two vectors *E* and *F* are in opposite directions with the same magnitude, as shown in Fig. 2–1(c).

Note that, in a correct equation, if one term is a vector, every other term must be a vector of the same dimensions. Thus, in the equation *C* = *mD*, if *C* is a directed length and *m* is time, *D* must be a vector with the dimensions $[L/T]$, such as velocity, so that the dimension of the term *mD* is the same as that of *C*.

2–2. Addition and subtraction of vectors

The most fundamental operation in Vector Analysis is addition. It will be seen that all other operations are solely based on the applicability of this rule of addition. Thus, if a directed physical quantity follows this rule to yield meaningful results, it will follow other rules in Vector Analysis.

The *sum* of two vectors *A* and *B* is defined as follows. Draw from the end of *A* the vector *B*; then, the vector directed from the beginning of *A* to the end of *B* is the sum (*A* + *B*), as shown in Fig. 2–2. This addition gives the sum, which is of course a vector, in direction and in magnitude, but not in location, which is not required for the description of the vector.

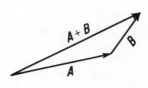

Fig. 2–2

This definition is obviously meaningful when the two vectors are linear displacements. By common sense, we know that the resultant displacement due to two successive displacements A and B is the vector $(A+B)$. Similar argument will indicate that linear velocities can also be added in this manner. Take forces as another example. It is an experimental fact that the joint effect of two forces A and B on the motion of a particle is the same as that of a force equal to $(A+B)$. Thus, forces can be added in this manner, at least when their effect on the motion of a particle is considered.

However, an important question is whether this definition of addition is equally applicable to all other directed quantities to yield meaningful results. The answer is *No*, it is not applicable to every one of them. For example, take finite angular displacements. An angular displacement has a magnitude equal to the angle of turn. It also has a direction, as represented by the direction of the axis of rotation, for instance. However, according to the definition above, we cannot add two finite angular displacements about different axes to obtain the resultant angular displacement. In Fig. 2–3, let the sphere first be rotated

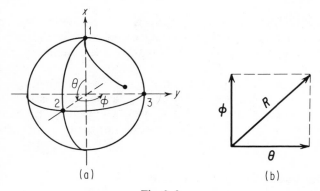

Fig. 2–3

through 90° about the y axis, and then through 90° about the x axis. In this process, a particle at point 1 is first moved to point 2, and then to point 3. Vector addition, as defined above, gives the total angular displacement as one with a magnitude of $\sqrt{2}$ times 90° about an axis in the x-y plane, as indicated by the vector R in Fig. 2–3(b). This angular displacement does not bring point 1 to point 3. Thus, vector addition cannot be applied to finite angular displacements to yield physically meaningful results. (In his future studies of Mechanics, the student will find that infinitesimal angular displacements, angular velocity and acceleration do follow this rule of vector addition).

With vector addition, as defined above, the following rules become obvious:

(a) Vector addition is commutative; i.e.,

$$A+B = B+A \tag{2–1}$$

In Fig. 2–4, the two vectors $(A+B)$ and $(B+A)$ can be seen to be equal in magnitude and in the same direction, and therefore are equal. The same result can also be obtained graphically with a parallelogram, as shown in Fig. 2–4.

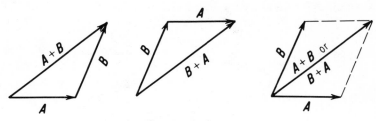

Fig. 2–4

(b) Vector addition is associative; i.e.,

$$(C+D)+E = C+(D+E) \tag{2-2}$$

This equality is illustrated in Fig. 2–5. Thus, the order of addition is immaterial, and the definition of vector addition can be extended to the case of

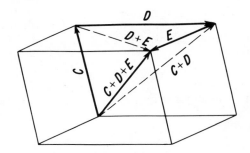

Fig. 2–5

more than two vectors. For example, in order to find the sum of C, D, and E, place the beginning of D to C, and then E to D, as shown in Fig. 2–5. or in any other order. The sum of the three is given by the vector directed from the beginning of the first vector to the end of the last vector thus put together. Consequently, it is very easy to find the sum of vectors graphically when the vectors are all parallel to a plane. These vectors can be moved into this plane without any change in magnitude

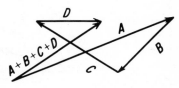

Fig. 2–6

and direction, and be added together graphically, as shown in Fig. 2–6. The figure formed by the vectors and their sum is called a *vector polygon*.

Subtraction of a vector is defined as the addition of its negative; i.e.,

$$A - B = A + (-B) \tag{2-3}$$

where $(-B)$ has been defined as a vector with the same magnitude as B, but in a direction opposite to B. See Fig. 2–7.

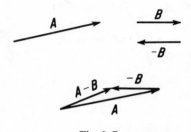

Fig. 2–7

Example 2–1. A boat B is sailing along a straight course at a velocity V_B of 30 mph. A man A on the boat is walking across the boat at a velocity V_{AB} of 11 fps relative to the boat. What is the absolute velocity V_A of the man? By absolute velocity here, we mean the velocity relative to the earth.

Using fps as the unit of velocity, we have V_B=absolute velocity of B=44 fps, and V_{AB}=velocity of A relative to B=11 fps. From Mechanics, we have for relative motion:

$$V_A = V_{AB} + V_B \tag{2-4}$$

With a scale of 1 in. to 20 fps, Fig. 2–8 is constructed according to Eq. (2–4).

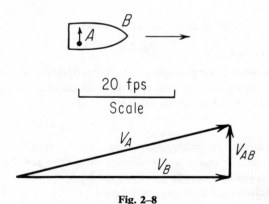

Fig. 2–8

From this figure, we obtain V_A=45.4 fps in the direction indicated in the vector polygon.

Problems

2–1. In Fig. 2–9, *A*, *B*, and *C* represent the successive displacements of a particle in direction and magnitude. Demonstrate graphically that the total displacement is the same for the following cases: (a) *A*, *B*, and then *C*; (b) *B*, *C*, and then *A*; and (c) *C*, *A*, and then *B*.

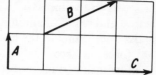

Fig. 2–9

2–2. The current in a river with parallel sides is 5 mph. A boat starting from one side keeps headed perpendicular to the shore and moves at 8 mph across. If the river is 2 miles wide, what is the total displacement of the boat on reaching the other shore? (Hint: first find the absolute velocity of the boat.)   *Ans.* 2.36 miles

2–3. At noon, boat *B* is 10 miles to the east of boat *A*. Boat *A* sails due north at a speed of 0.732 mph, and boat *B* is moving southwest at 1.414 mph. What is the shortest distance between these boats, and when does this occur? (Hint: first find relative velocity V_{BA}).   *Ans.* 8.66 miles at 2:30 p.m.

2–3. Statics of a particle

Classical Mechanics may be considered to be based on Newton's laws, which may be summarized as follows:

(a) Law of motion: the motion of a particle of mass *m*, subject to forces whose sum is *P*, is given by

$$P = k \frac{d}{dt}(mv) \qquad (2\text{–}5)$$

where *v* is the velocity of the particle, *t* is time and *k* is a constant whose value depends on the units used; e.g., $k = 1$ when *P* is in lb, *t* in sec, *v* in fps, and *m* in slugs; or when *P* is in dynes, *t* in sec, *v* in cm/sec, and *m* in grams. At this moment, we are not going to define the derivative of a vector variable. For a particle in equilibrium (i.e., with constant velocity, including in particular the case of no motion), Eq. (2–5) is reduced to

$$P = \sum F = 0 \qquad (2\text{–}6)$$

where $\sum F$ stands for the vector sum of the forces acting on a particle. This equation states the necessary and sufficient condition for equilibrium of a particle, and is called the *equation of Statics* of a particle.

(b) Law of action and reaction: when two particles exert forces on each other, these forces are equal in magnitude and opposite in direction.

A particle is defined as a mass of zero size, and is therefore only an imaginary thing created for the convenience of discussion. In dealing with the physical system, one has to consider a body of finite size. Since the forces acting on a particle are necessarily concurrent, it seems wise at this moment to limit the application of Eqs. (2–5) and (2–6) to bodies under concurrent forces, until further extension of their applications.

When the equation of motion is applied to a body of finite size, a question arises as to the forces which should be included in the equation. Should the action and reaction among the particles of the body be included? The answer is that, according to the law of action and reaction, the sum of all these internal forces is zero. Only forces applied on the body from external sources need be included in the equation. Thus, in using the equation in a particular problem, it is important to make clear what is the particle or body under consideration, so that a force can be classi-

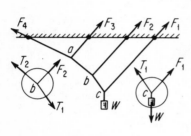

Fig. 2–10

fied as either internal or external. This body may be the whole or a portion of an object, and is called a *free-body*. In the system of strings shown in Fig. 2–10, we may isolate a portion near point c as a free body. For this free body, the external forces are the gravitational force W, and the tensile forces of magnitude T_1 and F_1 from the adjacent portions of strings. We may also isolate a portion near point b as a

free body. Note that, on this free body, the tensile force of magnitude T_1 is equal and opposite to that acting on c, according to the law of action and reaction. If we consider the whole string system as a free body, the external forces are then $F_1,\ F_2,\ F_3,\ F_4,$ and W. The pair of forces of magnitude T_1 in string bc are action and reaction between particles internal to the free body in question, and are therefore internal forces.

Example 2–2. A circular cylinder weighing 100 lb rests in the angle between two smooth planes inclined at 30° and 45° to the horizontal, as shown in Fig. 2–11(a). Find the reactions between the planes and the cylinder.

Take the cylinder as a free body, so as to study the reactions from the planes. The external forces acting on this free body include the weight W and the reactions F_1 and F_2. With no friction between the cylinder and the planes, F_1 and F_2 are normal to the contacting surfaces. The weight W of the cylinder may be assumed to be concentrated at its center. The cylinder is therefore in equilibrium under the action of three concurrent forces. According to Eq. (2–6),

$$\sum F = F_1 + F_2 + W = 0$$

According to this equation, the vector polygon formed by these three forces must close. In this problem, the directions of these forces are known.

The unknowns are the magnitudes F_1 and F_2, which can be determined as follows. Draw W to scale, as shown in Fig. 2–11(b). From points a and b, draw lines bc and ac in the directions of F_1 and F_2, respectively. Then bc and ac give F_1 and F_2, respectively. From the vector polygon, we obtain $F_1 = 52$ lb and $F_2 = 73$ lb.

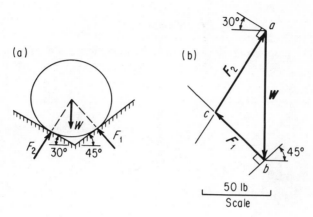

Fig. 2–11

Example 2–3. The system shown in Fig. 2–12(a) is in equilibrium. The pulley is smooth, so that the tension in the string may be considered to be

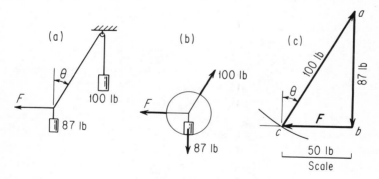

Fig. 2–12

uniform throughout its length. Find the magnitude of the horizontal force F and the angle θ.

Take the 87-lb weight as a free body, so as to study F and the angle θ. The external forces acting on this free body include the weight of 87 lb, the tensile force of 100 lb from the string, and F. This free body is in equilibrium under three concurrent forces. According to Eq. (2–6), the vector polygon formed by these forces must close.

In this case, the two unknowns are the direction of the string and the magnitude F. The closed vector polygon can be constructed with a radius ac representing 100 lb and a horizontal line from point b, as shown in Fig. 2–12(c). From the vector polygon, we have $F = 50$ lb and $\theta = 30°$.

Problems

2–4. Determine graphically the forces in the strings shown in Fig. 2–13.

Ans. 146 lb and 179 lb

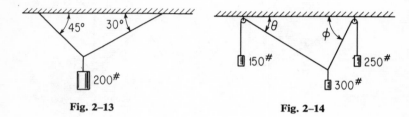

Fig. 2–13   Fig. 2–14

2–5. Determine graphically the angles θ and ϕ in the system shown in Fig. 2–14. The pulleys are very smooth, so that the tension in each string can be considered uniform throughout its length.   *Ans.* 33.7° and 60.0°

2–6. In Fig. 2–15, the mass m_1 is in equilibrium under the gravitational forces exerted by the other five masses. The magnitude of the force exerted on m_1 by

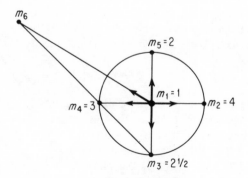

Fig. 2–15

any mass m at a distance r is proportional to mm_1/r^2. Masses m_2, m_3, m_4, and m_5 are situated on a circle of radius R, with m_1 at the center. Mass m_6 lies on the straight line passing through m_3 and m_4. Find the location and magnitude of m_6.   *Ans.* 5.59 unit mass

2-4. Vector addition—Algebraic methods

Algebraic formulas can be written for the magnitude and the direction of the sum of vectors. From Fig. 2–16, we have for the vector sum $(A+B)$:

$$|(A+B)|^2 = (A+B \cos \phi)^2 + (B \sin \phi)^2 = A^2 + 2AB \cos \phi + B^2 \qquad (2\text{-}7)$$

and

$$\tan \theta = \frac{B \sin \phi}{A + B \cos \phi} \qquad (2\text{-}8)$$

where angles ϕ and θ are in the plane containing the vectors A and B. When

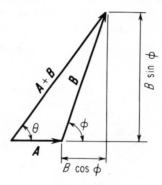

Fig. 2–16

there are more than two vectors to be added, this method can be used repeatedly, but becomes tedious, especially when the vectors are not parallel to one plane.

A generally more satisfactory algebraic method is the use of the components of vectors. By the *component* of a vector on an axis, we mean the projection of the vector on this axis. We may write, for the magnitude of the component of A on the axis s:

$$A_s = A \cos \theta \qquad (2\text{-}9)$$

where θ is the angle between the positive directions of axis s and the vector A. When they are not intersecting, a line parallel to axis s is used, as shown in Fig. 2–17. When the angle θ is between 90° and 270°, A_s becomes negative, meaning that the component is in a direction opposite to the axis s. (In computation, it is more

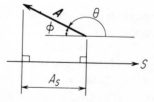

Fig. 2–17

convenient to take the smaller angle between the vector and the axis, such as ϕ in Fig. 2–17. Then, $A_s = \pm A \cos \phi$, where the plus or minus sign is used according to the direction of the component along the axis.) The components most often used are those on rectangular coordinate axes. Let i be a unit vector (with a magnitude equal to one unit) in the direction of the x axis. Then the x component of the vector A can be expressed, in direction as well as in magnitude, as $A_x i$. Similarly, let j and k be the unit vectors in the directions of the y and z axes, respectively. The y and z components of the vector A can be written as $A_y j$ and $A_z k$ respectively, where

$$\left. \begin{array}{l} A_x = A \cos (i, A) \\ A_y = A \cos (j, A) \\ A_z = A \cos (k, A) \end{array} \right\} \quad (2\text{-}10)$$

where angle (i, A) is the angle between the positive directions of vectors i and A, and so on. When these three axes are rectangular axes, the sum of the three components is equal to the vector itself, as can be seen in Fig. 2–18.

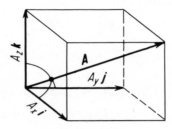

Fig. 2–18

Thus, with rectangular axes x, y and z,

$$A = A_x i + A_y j + A_z k \quad (2\text{-}11)$$

Note that, if a vector is zero in magnitude, all its components must be zero individually; i.e.,

$$A = 0: \quad \left\{ \begin{array}{l} A_x = 0 \\ A_y = 0 \\ A_z = 0 \end{array} \right. \quad (2\text{-}12)$$

Note that an equation with vector terms is equivalent to three equations with scalar terms.

It will now be shown that the component on any axis of a sum of a number of vectors is equal to the sum of their components on this axis. Let the x axis be the axis under consideration, and $R = A + B + \ldots$ We have

$$\begin{aligned} R &= (A_x i + A_y j + A_z k) + (B_x i + B_y j + B_z k) + \ldots \\ &= (A_x + B_x + \ldots) i + (A_y + B_y + \ldots) j + (A_z + B_z + \ldots) k \\ &= R_x i + R_y j + R_z k \end{aligned}$$

Thus

$$\left. \begin{array}{l} R_x = A_x + B_x + \ldots \\ R_y = A_y + B_y + \ldots \\ R_z = A_z + B_z + \ldots \end{array} \right\} \quad (2\text{-}13)$$

The magnitude of the vector R can be computed from its components, as follows. Find the magnitude of the sum of the vectors $R_x i$ and $R_y j$. This vector sum lies in the x-y plane and, according to Eq. (2–7), has a magnitude $\sqrt{R_x^2 + R_y^2}$. Then, add this vector to $R_z k$ to obtain R. Again according to Eq. (2–7), we have the magnitude R:

$$R = \sqrt{R_x^2 + R_y^2 + R_z^2} \qquad (2\text{–}14)$$

The direction of R can be expressed with the directional cosines:

$$\left. \begin{array}{c} \cos(i, R) = \dfrac{R_x}{R} \\[2mm] \cos(j, R) = \dfrac{R_y}{R} \\[2mm] \cos(k, R) = \dfrac{R_z}{R} \end{array} \right\} \qquad (2\text{–}15)$$

By substituting the values of R_x, R_y, and R_z from Eqs. (2–15) into Eq. (2–14), we have

$$\cos^2(i, R) + \cos^2(j, R) + \cos^2(k, R) = 1 \qquad (2\text{–}16)$$

When two of the cosines are known, the third is determined. Thus, any two of the three cosines are enough to determine the direction of the vector completely.

In summary, the vector sum R of several vectors can be obtained as follows. Decompose each vector into components, according to Eqs. (2–10). Find the components of the sum R by using Eqs. (2–13). Compute the magnitude and the direction of R, according to Eqs. (2–14) and (2–15).

Example 2–4. Find the resultant displacement due to the four displacements A, B, C, and D shown in Fig. 2–19.

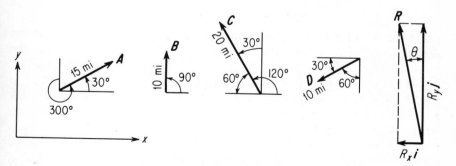

Fig. 2–19

First, decompose each vector into its components. The z component of each of these vectors is zero. Let $R = A + B + C + D$. We have $R_z = 0$.

Vector A: $A = 15$ miles

$\cos(i, A) = \cos 30° = \sqrt{3}/2$; $A_x = A\cos(i, A) = 13.0$ miles
$\cos(j, A) = \cos 300° = \cos 60° = \frac{1}{2}$; $A_y = A\cos(j, A) = 7.5$ miles

Vector B: $B = 10$ miles

$\cos(i, B) = \cos 90° = 0$; $B_x = 0$
$\cos(j, B) = \cos 0 = 1$; $B_y = 10$ miles

Vector C: $C = 20$ miles

$\cos(i, C) = \cos 120° = -\cos 60° = -\frac{1}{2}$; $C_x = -10$ miles
$\cos(j, C) = \cos 30° = \sqrt{3}/2$; $C_y = 17.3$ miles

(The student would probably find it more convenient to use the smaller angle between the vector and the axis, and then add a plus or minus sign to the component, depending on whether the component is in the same direction as or in an opposite direction to the axis. In the case of vector C, the smaller angle between the vector and the x axis is 60°, and the x component of C can be seen to be in a direction opposite to the x axis. Thus, C_x can be computed as $-C\cos 60°$ or -10 miles.)

Vector D: $D = 10$ miles

$D_x = -D\cos 30° = -8.7$ miles
$D_y = -D\cos 60° = -5.0$ miles

According to Eqs. (2–13), the components of the sum R are

$R_x = A_x + B_x + C_x + D_x = 13.0 + 0 - 10.0 - 8.7 = -5.7$ miles
$R_y = A_y + B_y + C_y + D_y = 7.5 + 10.0 + 17.3 - 5.0 = 29.8$ miles

According to Eq. (2–14), the magnitude of R is $\sqrt{(-5.7)^2 + 29.8^2}$, or 30.3 miles. According to Eq. (2–15), the direction of R is given by

$$\cos(j, R) = 29.8/30.3 = 0.983$$

i.e., $\theta = 10.5°$, as shown in Fig. 2–19. Since we also know $\cos(k, R) = 0$, the direction of R is completely determined.

Example 2–5. Two circular cylinders are piled in a rectangular ditch, as shown in Fig. 2–20(a). Find the reaction between the cylinders and the reactions against the bottom and the walls of the ditch. The smaller cylinder weighs 90 lb and the larger cylinder 160 lb. They are made of homogeneous materials, so that the weight of each can be considered as concentrated at its center, if the whole cylinder is included in a free body.

Each cylinder is in equilibrium under concurrent forces, as shown in

Fig. 2–20(b) and (c). Thus, for each cylinder we have, according to Eqs. (2–6) and (2–12),

$$\sum \boldsymbol{F} = 0: \quad \begin{cases} \sum F_x = 0 \\ \sum F_y = 0 \\ \sum F_z = 0 \end{cases}$$

Since all the forces are in the x-y plane, we always have $\sum F_z = 0$. With the other two equations, we can determine two unknowns of the forces acting on each free body. This is true of all free bodies in equilibrium under coplanar concurrent forces.

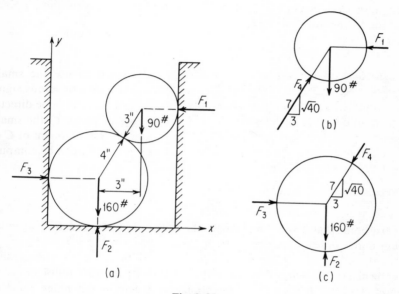

Fig. 2–20

With the smaller cylinder as a free body, as shown in Fig. 2–20(b), the two unknowns are the magnitudes F_1 and F_4. The direction of $\boldsymbol{F}_4$ is determined from the fact that the reaction must act along the line joining the centers of the cylinders. The components of the forces are:

Force $\boldsymbol{F}_1$: x component $= -F_1$; y component $= 0$
Force $\boldsymbol{F}_4$: x component $= F_4 \cdot 3/7$; y component $= F_4 \sqrt{40}/7$
Weight: x component $= 0$; y component $= -90$ lb

The equations of Statics are

$$\sum F_x = -F_1 + \frac{3}{7} F_4 = 0$$

$$\sum F_y = \frac{\sqrt{40}}{7} F_4 - 90 = 0$$

Solving, we have $F_1 = 42.7$ lb and $F_4 = 99.5$ lb.

With the larger cylinder as a free body, the two unknowns are the magnitudes F_2 and F_3. The equations of Statics are

$$\sum F_x = -\frac{3}{7} F_4 + F_3 = -42.7 + F_3 = 0$$

$$\sum F_y = F_2 - 160 - \frac{\sqrt{40}}{7} F_4 = F_2 - 160 - 90 = 0$$

Solving, we have $F_3 = 42.7$ lb and $F_2 = 250$ lb.

Example 2–6. A weight of 100 lb is suspended with three strings attached to a ceiling, as shown in Fig. 2–21. Point *d* is located 2 ft directly under point 0. Find the forces in the strings.

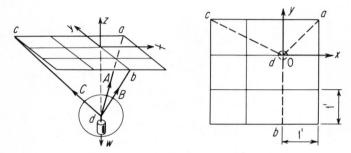

Fig. 2–21

Take point *d* as a free body under the forces *A*, *B*, *C*, and *W*. For equilibrium under noncoplanar concurrent forces, we have $\sum F = 0$; i.e., $\sum F_x = 0$, $\sum F_y = 0$, and $\sum F_z = 0$ for each free body. With three equations, three unknowns can be determined. The three unknowns in this problem are the magnitudes of *A*, *B* and *C*, their directions being determined by the directions of the strings.

To compute the components of the forces according to Eqs. (2–10), we must first find the directional cosines of the forces. Since they are acting along the strings, we can use

$$\frac{A_x}{A} = \cos (i, A) = \pm \frac{L_x}{L}$$

where L is the length of the string with tension A, L_x is the length of the projection of L on the axis, and the sign is plus or minus, depending on whether the component $A_x i$ is in the same direction as or the opposite direction to the axis. Similar equations can be written for the y and z components. From the figure, we have

String *ad*: $L_x = 1$, $L_y = 1$, $L_z = 2$, and $L = \sqrt{1^2 + 1^2 + 2^2} = \sqrt{6}$
String *bd*: $L_x = 0$, $L_y = 2$, $L_z = 2$, and $L = \sqrt{0^2 + 2^2 + 2^2} = \sqrt{8}$
String *cd*: $L_x = 2$, $L_y = 1$, $L_z = 2$, and $L = \sqrt{2^2 + 1^2 + 2^2} = 3$

Thus, we have the components of the forces:

Force A: $A_x = A/\sqrt{6}$, $A_y = A/\sqrt{6}$, $A_z = 2A/\sqrt{6}$

Force B: $B_x = 0$, $B_y = -2B/\sqrt{8}$, $B_z = 2B/\sqrt{8}$

Force C: $C_x = -2C/3$, $C_y = C/3$, $C_z = 2C/3$

Force W: $W_x = 0$, $W_y = 0$, $W_z = -100$ lb

For equilibrium,

$$\sum F_x = \frac{1}{\sqrt{6}} A - \frac{2}{3} C = 0$$

$$\sum F_y = \frac{1}{\sqrt{6}} A - \frac{2}{\sqrt{8}} B + \frac{1}{3} C = 0$$

$$\sum F_z = \frac{2}{\sqrt{6}} A + \frac{2}{\sqrt{8}} B + \frac{2}{3} C - 100 = 0$$

Solving, we have $A = 54.5$ lb, $B = 47.1$ lb, and $C = 33.3$ lb.

Problems

2–7. Find the forces in the strings shown in Fig. 2–22. Use an algebraic method.

Ans. 7.3 lb and 9.0 lb

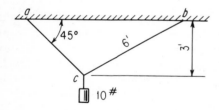

Fig. 2–22

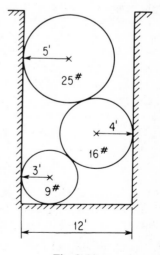

Fig. 2–23

2–8. Three cylinders are piled in a rectangular ditch, as shown in Fig. 2–23. Find the reaction between the small cylinder and the wall.   *Ans.* 41.8 lb

2–9. Find the tension in the bar *ab* shown in Fig. 2–24. The bars are pin-jointed, so that the stresses act along the bars.   *Ans.* 234 lb

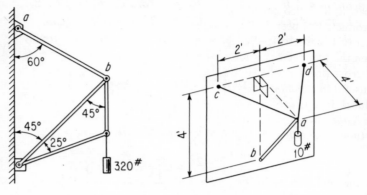

Fig. 2–24   Fig. 2–25

2–10. Solve Problem 2–5 by using an algebraic method.

2–11. Find the forces in the three members of the structure shown in Fig. 2–25.
                                                                        Ans. 14.1 lb and 5.6 lb

2–12. Find the forces in the members *ac, be* and *bd* in the derrick shown in Fig. 2–26. The members *ab, bc,* and *ac* are all in the $x - y$ plane. The weight *W* is such that the tension in cable *bc* is one ton.   *Ans.* 2268 lb and 1964 lb

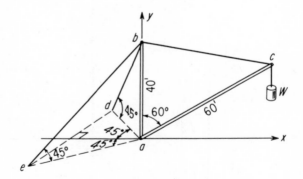

Fig. 2–26

2–5. Scalar product of two vectors

Some physical quantities can be described with a combination of two vectors, in a manner somewhat similar to the product of two scalar quantities. There are two such combinations, and they are called the products of two vectors. One of these products has been so defined that the result is a scalar quantity, and is called the scalar product of two vectors. The scalar product is usually expressed with a dot between the two vectors, such as $A \cdot B$, and, for this reason, it is also called the dot product of two vectors. The other of the two products has been so defined as to give a vector, and is called the vector product of two vectors. The vector product is usually expressed with a cross between the two vectors, such as $A \times B$, and, for this reason, it is also known as the cross product of two vectors. These products have been so defined as to be useful in the analysis of directed quantities. The scalar product is to be introduced in this article.

The *scalar product* of two vectors A and B is defined as the product of the magnitudes A and B and the cosine of their included angle; i.e.,

$$A \cdot B = AB \cos (A, B) \qquad (2\text{--}17)$$

When the included angle is between 90° and 270°, the scalar product is a negative quantity. Also, we have $A \cdot B = 0$ when $A = 0$, or $B = 0$, or A is perpendicular to B. Thus, if $A \cdot B = 0$ and A is not zero, it does not follow that B is zero.

Inasmuch as $\cos (B, A) = \cos (A, B)$, it is evident that the scalar product is commutative; i.e.,

$$A \cdot B = B \cdot A \qquad (2\text{--}18)$$

That the scalar product is distributive can be shown as follows. The scalar product $A \cdot B$ may be considered as the product of the scalar magnitude A

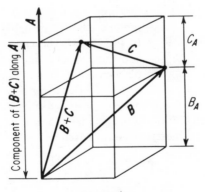

Fig. 2–27

and the magnitude B_A of the component of B in the direction of A. Thus, $A \cdot (B + C)$ is equal to the product of A and the component of the vector $(B + C)$ in the direction of A. But this component is equal to the sum of the components of B and C in the direction of A (see Eq. (2–13) and Fig. 2–27).

The product $A \cdot (B+C)$ is therefore equal to the sum of (a) the product of A and B_A, and (b) the product of A and C_A. Thus,

$$A \cdot (B+C) = A \cdot B + A \cdot C \tag{2-19}$$

When rectangular axes are used, the scalar product of two vectors can be obtained from the components of the two vectors. With i, j, and k representing the unit vectors along the x, y, and z axes respectively, we have, according to Eq. (2–17),

$$\left. \begin{aligned} i \cdot i = j \cdot j = k \cdot k = 1 \\[6pt] i \cdot j = j \cdot k = k \cdot i = i \cdot k = k \cdot j = j \cdot i = 0 \end{aligned} \right\} \tag{2-20}$$

Thus,

$$\begin{aligned} A \cdot B &= (A_x i + A_y j + A_z k) \cdot (B_x i + B_y j + B_z k) \\ &= A_x B_x (i \cdot i) + A_x B_y (i \cdot j) + A_x B_z (i \cdot k) \\ &\quad + A_y B_x (j \cdot i) + A_y B_y (j \cdot j) + A_y B_z (j \cdot k) \\ &\quad + A_z B_x (k \cdot i) + A_z B_y (k \cdot j) + A_z B_z (k \cdot k) \end{aligned}$$

That is,

$$A \cdot B = A_x B_x + A_y B_y + A_z B_z \tag{2-21}$$

The definition of the scalar product has been made so as to be useful in the analysis of directed quantities. One can find the angle between two known vectors by computing their scalar product (see Example 2–7). One can also find the projection of one known vector on another by so doing (see Example 2–8). One can show that two nonzero vectors are perpendicular to each other by showing that their scalar product is zero. In many physical problems, the scalar product represents a meaningful quantity. Take, for example, the work done by constant forces in moving a body through a linear displacement. In Fig. 2–28 is shown a mass m moved under constant forces F and R through a linear displacement s during interval $(t_2 - t_1)$. The velocity v of m changes in magnitude but not in direction. Since the forces are constant, in magnitude as well as in direction, Newton's equation of motion indicates that the time rate of change of mv is constant. Eq. (2–5) can therefore be rewritten as

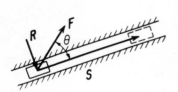

Fig. 2–28

$$F + R = \frac{mv_2 - mv_1}{t_2 - t_1}$$

and the mean v during $(t_2 - t_1)$ is $(v_1 + v_2)/2$, and s is therefore $(v_1 + v_2)(t_2 - t_1)/2$. Take the scalar product of s and each side of the equation:

$$\begin{aligned} F \cdot s + R \cdot s &= \frac{(mv_2 - mv_1) \cdot s}{t_2 - t_1} = \frac{(mv_2 - mv_1) \cdot (v_1 + v_2)}{2} \\ &= \frac{mv_2^2}{2} - \frac{mv_1^2}{2} \end{aligned}$$

Thus, the scalar product of the forces and the displacement is equal to the change of $mv^2/2$ of the mass. The scalar products $\boldsymbol{F}\cdot\boldsymbol{s}$ and $\boldsymbol{R}\cdot\boldsymbol{s}$ are called the *work* done during displacement $\boldsymbol{s}$ by forces $\boldsymbol{F}$ and $\boldsymbol{R}$, respectively. The quantity $mv^2/2$ is called the *kinetic energy* of mass m in linear motion. Thus, the increase of kinetic energy of a body in linear motion is equal to the total work done by all the forces acting on the body.

From Eqs. (2–17) and (2–19), we can learn something about the work done by a force $\boldsymbol{F}$. When $\boldsymbol{F}$ is perpendicular to the displacement $\boldsymbol{s}$, no work is being done by the force, and the kinetic energy of the body is not changed by the action of this force. When $\boldsymbol{F}$ is in the same direction as $\boldsymbol{s}$, a positive work is done by $\boldsymbol{F}$ on the body, tending to increase its speed. When $\boldsymbol{F}$ is in an opposite direction to $\boldsymbol{s}$, a negative work is done by $\boldsymbol{F}$ on the body, tending to decrease its speed. In light of Eq. (2–19), the work done by a constant force A in successive displacements B, C, etc. is equal to the work that would be done by A through a displacement equal to $(B+C+\ldots)$. Thus, the work done by a constant force is independent of the path. Equation (2–19) also indicates that the work done by forces B, C, $\ldots$ in the same displacement A is equal to that done by a force $(B+C+\ldots)$ in A.

Example 2–7. Find the altitude of the sun at New York City (long. 74° W, lat. 41° N) when it is noon at Greenwich, England, on the day of Summer solstice.

In Fig. 2–29 is shown the globe with the y axis as its polar axis. The sun is placed in the x-y plane, so that a vector S directed to the sun is parallel to the x-y plane. When it is noon at Greenwich, this town lies in the x-y plane. Let N be a vector directed vertically at New York. The altitude of the sun at New York is

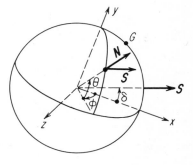

Fig. 2–29

equal to 90° minus the angle between the vectors N and S. This angle can be determined from the scalar product of the two vectors:

$$\boldsymbol{N}\cdot\boldsymbol{S} = NS \cos{(N, S)} = N_x S_x + N_y S_y + N_z S_z$$

Here, we have $N_y = N \sin\theta$, $N_x = N \cos\theta \cos\phi$, $N_z = N \cos\theta \sin\phi$, $S_x = S \cos\delta$, $S_y = S \sin\delta$, and $S_z = 0$. Thus,

$$\cos{(N, S)} = \cos\theta \cos\phi \cos\delta + \sin\theta \sin\delta$$

In this case, we have the difference ϕ in longitude$=74°$, the latitude θ of New York$=41°$, and on summer solstice the declination δ of the sun$=23.5°$. With these values, we obtain $\cos{(N, S)}=0.45$. The angle between N and S is therefore 63°, and the altitude of the sun at New York is $90°-63°=27°$. This occurs at noon in Greenwich; i.e., 7 a.m. EST in New York.

Example 2–8. Point *P* is located in the *x-y* plane by its coordinates (x, y).

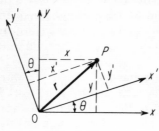

The *x'* and *y'* axes lie in the *x-y* plane, and are oriented at an angle θ with the *x* and *y* axes, respectively, as shown in Fig. 2–30. Express the coordinates (x', y') of *P* in terms of coordinates *x* and *y*.

Let *r* be the location vector directed from the origin to *P*. It can be seen that *r* can be expressed as the sum of known vectors:

Fig. 2–30

$$r = xi + yj$$

The coordinate *x'* is the component of *r* along the *x'* axis. With *i'* as a unit vector along this axis, this component can be computed as follows:

$$
\begin{aligned}
x' &= r \cos (r, i') = r \cdot i' \\
&= (xi + yj) \cdot i' = x\, i \cdot i' + y\, j \cdot i' \\
&= x \cos (i, i') + y \cos (j, i')
\end{aligned}
\tag{2-22}
$$

With $\cos (i, i') = \cos \theta$ and $\cos (j, i') = \cos (90° - \theta) = \sin \theta$,

$$x' = x \cos \theta + y \sin \theta$$

Similarly, we can show that

$$y' = x \cos (i, j') + y \cos (j, j') \tag{2-23}$$

or

$$y' = -x \sin \theta + y \cos \theta$$

Example 2–9. A particle of mass *m* is projected upward from a platform, as shown in Fig. 2–31, with a velocity v_0 on leaving the projector. Find the maximum height the particle will reach and its speed on reaching the floor at *a*.

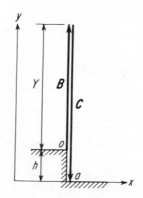

Fig. 2–31

After leaving the projector, the particle is under one constant force, the gravitational force $F = -mg\,j$, where j is the unit vector along the y axis, as shown in the figure, and g is the gravitational force per unit mass.* Let $B = Yj =$ displacement on reaching the maximum height. The work done by F is

$$F \cdot B = (-mg\,j) \cdot (Yj) = -mg\,Y$$

This work is equal to the increase of kinetic energy of the particle. Since the velocity is zero at the maximum height,

$$-mg\,Y = 0 - \frac{1}{2}\,mv_o^2$$

$$Y = \frac{v_o^2}{2g}$$

To reach the floor, we have displacement $C = -(Y+h)\,j$. The work done by F along C is

$$F \cdot C = (-mg\,j) \cdot [-(Y+h)\,j] = mg(Y+h)$$

Since, in this displacement, the particle starts with zero velocity,

$$mg\,(Y+h) = \frac{1}{2}\,mv_a^2 - 0$$

$$v_a^2 = 2g(Y+h) = v_o^2 + 2gh$$

Note that the total work done by the constant force F through the displacements B and C is mgh, which is equal to the work done by F in a displacement $-h\,j$ directly from o to a.

Problems

2–13. With reference to three rectangular coordinate axes, point P is located at (3, 4, 0), point Q at (8, 6, 0), and point R at (1, 2, 2). Point O is the origin. Find the angle between the lines OP and OQ, and that between the lines OP and OR.   *Ans.* 16.2° and 42.9°

2–14. The x, y, and z axes are rectangular coordinate axes, and x', y', and z' axes form another set of rectangular coordinate axes. Both sets have the same origin. Point P is located by coordinates (x, y, z). Show that the coordinates (x', y', z') for P in terms of x, y, and z are

$$x' = x \cos (i, i') + y \cos (j, i') + z \cos (k, i'), \text{ etc.}$$

2–15. A train is travelling in a NE direction on a one per cent grade (rise=1 ft per 100 ft). A horizontal wind exerts a force of 200 lb toward the west on the train.

---

* In accordance with Newton's law of motion, Eq. (2.5), g is also the gravitational acceleration, when proper units are used to make $k=1$. The unit of g may be ft/sec², which is the same as lb/slug, or cm/sec², which is the same as dynes/gm. Its value is about 32.2 ft/sec², or 980 cm/sec².

Find the work done against the wind resistance per mile of travel. (Hint: The work done by the engine against wind resistance is equal and opposite to the work done by the wind force on the train.)   *Ans.* 746,000 ft-lb

2–16. A body weighing 100 lb is thrown out from a platform as shown in Fig. 2–32. Find the work done by the gravitational force on the body, and the speed on reaching point *b*. The initial speed at point *a* is 8 fps. (Hint: The curved path may be considered to consist of a series of short linear displacements.)

Ans. 500 ft-lb and 19.6 fps

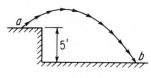

Fig. 2–32

2–6. Vector product of two vectors

Some vector quantities can be expressed as a combination of two vectors, in a manner somewhat similar to the product of two scalars. This combination of two vectors to yield a vector is called a *vector product* of two vectors, or the cross product of two vectors, as it is usually expressed with a cross between the two vectors; e.g., $A \times B$.

Let θ be the smaller angle between two vectors A and B. The magnitude of the vector product $(A \times B)$ is defined as

$$|(A \times B)| = AB \sin \theta \qquad (2\text{–}24)$$

The direction of the vector product is defined as perpendicular to the plane containing A and B, in the direction in which a right-handed screw advances when turned from A towards B through the angle θ. Let e be a unit vector in this direction, as shown in Fig. 2–33. Then, in magnitude and in direction,

$$A \times B = AB \sin \theta \, e \qquad (2\text{–}25)$$

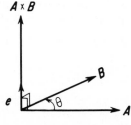

Fig. 2–33

The vector product is zero if $A=0$, or $B=0$, or A is parallel to B ($\theta=0$ or π). Thus, if $A \times B = 0$ and A is not zero, it does not follow that B is zero. Since the direction of advance of a right-handed screw is reversed when turned from B towards A, instead of from A towards B,

$$B \times A = -(A \times B) \tag{2-26}$$

The vector product of two vectors is therefore *not* commutative. However, it can be shown as follows that the vector product is distributive. Take any three vectors A, B, and C, as shown in Fig. 2–34. The vector products

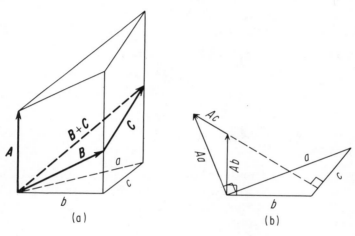

Fig. 2–34

$A \times (B+C)$, $A \times B$, and $A \times C$ are, by the definition of the vector product, all lying in the plane perpendicular to A. Let the lengths a, b, and c be the projections of the vectors $(B+C)$, B, and C, respectively, on this plane. The vector product $A \times (B+C)$ is perpendicular to the parallelogram with sides A and $(B+C)$, and according to Eq. (2–24), has a magnitude equal to the area of the parallelogram. Thus, $A \times (B+C)$ can be shown in Fig. 2–34(b) with a magnitude $A \cdot a$. Similarly, $A \times B$ is perpendicular to the line of length b with a magnitude $A \cdot b$, and $A \times C$ is perpendicular to the line of length c with a magnitude $A \cdot c$. The two triangles in Fig. 2–34(b) are therefore similar. Thus,

$$A \times (B+C) = (A \times B) + (A \times C) \tag{2-27}$$

When rectangular coordinate axes are used, the vector product of two vectors can be obtained from the components of the vectors. As the vector product has been defined with the right-hand convention, it is necessary here to adopt a convention of the arrangement of the coordinate axes. It is the convention to use the right-hand rule; i.e., the z axis is in the direction of advance of a right-handed screw when turned from the x axis towards the y axis. With this convention, we have

$$\left.\begin{array}{lll} i \times j = & k & j \times k = & i & k \times i = & j \\ j \times i = & -k & k \times j = & -i & i \times k = & -j \\ i \times i = & 0 & j \times j = & 0 & k \times k = & 0 \end{array}\right\} \quad (2\text{--}28)$$

Thus, according to Eqs. (2–27) and (2–28),

$$\begin{aligned} A \times B &= (A_x i + A_y j + A_z k) \times (B_x i + B_y j + B_z k) \\ &= A_x B_x (i \times i) + A_x B_y (i \times j) + A_x B_z (i \times k) \\ &\quad + A_y B_x (j \times i) + A_y B_y (j \times j) + A_y B_z (j \times k) \\ &\quad + A_z B_x (k \times i) + A_z B_y (k \times j) + A_z B_z (k \times k) \\ &= 0 + A_x B_y k - A_x B_z j - A_y B_x k + 0 + A_y B_z i + A_z B_x j - A_z B_y i + 0 \end{aligned}$$

Collecting terms, we have the three components of the vector product:

$$A \times B = (A_y B_z - A_z B_y)\, i + (A_z B_x - A_x B_z)\, j + (A_x B_y - A_y B_x)\, k \quad (2\text{--}29)$$

This equation can be written in a shorthand form as a determinant:

$$A \times B = \begin{vmatrix} i & j & k \\ A_x & A_y & A_z \\ B_x & B_y & B_z \end{vmatrix} \quad (2\text{--}30)$$

With the components known, the magnitude and the direction of the vector product can be easily determined, as indicated by Eqs. (2–14) and (2–15).

The vector product of two vectors has been so defined as to be useful in the analysis of directed quantities. One can find the area of a parallelogram formed by two vectors as two nonparallel sides by finding the magnitude of their vector product (see the proof of Eq. (2–27)). One can show that two nonzero vectors are parallel by showing that their vector product is zero. Many directed physical quantities can be represented by the vector product of two vectors. Take, for example, the linear velocity v of a particle on a solid body rotating at angular velocity ω about an axis. The angular velocity ω is a vector with a magnitude equal to the speed of rotation, and a direction as indicated by the direction of the axis of rotation according to the right-hand rule, as shown in Fig. 2–35. Let r be the vector directed from any point a on the axis of rotation to the particle P in question. Let θ denote the angle between r and ω which has been placed, for convenience, on the axis of rotation. It can be seen that point P is actually at a distance $r \cdot \sin \theta$ from the axis of rotation. The linear velocity v therefore has a magnitude $\omega r \cdot \sin \theta$ and a direction perpendicular to the plane aOP which contains the axis of rotation and r. Thus, the linear velocity v can be completely described in magnitude and in direction by

$$v = \omega \times r \quad (2\text{--}31)$$

Note that $v = -r \times \omega$.

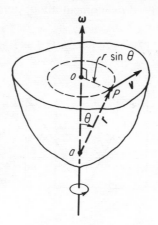

Fig. 2–35

For another example of vector products, take the moment M of a force F about a point a. That this quantity M is useful in the study of Mechanics will be shown in the following article. The *moment* M of F about point a is defined as

$$M = r \times F \qquad (2\text{–}32)$$

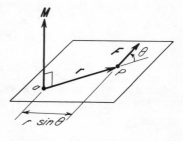

where r is the vector directed from moment center a to P, the point of application of F. The magnitude M is equal to $rF \cdot \sin \theta$ (see Fig. 2–36). The distance $r \cdot \sin \theta$ is the distance from the moment center to the line of action of F, and is usually called the *moment arm* of F about a. The moment M, being a vector, can be resolved into components along axes. The component of M along an

·Fig. 2–36

axis through the moment center is also called the (scalar) moment of F about this axis. From Eq. (2–25), we know that M is zero if the line of action of F passes through the moment center, since $\sin \theta = 0$. The component of M along an axis parallel to F is zero since, by definition, M is perpendicular to F. From Eq. (2–27), we know that the sum of the moments of several concurrent forces (with same r) is equal to the moment of the sum of the forces:

$$(r \times F_1) + (r \times F_2) + \ldots = r \times (F_1 + F_2 + \ldots)$$

It follows immediately that the moment of a force can be computed as the sum of the moments of its components (see Example 2–10).

Example 2–10. A force in lb, $F = 2i + 3j$, is located at $(2, -1, 0)$, the unit of length being the foot. Find its moment about point a at $(1, 1, 0)$.

As shown in Fig. 2–37,

$$r = (2-1)\,i + (-1-1)\,j = i - 2j$$

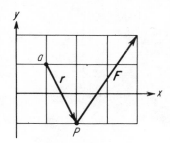

Fig. 2–37

Thus, according to Eqs. (2–30) and (2–32),

$$M = r \times F = \begin{vmatrix} i & j & k \\ r_x & r_y & r_z \\ F_x & F_y & F_z \end{vmatrix}$$

For a force in the x-y plane about a moment center in this plane, $F_z = 0$, $r_z = 0$, and

$$\begin{aligned} M &= (r_x F_y - r_y F_x)\,k \\ &= [1 \times 3 - (-2) \times 2]\,k \\ &= 7\,k \qquad \text{(i.e., 7 ft-lb in the } z \text{ direction)} \end{aligned}$$

Note that this moment is equal to the sum of the moments $r_x F_y k$ and $-r_y F_x k$ of the components F_y and F_x with moment arms r_x and r_y respectively about point a.

Problems

2–17. A globe is shown rotating about an axis in the direction of oa in Fig. 2–38. Find the x, y, and z components of the linear velocity of a point at Latitude $30°$ N on the globe as the point passes the plane oab as shown, by using Eqs. (2–30) and (2–31). The globe is 4 ft in diameter and is rotating at a speed of one revolution per second.   *Ans.* 7.7 $(-i+j)$ fps

2–18. Given force $F = i + j - 2k$ acting at point $P\,(1, 2, 1)$; find its moment about the origin and the x component of this moment. Also find its moment about point $a\,(2, 0, 0)$ on the x axis, and the x component of this moment. (This problem demonstrates that the moment of a force about an axis is independent of the location of the moment center, as long as it remains on the axis.)   *Ans.* $M_x = -5$

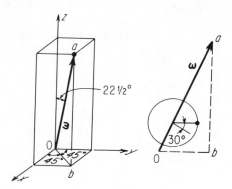

Fig. 2–38

2–19. A pair of parallel forces, equal in magnitude but opposite in direction, is called a *couple*. In Fig. 2–39 is shown a couple with forces F and $-F$. Find the moment of this couple (i.e., the sum of the moments of the two forces) about point b. With a as the vector directed from the point of application of $-F$ to that of F, demonstrate that this moment is equal to $(a \times F)$, which is independent of the location of the moment center.

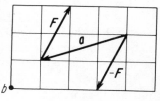

Fig. 2–39

2–20. It can be proved that the following scalar triple products are equal:

$$A \cdot (B \times C) = B \cdot (C \times A) = C \cdot (A \times B) \tag{2-33}$$

Verify the first equality by using the rectangular components of the vectors. You may put the x axis along A and the $x-y$ plane parallel to B without loss of generality.

2–21. It can be proved that the vector triple product

$$A \times (B \times C) = B(A \cdot C) - C(A \cdot B) \tag{2-34}$$

Verify this expression by using the rectangular components of the three vectors.

2–7. Equilibrium of bodies of finite size

From Newton's law of motion, $\sum F = d(mv)/dt$, we have the necessary and sufficient conditions of equilibrium of a single particle. A necessary condition is one which must be satisfied when a particle is in equilibrium. When a particle is known to be in equilibrium (i.e., $d(mv)/dt = 0$), we have from Newton's law $\sum F = 0$ as a necessary condition. A sufficient condition is one which, if satisfied, always produces equilibrium. When $\sum F$ is known to be zero, Newton's law indicates that $d(mv)/dt = 0$; i.e., the particle is in equilibrium. Thus, $\sum F = 0$ is also a sufficient condition of equilibrium of a particle. We now proceed to find necessary and sufficient conditions of equilibrium of a body of finite size. One must first realize the difference between the two kinds of conditions which may not be identical. Attention is called to the fact that, in the following discussion, nothing other than Newton's law is used in finding these conditions.

Given a body in equilibrium (with every particle in equilibrium), we have, as a necessary condition of equilibrium of each particle, $\sum F = 0$ on each particle. These forces include forces from external sources and the reactions from the other particles of the body. Summing up all the forces on all the particles of the body, we have $\sum F_i + \sum F_e = 0$, where $\sum F_e$ is the sum of all the external forces on the body, and $\sum F_i$ is the sum of all the internal actions and reactions among the particles of the body. Since for each action there is an equal and opposite reaction, we have $\sum F_i = 0$. Thus $\sum F_e = 0$ or simply

$$\sum F = 0 \qquad (2\text{–}35)$$

where $\sum F$ is the sum of all external forces on the body. This is a necessary condition that must be satisfied when a body is in equilibrium.

We can make up other necessary conditions for equilibrium. One that will be found useful is obtained by considering the moments of the forces. Consider the forces on one of the particles. These forces are concurrent and, therefore, the sum of their moments about any moment center is equal to that of their sum, which is zero, since $\sum F = 0$ for equilibrium of the particle. Since the moment of the forces on each particle is zero, the sum of the moments of all the internal and external forces on the body is zero. And since each pair of internal action and reaction is colinear, equal and opposite, the sum of the moments of the internal forces is zero. Thus

$$\sum M = 0 \qquad (2\text{–}36)$$

where $\sum M$ is the sum of moments of all the external forces on the body about any moment center. This is another necessary condition of equilibrium.

While one can make up other necessary conditions of equilibrium, Eqs. (2–35) and (2–36) are the ones found to be useful later. However, they are not sufficient conditions of equilibrium; i.e., they do not guarantee equilibrium. For example, apply a pair of equal and opposite forces to the two ends of a rubber cylinder. Equations (2–35) and (2–36) are satisfied, and yet the body is not in equilibrium, but is being deformed.

It can be shown, however, that if a body is rigid (i.e., not deformable), Eqs. (2–35) and (2–36) are also sufficient conditions of equilibrium. In reality, no material is absolutely rigid. In practice, one can ignore the deformations if they are small. To show that these equations are sufficient conditions for equilibrium, take a rigid body with $\sum F=0$ and $\sum M=0$. We are not yet sure that the body is in equilibrium. To produce equilibrium, one can introduce the following constraints, as shown in Fig. 2–40, in addition to the given forces: a hinge at point A, so that the body cannot move away from this point; a sleeve at point B, so that the body can now only rotate about AB; and a hanger at C, so that the body is now completely fixed since it is not deformable. We have introduced six components of forces to the body, three at A, two at B and one at C. Now that the body is definitely in equilibrium, we have, according to the necessary conditions, Eqs. (2–35) and (2–36),

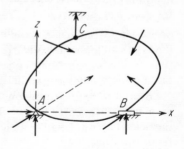

Fig. 2–40

$$\sum (\text{given } F)+\sum (\text{added } F) = 0$$
$$\sum (M \text{ of given } F)+\sum (M \text{ of added } F) = 0$$

Since we have given $\sum F = 0$ and $\sum M = 0$,

$$\sum (\text{added } F) = 0$$
$$\sum (M \text{ of added } F) = 0$$

Here, we have two vector equations or six scalar equations, from which the six added components of forces can be determined. It is not difficult to verify that these equations give zero value for all the six added components. This means that no additional constraints are necessary to produce equilibrium, once we have $\sum F=0$ and $\sum M=0$ on a rigid body. Thus, Eqs. (2–35) and (2–36) are also sufficient conditions of equilibrium of a rigid body. Note that we need the equation $\sum M=0$ as well as $\sum F=0$ in this proof, because we have to introduce, during the proof, six constraints to the body. Six scalar equations are needed to show that these constraints are not necessary.

Given a body in equilibrium, we have from Eqs. (2–35) and (2–36):

$$\sum F = 0 \quad \begin{cases} \sum F_x = 0 \\ \sum F_y = 0 \\ \sum F_z = 0 \end{cases}$$

$$\sum M = 0 \quad \begin{cases} \sum M_x = 0 \\ \sum M_y = 0 \\ \sum M_z = 0 \end{cases}$$

While there are six scalar equations, some of them may not furnish useful information for some particular force systems. For example, for coplanar concurrent forces on a free body as in Example 2–5, four of these equations

($\sum F_z = 0$, $\sum M_x = 0$, $\sum M_y = 0$, and $\sum M_z = 0$) take the form $0 = 0$. Therefore, only two of the equations are useful. Thus, for a particular system of forces in equilibrium, there is a fixed number of useful equations that can be written for each free body:

Concurrent parallel forces	1
Coplanar concurrent forces	2
Noncoplanar concurrent forces	3
Coplanar parallel forces	2
Coplanar nonconcurrent nonparallel forces	3
Noncoplanar parallel forces	3
Noncoplanar nonconcurrent nonparallel forces	6

Examples of the second and third systems are given in Examples 2–5 and 2–6. Examples of the last four systems are given in Examples 2–11 to 2–14 below.

To determine the number of unknowns involved in a problem, one should remember that, for a force in space, a full description consists of a magnitude and two angles (see remarks following Eq. (2–16)), or the magnitude of its three components. In any case, three values are required for its full description. If a force in space is unknown in magnitude as well as in direction, there are three unknowns involved (e.g., reaction at point b in Example 2–14). If a force is known in direction but unknown in magnitude, there is only one unknown involved (e.g., the magnitude F_6 in the same example). In the case of forces in a plane, one of the directional cosines is known, since the forces are all perpendicular to the axis which is perpendicular to this plane. Thus, for a force in a plane, a full description consists of a magnitude and one additional angle, or the magnitudes of two components of the force. Therefore, in a problem with coplanar forces, a force unknown in magnitude and in direction is equivalent to two unknowns (e.g., reaction at the bottom of the ladder in Example 2–12). A force unknown in magnitude but known in direction gives one unknown (e.g., reaction at the top of the same ladder).

Very often, a problem cannot be solved by applying the equations of Statics directly to the whole physical system. Take, for example, the system of strings shown in Fig. 2–10. With the whole system as a free body, we have four unknowns (F_1, F_2, F_3, and F_4), while the number of useful equations of Statics for the coplanar forces is three. However, this problem can be solved by choosing free bodies with care. With point c as a free body, we have two equations of Statics for two unknowns, including F_1. With F_1 determined, the other three unknowns can then be solved for by using the whole system as a free body.

Problems that can be solved by using the equations of Statics alone are called *statically-determinate problems*. The system shown in Fig. 2–10 is an example of these problems. But there are problems which cannot be solved by using the equations of Statics alone, no matter how the free bodies are chosen. For example, take the case of a four-legged table with a load near the center of the table top. For this system of parallel forces, there are three useful equations of Statics. One more equation is necessary for the determination of the four unknown supporting forces. This additional equation is written according to the elastic properties of the legs and the table top. That the supporting forces depend on the elastic properties of the system can easily be demonstrated by considering the following two cases. When the four legs are similar, the load on each leg is nearly the same. When one leg is made of rubber while the others are heavy steel posts, the rubber leg will offer practically no support. Such problems are called *statically-indeterminate problems*, which are beyond the scope of this chapter. It suffices to say here that, if one or more components of the reactions can be removed without disturbing the configuration of the system, the system is statically indeterminate. In the system of strings in Fig. 2–10, none of the reactions can be removed (by disconnecting a string) without disturbing the system. This system is therefore statically determinate. On the other hand, one of the reactions on the four-legged table can be removed without disturbing the system. This system is therefore statically indeterminate.

Example 2–11. Find the reactions F_3 and F_4 supporting the block under the action of two parallel forces F_1 and F_2, as shown in Fig. 2–41. The symbol at F_3 represents a "roller," where the reaction is always normal to the contacting surfaces. The symbol at F_4 represents a "hinge," where the reaction must pass.

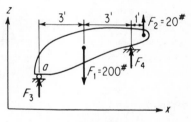

Fig. 2–41

Here, we have a system of coplanar parallel forces. Let this plane be the x-z plane with the z axis vertically upward. For any *one* of the forces in this direction, we have $F_y=0$ and $F_x=0$. Thus, with moment center at any point in the x-z plane ($r_y=0$), the moment is

$$M = r \times F = \begin{vmatrix} i & j & k \\ r_x & 0 & r_z \\ 0 & 0 & F_z \end{vmatrix} = -r_x F_z j$$

Since there are no x and y components of forces and no x and z components of moments, the useful equations from Eqs. (2–35) and (2–36) are $\sum F_z=0$ and $\sum M_y=0$. With two equations for a free body, two unknowns can be determined. Taking the whole block as a free body, we have two unknowns, F_3 and F_4:

$$\sum F_z = F_3 - 200 + F_4 + 20 = 0$$

and, with moment center at point a on one of the two unknowns, as shown,

$$\sum M_y = -F_3 \times 0 + 200 \times 3 - F_4 \times 6 - 20 \times 7 = 0$$

Solving, we obtain $F_3 = 103.3$ lb and $F_4 = 76.7$ lb.

At the start, we have assumed the directions of F_3 and F_4. If the assumed direction of a force is incorrect, a negative value for its magnitude will be obtained. Here, we have positive values for F_3 and F_4, indicating that the assumed directions for them are correct.

Example 2–12. A ladder rests with its upper end against a smooth wall and its lower end against a block on the floor, as shown in Fig. 2–42. Find the reactions at the two ends of the ladder.

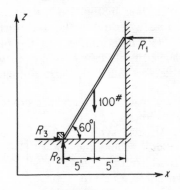

Fig. 2–42

The ladder is under transverse load, and is therefore not under axial tension or compression. The reactions do not act along the ladder. Since the wall is smooth, reaction R_1 must be perpendicular to the wall. The reaction at the bottom is unknown in magnitude and in direction, and can be represented by two unknown components.

Here, we have a system of coplanar nonconcurrent and nonparallel forces. Placing all the forces in the x-z plane, we have no y components of forces. With the moment center in the x-z plane, we have, for any one of the forces,

$$M = \begin{vmatrix} i & j & k \\ r_x & 0 & r_z \\ F_x & 0 & F_z \end{vmatrix} = (r_z F_x - r_x F_z) j$$

Thus, for equilibrium under coplanar, nonconcurrent and nonparallel forces, we have three useful equations of statics for each free body. With the whole ladder as a free body, we have $\sum M_y = 0$, $\sum F_x = 0$, and $\sum F_z = 0$. There are three unknown components of forces on this free body. In taking moments, it is convenient to choose a moment center on the line of action of one or more of the unknowns.

With the moment center at the lower end of the ladder, we have

$$\sum M_y = +100 \times 5 - R_1 \times 10\sqrt{3} = 0$$
$$\sum F_x = R_3 - R_1 = 0$$
$$\sum F_z = R_2 - 100 = 0$$

Solving, we obtain $R_1 = R_3 = 28.8$ lb, and $R_2 = 100$ lb.

Example 2–13. Find the three reactions supporting the plate in Fig. 2–43 under a 100-lb load.

Here, we have a system of noncoplanar parallel forces. With the z axis parallel to the forces, we have no x and y components of forces. With any moment center, any one of the forces gives

$$M = \begin{vmatrix} i & j & k \\ r_x & r_y & r_z \\ 0 & 0 & F_z \end{vmatrix} = r_y F_z\, i - r_x F_z\, j$$

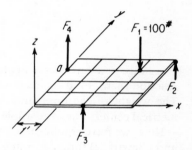

Fig. 2–43

There is no z component of moment. Thus, for equilibrium under this system of forces, there are three useful equations of Statics for each free body: $\sum F_z = 0$, $\sum M_x = 0$, and $\sum M_y = 0$. With the whole plate as a free body, there are three unknowns, F_2, F_3, and F_4.

Choosing the moment center a on the line of action of one of the unknowns, we have:

Force	F_z	r_x	r_y
F_1	-100 lb	3 ft	0 ft
F_2	F_2	4	1
F_3	F_3	2	-3
F_4	F_4	0	0

Thus

$$\sum F_z = \qquad\qquad\qquad -100 + F_2 + F_3 + F_4 = 0$$
$$\sum M_x = \sum r_y F_z = \qquad\qquad 0 + F_2 - 3F_3 + 0 = 0$$
$$\sum M_y = \sum -r_x F_z = -3 \times (-100) - 4F_2 - 2F_3 + 0 = 0$$

Solving, we obtain $F_2 = 64.3$ lb, $F_3 = 21.4$ lb, and $F_4 = 14.3$ lb.

Example 2-14. A rectangular trap door weighs 100 lb and is hinged at points *a* and *b*, as shown in Fig. 2-44. The door is held open with a cable.

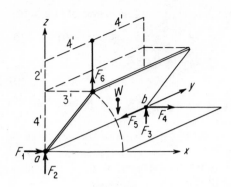

Fig. 2-44

The hinge at *a* has been so constructed that there is no *y* component in the reaction there. Find the reactions at the hinges and the tension in the cable. The weight of the door may be considered to be concentrated at its geometrical center, when the whole door is included in a free body.

Here, we have equilibrium under a system of noncoplanar, nonconcurrent and nonparallel forces. For any one of the forces,

$$M = r \times F = (r_y F_z - r_z F_y)\,i + (r_z F_x - r_x F_z)\,j + (r_x F_y - r_y F_x)\,k$$

All six scalar equations of Statics are useful. With the whole door as a free body, the six unknowns are: F_1 and F_2 at hinge *a*; F_3, F_4, and F_5 at hinge *b*; and F_6, the tension in the cable. The direction of F_6 is determined by the direction of the cable. From Fig. 2-44, we have the projections of the length of the cable: $L_x = 3$ ft, $L_y = 4$ ft, and $L_z = 2$ ft. The length of the cable L is therefore $\sqrt{3^2 + 4^2 + 2^2} = \sqrt{29}$ ft.

With point *a* as the moment center, we have

Force	F_x	F_y	F_z	r_x	r_y	r_z
F_1	F_1	0	0	0	0	0
F_2	0	0	F_2	0	0	0
F_3	0	0	F_3	0	8	0
F_4	F_4	0	0	0	8	0
F_5	0	$-F_5$	0	0	8	0
F_6	$\dfrac{-3}{\sqrt{29}}F_6$	$\dfrac{4}{\sqrt{29}}F_6$	$\dfrac{2}{\sqrt{29}}F_6$	3	0	4
W	0	0	-100	$\dfrac{3}{2}$	4	2

Thus

$$\sum F_x = F_1 + F_4 - \frac{3}{\sqrt{29}} F_6 = 0$$

$$\sum F_y = -F_5 + \frac{4}{\sqrt{29}} F_6 = 0$$

$$\sum F_z = F_2 + F_3 + \frac{2}{\sqrt{29}} F_6 - 100 = 0$$

$$\sum M_x = \sum r_y F_z - \sum r_z F_y = 8F_3 - \frac{16}{\sqrt{29}} F_6 - 400 = 0$$

$$\sum M_y = \sum r_z F_x - \sum r_x F_z = -\frac{18}{\sqrt{29}} F_6 + 150 = 0$$

$$\sum M_z = \sum r_x F_y - \sum r_y F_x = -8F_4 + \frac{12}{\sqrt{29}} F_6 = 0$$

Solving, we obtain $F_1 = 12\frac{1}{2}$ lb, $F_2 = 16\frac{2}{3}$ lb, $F_3 = 66\frac{2}{3}$ lb, $F_4 = 12\frac{1}{2}$ lb, $F_5 = 33\frac{1}{3}$ lb, and $F_6 = 45$ lb.

Problems

2–22. Find the reactions supporting the beam shown in Fig. 2–45.

Ans. 80 lb and 270 lb

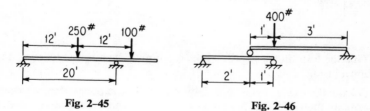

Fig. 2–45   Fig. 2–46

2–23. Find the four reactions in the system of beams shown in Fig. 2–46.

Ans. 300 lb and 100 lb; 100 lb and 200 lb

2–24. Find the force P required for balancing a weight of 1000 lb in each of the two systems of pulleys shown in Fig. 2–47. The pulleys are very smooth, so that the tension in each string is practically uniform. The radius of the pulleys is r. The weight of the pulleys is negligible. What should be the distance c in the system shown in Fig. 2–47(b)?   *Ans.* 125 lb, 143 lb, and $3r/7$

2–25. A cantilever beam is a beam with one end free of support, while the other end is built inside a solid support, as shown in Fig. 2–48(a). As far as the over-hanging portion of the beam is concerned, the reaction at the built-in support can be replaced by a couple of moment M ($M = fd$) and a vertical force V, as shown in Fig. 2–48(b). Find the reactions M and V acting on the beam.

Ans. 3000 lb-ft and 100 lb

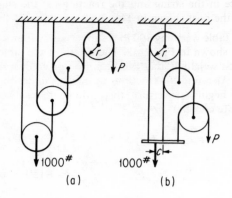

Fig. 2–47

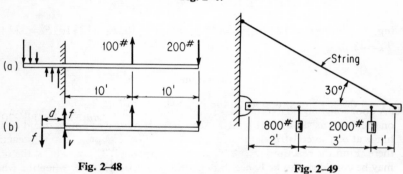

Fig. 2–48   Fig. 2–49

2–26. Find the force in the string and the reaction at the hinge supporting the beam shown in Fig. 2–49.   *Ans.* 3860 lb and 3460 lb

2–27. A smooth circular cylinder weighing 1000 lb is supported by a string and a beam, as shown in Fig. 2–50. One end of the beam is hinged at the wall, and the other end rests on a smooth floor. The weight of the beam is negligible. Find the reaction on the floor.   *Ans.* 700 lb

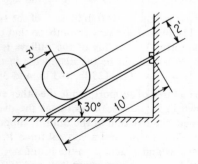

Fig. 2–50

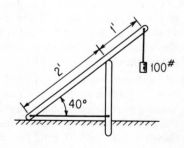

Fig. 2–51

2-28. Find the force in the string and the reactions at the smooth floor and the smooth top of the post shown in Fig, 2-51.   *Ans.* 74 lb, 12 lb, and 115 lb

2-29. A rectangular table weighing 100 lb is supported by four legs at the midpoints of the sides, as shown in Fig. 2-52. The length of the table is twice its width. Find the greatest weight W that can be put on one corner of the table without overturning it. Also find the reactions at the legs under this condition. (Hint: When the table begins to overturn, there will be no reaction under the two legs near the opposite corner.)   *Ans.* 100 lb

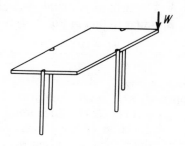

Fig. 2-52

2-30. A door weighing 30 lb is held open under the action of à 10-lb weight by a nail on the floor, as shown in Fig. 2-53. The door is hinged at points *a* and *b*. The hinge at *a* is so constructed that there is no vertical component in the reaction there. Find the reactions at the hinges and at the nail. The weight of the door may be considered to be concentrated at its geometrical center when the whole door is included in a free body.   *Ans.* 7.4 lb, 31.2 lb, and 7.1 lb

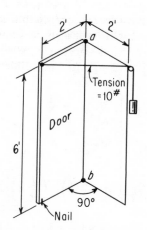

Fig. 2-53

2–8. Derivative of a vector

This topic of the derivative of a vector does not rightfully belong to a chapter on Vector Algebra. However, as the derivative of a vector has appeared in Eq. (2–5), and since some formulas can be presented more concisely in terms of such derivatives in later chapters, a definition and some simple formulas are included herewith.

Just as a scalar quantity can vary with another quantity, a vector may be a function of a scalar quantity. For example, the velocity v of a particle may vary with time; i.e., $v(t)$. The definition of the derivative of any vector $v(t)$ with respect to a scalar is similar to that in Eq. (1–4) for scalar functions:

$$\frac{d}{dt}\,v(t) \equiv \lim_{\Delta t \to 0} \frac{v(t+\Delta t)-v(t)}{\Delta t} = \lim_{\Delta t \to 0} \frac{\Delta v}{\Delta t} \tag{2–37}$$

The vector Δv is shown in Fig. 2–54 for a finite Δt. As Δt decreases, the vector $v(t+\Delta t)$ will approach $v(t)$, and the end of the former vector will trace

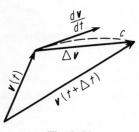

a curve C. The direction of Δv is indicated by the direction of the chord. As Δt approaches zero, this direction is given by the tangent of the curve C at the end of the vector $v(t)$. (The student should realize that, as v is not a linear measurement and the two vectors do not occur at the same place or at the same time, there is actually no such curve as C. This curve is used only for instruction purpose to show the direction of the vector dv/dt.)

Fig. 2–54

It should be noted that the derivative is zero only when the vector is constant in direction as well as in magnitude. In particular, if a vector is constant in magnitude but changes in direction, its derivative, according to a construction like Fig. 2–54, is perpendicular to the vector. It will also be shown algebraically later that $v \cdot (dv/dt)=0$ if the magnitude v is constant.

With the definition in Eq. (2–37), it is not difficult to derive the following useful formulas:

$$\frac{d}{dt}\,(A+B) = \frac{d}{dt}\,A + \frac{d}{dt}\,B \tag{2–38}$$

$$\frac{d}{dt}\,(u\,A) = u\frac{d}{dt}\,A + A\frac{d}{dt}\,u \tag{2–39}$$

$$\frac{d}{dt}\,(A \cdot B) = A \cdot \left(\frac{d}{dt}\,B\right) + \left(\frac{d}{dt}\,A\right) \cdot B \tag{2–40}$$

$$\frac{d}{dt}\,(A \times B) = A \times \left(\frac{d}{dt}\,B\right) + \left(\frac{d}{dt}\,A\right) \times B \tag{2–41}$$

For example,

$$\frac{d}{dt}(A \cdot B) = \lim_{\Delta t \to 0} \frac{(A+\Delta A)\cdot(B+\Delta B)-A \cdot B}{\Delta t}$$

$$= \lim_{\Delta t \to 0} \frac{A \cdot \Delta B + \Delta A \cdot B + \Delta A \cdot \Delta B}{\Delta t}$$

As Δt approaches zero, ΔA and ΔB also approach zero, and the higher-order term $\Delta A \cdot \Delta B$ disappears in comparison with the other terms. Thus, Eq. (2–40) results. As an illustration of its application, let us show algebraically that dv/dt is perpendicular to v if the magnitude v is constant:

$$2v \cdot \left(\frac{d}{dt} v\right) = \frac{d}{dt}(v \cdot v) = \frac{d}{dt}(v^2) = 0$$

When a fixed rectangular coordinate system is used, we can express the derivative of a vector in terms of the derivatives of its components. Since the unit vectors i, j, and k are constant, we have

$$\frac{d}{dt} A = \frac{d}{dt}(A_x i + A_y j + A_z k) = \frac{dA_x}{dt} i + \frac{dA_y}{dt} j + \frac{dA_z}{dt} k \qquad (2\text{--}42)$$

As examples of derivatives of vectors, take the velocity v and the acceleration a of a particle. If $r(t)$ is the location vector directed from a fixed origin to the particle, we have

$$v \equiv \frac{d}{dt} r \qquad (2\text{--}43)$$

$$a \equiv \frac{d}{dt} v = \frac{d^2}{dt^2} r \qquad (2\text{--}44)$$

If the position of the particle is expressed in terms of its coordinates, i.e.,

$$r = xi + yj + zk$$

then, by virtue of Eq. (2–42),

$$v = \frac{dx}{dt} i + \frac{dy}{dt} j + \frac{dz}{dt} k \qquad (2\text{--}45)$$

and

$$a = \frac{d^2x}{dt^2} i + \frac{d^2y}{dt^2} j + \frac{d^2z}{dt^2} k \qquad (2\text{--}46)$$

Thus, for a particle of constant mass m, Newton's equation of motion can be written as

$$\left. \begin{array}{l} \sum F_x = m \dfrac{d^2x}{dt^2} \\[2mm] \sum F_y = m \dfrac{d^2y}{dt^2} \\[2mm] \sum F_z = m \dfrac{d^2z}{dt^2} \end{array} \right\} \qquad (2\text{--}47)$$

where $x(t)$, $y(t)$, and $z(t)$ locate the particle.

Example 2–15. A car is running on a circular track with constant speed v so that its position is given by $x = R \cos \omega t$, $y = R \sin \omega t$, and $z = 0$, where $\omega = v/R$ (see Fig. 2–55). Find its velocity and acceleration.

From the fact that the derivative of a vector of constant magnitude is perpendicular to the vector, we have in this case v $(= dr/dt)$ perpendicular to r, since the magnitude r from the origin is constant, and a $(= dv/dt)$ perpen-

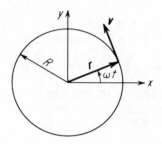

Fig. 2–55

dicular to v, since the speed v is constant. We can also arrive at this conclusion by using Eqs. (2–45) and (2–46).

Here, we have

$$r = (R \cos \omega t)\, i + (R \sin \omega t)\, j$$

Thus

$$v = \frac{d}{dt} r = (-R\omega \sin \omega t)\, i + (R\omega \cos \omega t)\, j$$

and

$$a = \frac{d}{dt} v = (-R\omega^2 \cos \omega t)\, i + (-R\omega^2 \sin \omega t)\, j$$

It can be easily verified that $r \cdot v = 0$ and $v \cdot a = 0$; i.e., r is perpendicular to v, and v is perpendicular to a. Note that $a = -R\omega r$; i.e., a is directed opposite to r towards the center, and has a magnitude equal to $R\omega r$ or v^2/R. Thus, for a particle with a constant speed in a circular path,

$$a = \frac{v^2}{R} \tag{2–48}$$

CHAPTER 3

APPLICATIONS OF INTEGRAL CALCULUS

3–1. The definite integral

Suppose it is necessary to compute the length of a trip from observations on a speedometer. If the speed f is found to be constant throughout the duration T of travel, the distance S travelled is simply $S=fT$. However, if the speed varies during the journey, this simple relationship is no longer valid. A way of computing the distance S is to divide the total time taken into a number of periods of Δt. Let N be the number of periods. During the ith period, the distance of travel is approximately $f_i \Delta t$, where f_i is a speed at some instant in this period. The total distance S is therefore approximately equal to

$$S \doteq f_1 \Delta t + f_2 \Delta t + \ldots = \sum_{i=1}^{N} f_i \Delta t$$

This value of S is not exact because, during each period, the speed f is not constant. However, if the length of each period is shortened while the number of periods is increased, the variation of f during each period is reduced. When Δt is made infinitesimally small, the variation of f during each period approaches zero as a limit. Thus,

$$S = \operatorname*{Lim}_{\Delta t \to 0} \sum_{t=a}^{t=b} f(t) \, \Delta t$$

where a and b are the values of t at the beginning and the end of the trip, respectively. The expression on the right-hand side of this equation is called a *definite integral*, and is usually written as

$$\int_a^b f(t) \, dt \equiv \operatorname*{Lim}_{\Delta t \to 0} \sum_{t=a}^{t=b} f(t) \, \Delta t \tag{3.1}$$

The integral sign is a modification of the letter S, designating a sum. This expression is read "integral from a to b of $f(t)\ dt$." It can be seen from Fig. 3-1 that the definite integral is represented graphically by the area under the curve of $f(t)$ vs. t between the limits a and b.

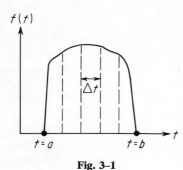

According to the definition of the definite integral, we have

$$\int_b^a f(t)\ dt\ =\ -\int_a^b f(t)\ dt \qquad (3\text{-}2)$$

since the sign of Δt in going from a to b is opposite to that in going from b to a. Also, we have

Fig. 3-1

$$\int_a^m f(t)\ dt + \int_m^b f(t)\ dt\ =\ \int_a^b f(t)\ dt \qquad (3\text{-}3)$$

and

$$\int_a^b [f(t) + F(t)]\ dt\ =\ \int_a^b f(t)\ dt + \int_a^b F(t)\ dt \qquad (3\text{-}4)$$

It should be mentioned that a definite integral is a constant. We have

$$\int_a^b f(t)\ dt\ =\ \int_a^b f(u)\ du\ =\ \int_a^b f(x)\ dx \qquad (3\text{-}5)$$

The variable used under the integral sign is immaterial, and is usually called a dummy variable.

3-2. The indefinite integral

We have seen that, to compute the total distance of a trip, we arrive at a definite integral between $t=a$ at the beginning and $t=b$ at the end of the

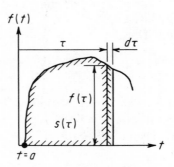

Fig. 3-2

trip. The same expression can be used to represent the distance $s(\tau)$ covered from $t=a$ up to any time $t=\tau$ (see Fig. 3–2):

$$s(\tau) = \int_a^\tau f(t)\,dt \qquad (3-6)$$

Obviously, the value of s varies with the value of τ; i.e., s is a function of τ. The integral $s(\tau)$ is called an *indefinite integral* of $f(\tau)$. We do not call it *the* indefinite integral, because a different value of $s(\tau)$ is obtained by using a different limit a without change of the function f. It might seem that we should have called $s(\tau)$ an integral of $f(t)$ instead of $f(\tau)$. Actually, the variable used under the integral sign is immaterial (see Eq. (3–5)).

We are now going to find the link between the integral calculus and the differential calculus. This link provides a method of evaluating an integral without going through the process of adding a large number of quantities as suggested by Eq. (3–1). We differentiate $s(\tau)$ with respect to τ. By definition, (see Eq. (1–4)),

$$\frac{ds}{d\tau} = \lim_{\Delta\tau\to 0} \frac{s(\tau+\Delta\tau)-s(\tau)}{\Delta\tau}$$

According to Eqs. (3–6) and (3–3),

$$s(\tau+\Delta\tau)-s(\tau) = \int_a^{\tau+\Delta\tau} f(t)\,dt - \int_a^\tau f(t)\,dt = \int_\tau^{\tau+\Delta\tau} f(t)\,dt$$

As $\Delta\tau\to 0$, the value of $f(t)$ during the interval from $t=\tau$ to $t=(\tau+\Delta\tau)$ approaches $f(\tau)$ as a limit. Thus

$$\frac{ds}{d\tau} = \lim_{\Delta\tau\to 0} \frac{\int_\tau^{\tau+\Delta\tau} f(t)\,dt}{\Delta\tau} = \frac{f(\tau)\,\Delta\tau}{\Delta\tau} = f(\tau) \qquad (3-7)$$

In our physical example, this result is not surprising. It simply states that the rate of change of distance s at any time τ is equal to the speed f at this instant. However, Eq. (3–7) is the basic link between the differential and integral calculus. This equation states that differentiation of an indefinite integral $s(\tau)$ of a given function $f(\tau)$ always gives us back the same function $f(\tau)$. Thus, to integrate $f(\tau)$ is to find a function $s(\tau)$ which, upon differential, gives $f(\tau)$.

In computing the distance from the starting point, we have used the time $t=a$ at the beginning of the trip as the lower limit of integration in Eq. (3–6). We can also compute the distance from a certain landmark which we pass at $t=m$. In this case, we use $t=m$ as the lower limit of integration. The two distances thus obtained differ by a definite value which is the distance between the starting point and the landmark. This fact is stated by Eq. (3–3):

$$\int_a^m f(t)\,dt + \int_m^\tau f(t)\,dt = \int_a^\tau f(t)\,dt$$

Since the first integral has constants for the two limits, and is therefore a constant, we have

$$\int_m^\tau f(t)\, dt = \int_a^\tau f(t)\, dt + \text{constant } C = s(\tau) + C$$

Thus, if $s(\tau)$ is an indefinite integral of $f(\tau)$, the family of functions $[s(\tau) + C]$ represents other indefinite integrals of the same function $f(\tau)$. The value of C depends on the choice of the lower limit of integration. The indefinite integrals of $f(\tau)$ can therefore be written as

$$\int f(\tau)\, d\tau = \int_m^\tau f(t)\, dt = s(\tau) + C \qquad (3\text{--}8)$$

where C depends on the value of m and is called the *constant of integration*.

A definite integral can now be evaluated, instead of by summation as indicated by Eq. (3–1), by first finding the indefinite integrals. According to Eq. (3–3),

$$\int_a^b f(t)\, dt = \int_m^b f(t)\, dt - \int_m^a f(t)\, dt = [s(b) + C] - [s(a) + C]$$
$$= s(b) - s(a)$$

which is usually written as

$$\int_a^b f(t)\, dt = s(\tau) \Big|_a^b = s(b) - s(a) \qquad (3\text{--}9)$$

Unfortunately, indefinite integrals are not always easy to find. Even for some very simple functions, the indefinite integrals may be very complicated. The student is advised to memorize the integrals of the more elementary functions, and to learn the method of integration by parts, the method by substitution, and the method by partial fractions. He should learn how to handle improper integrals; i.e., definite integrals, either with infinite interval of integration, or with an infinite discontinuity in the integrand. Discussions on these topics can be found in elementary textbooks on the Calculus. In solving problems, a table of integrals will be found very useful. Extensive lists of integrals can be found in Peirce and Foster's *A Short Table of Integrals*, Ginn, 1956, and Bierens de Haan's *Table of Definite Integrals*, Hafner, 1956.

In introducing the integral, the computation of the distance of travel from observed speed has been used as an example. The results thus obtained, however, are quite general. In the integral

$$\int_a^b f(t)\, dt \equiv \lim_{\Delta t \to 0} \sum_{t=a}^{t=b} f(t)\, \Delta t$$

if t represents the linear displacement of a particle and $f(t)$ is a varying force acting on the particle in the direction of the displacement, the product

$f(t)\,dt$ is the work done by the varying force in moving over the distance dt. Although the magnitude of the force changes from place to place, the integral of $f(t)\,dt$ is the work done by the varying force through a finite displacement. Numerous other examples can be cited. The student will encounter more examples in the following articles.

Example 3-1. The speed in mph of a car in a trip directed from A to B is $\sin t$, where t is the time in hours. The trip takes 2π hours. Find the distance from the starting point at the end of the trip, and the total mileage added to the car.

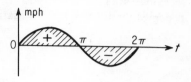

The plot of speed vs. time is shown in Fig. 3-3. During the interval from $t=\pi$ to $t=2\pi$, the speed is negative, mean-

Fig. 3-3

ing that the movement is actually directed from B to A. The total displacement is

$$\lim_{\Delta t \to 0} \sum_{t=0}^{t=2\pi} \sin t\,\Delta t = \int_0^{2\pi} \sin t\,dt = -\cos t \Big|_0^{2\pi} = 0$$

i.e., ending up at the starting point. However, the mileage is independent of the direction of travel. Thus, the added mileage is

$$\lim_{\Delta t \to 0} \sum_{t=0}^{t=2\pi} |\sin t|\,\Delta t = \int_0^{2\pi} |\sin t|\,dt = \int_0^{\pi} \sin t\,dt + \int_{\pi}^{2\pi} (-\sin t)\,dt$$

$$= 2\int_0^{\pi} \sin t\,dt = -2\cos t \Big|_0^{\pi} = 4 \text{ miles}$$

Care should be exercised when parts of the integral have negative values. In Fig. 3-3, the area between the curve and the t axis is partly positive and partly negative. The displacement is the algebraic sum of the two parts of the area, while the mileage is the sum of their absolute values.

Example 3-2. When a uniform bar of cross-sectional area A is under uniformly distributed tensile stress, the elongation e in the direction of the stress for a material obeying Hooke's law is given by

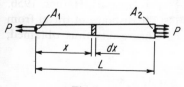

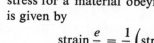

$$\text{strain } \frac{e}{L} = \frac{1}{E}\left(\text{stress } \frac{P}{A}\right) \quad (3\text{-}10)$$

or $e = PL/AE$, where L is the length of the bar, P is the applied force, and E is the Young's modulus of the material. By using

Fig. 3-4

Eq. (3-10), find the elongation of a bar with gradually varying cross-sectional area $A = A_1 + kx^2$, where $k = (A_2 - A_1)/L^2$ (see Fig. 3-4). The change of A with x is so gradual that the stress over each cross section may be considered to be uniformly distributed.

Across each cross section, the total tensile force is P. This bar may be considered as a large number of short bars, each Δx in length. For each of these short bars, the cross-sectional area is practically uniform throughout its length. Thus, for a short length Δx at x, the elongation is approximately $P\,\Delta x/E(A_1+kx^2)$. This value is approximate because, for finite Δx, the cross-sectional area A is not strictly uniform throughout Δx. However, as Δx becomes infinitesimal, the variation of A through Δx approaches zero. Thus

$$\text{Total elongation} = \lim_{\Delta x \to 0} \sum_{x=0}^{L} \frac{P\,\Delta x}{E(A_1+kx^2)} = \int_0^L \frac{P\,dx}{E(A_1+kx^2)}$$

$$= \frac{P}{E\sqrt{A_1 k}} \tan^{-1}\sqrt{\frac{k}{A_1}}\,x\;\Bigg|_0^L$$

$$= \frac{PL}{EA_1}\left[\sqrt{\frac{A_1}{A_2-A_1}}\,\tan^{-1}\sqrt{\frac{A_2-A_1}{A_1}}\right]$$

This result is dimensionally correct. As a check on a limiting case, consider the case where $A_1=A_2$. It can be shown that, as A_1 approaches A_2, this elongation becomes the same as that of a uniform bar (see Problem 1–41).

Example 3–3. Find the reactions F_1 and F_2 supporting the beam with a nonuniformly distributed load, as shown in Fig. 3–5. The load w (in lb per ft) is related to the distance x (in ft) from the support at F_1 by

$$w = 100 \sin \frac{\pi x}{10}$$

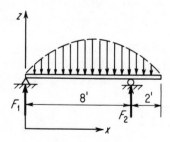

Fig. 3–5

The distributed load may be considered to be a series of loads of magnitude $w\,\Delta x$ each applied over a short distance Δx on the beam. For equilibrium under this system of coplanar parallel forces, two unknowns can be determined from the equations of Statics: $\sum M_y=0$ and $\sum F_z=0$. With moment center at F_1, the moment M_y of the load $w \, \Delta x$ located at x is $wx \, \Delta x$. Thus

$$\sum M_y = -\sum xF_z = -8F_2 + \lim_{\Delta x \to 0} \sum_{x=0}^{10} wx \, \Delta x = 0$$

giving

$$F_2 = \frac{1}{8} \int_0^{10} 100 \sin\left(\frac{\pi x}{10}\right) x \, dx = \frac{100}{8} \left(\frac{10}{\pi}\right)^2 \left(\sin\frac{\pi x}{10} - \frac{\pi x}{10}\cos\frac{\pi x}{10}\right)\Big|_0^{10}$$

$$= \frac{1250}{\pi}\,\text{lb}$$

Also

$$\sum F_z = F_1 + F_2 - \lim_{\Delta x \to 0} \sum_{x=0}^{10} w \, \Delta x = 0$$

giving

$$F_1 = \int_0^{10} 100 \sin\frac{\pi x}{10}\, dx - F_2 = \frac{2000}{\pi} - \frac{1250}{\pi} = \frac{750}{\pi}\,\text{lb}$$

Problems

(In solving the following problems, first show that the wanted quantity can be expressed as a summation, and then as an integral, in accordance with the definition in Eq. (3–1).)

3–1. Find the area bounded by the following two lines: $x = y^2/3$ and $x = 3$. Also find the length of the boundary of this area. *Ans.* 12 square units, 14.88 units

3–2. The atmospheric pressure at sea level is approximately equal to the weight of air directly above in the atmosphere. The density ρ of the air varies with the altitude according to the weather conditions. In a certain case, the variation of ρ with altitude z above sea level is $\rho = \rho_0 e^{-kz}$, where ρ_0 is the density of air at sea level, and k is a constant. Show that, by assuming that the atmosphere extends to infinite height, the atmospheric pressure at sea level is $\rho_0 g/k$, where g is the gravitational acceleration. (Hint: pressure = force per unit area, and weight per unit volume = ρg.)

3–3. The specific heat capacity of a material is the heat required per unit mass to raise its temperature by one unit. The specific heat capacity c of a certain material varies with temperature as follows:

$$c = 0.100\left[1.00 + 0.15\left(\frac{t}{100}\right) + 0.02\left(\frac{t}{100}\right)^2\right] \qquad \text{for } -200 < t < 100$$

where t is the temperature in °C, and c is in calories per gram per °C. Find the amount of heat required to raise the temperature of 100 grams of this material from −200°C to 100°C. *Ans.* 2835 cal

3–4. The diameter of the tires of a car decreases linearly with the number of turns of the wheels. In 10 million turns, the diameter decreases from 24 in. to 23 in. What is the distance covered in this 10 million turns? If the odometer gives correct mileage when the diameter is 24 in., what is the error of the reading for this 10 million turns?

3–5. The force F required to hold a linear spring with an extension x from its neutral length is kx, where k is called the *spring constant*. Such a spring is called linear because F varies linearly with x. For a certain linear spring, F is 100 lb when x is 5 in. Find the work done in slowly stretching the spring from $x = 2$ in. to $x = 6$ in., as shown in Fig. 3–6. (Hint: when the stretching is very slow, the rate of change of mv of the spring material is negligible. The force F can then be considered, in view of Newton's law of motion, to be in equilibrium with the spring resistance at all time.)   *Ans.* 320 in.-lb

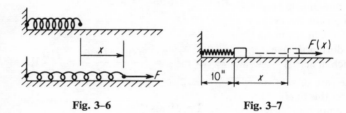

Fig. 3–6   Fig. 3–7

3–6. A block weighs 300 lb and is connected to a spring with a natural length of 10 in., as shown in Fig. 3–7. The spring constant is 20 lb per in. The coefficient of friction between the block and the floor is $\frac{1}{5}$ (i.e., the tangential component of the reaction opposing the relative motion is $\frac{1}{5}$ the normal component). Find the work done by the varying horizontal force F in moving the block slowly along the floor through a distance of 2 ft. Indicate the portion of this work spent in overcoming friction and that spent in stretching the spring.
                    Ans. 1440 in.-lb, 5760 in.-lb

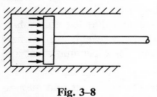

Fig. 3–8

3–7. A cylinder 15 sq in. in cross section is holding 150 cu in. of gas, as shown in Fig. 3–8. The pressure is then 100 lb per sq in. The gas then expands isothermally to 300 cu in. Find the work done by the gas on the piston during the expansion. (Hint: during expansion, the pressure varies. For isothermal expansion, it may be assumed that the product (pressure × volume) remain constant.)   *Ans.* 10,400 in.-lb

3–8. A linear spring in its unstressed condition is 3 ft long, and is fixed at one end at point A and attached at the other end to block B, as shown in Fig. 3–9. Verify that the work done by the varying force F in slowly moving block B through a distance of 4 ft along the frictionless slot is equal to the work required to stretch the spring slowly in any other way to the same final length of 5 ft.

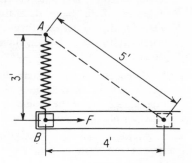

Fig. 3–9

3–9. The rate of sale (number sold per unit time) of a certain newly invented article through the first year is $1000t^2$ (for $0 < t < 12$), where t is the time in months, with $t = 0$ at the beginning of the year. The sale price per article also varies with time during this year, and is represented by $1/t$ dollars. The cost of production of each article is 2 cents. Find the total profit in the year.   *Ans.* $60,480

3–10. The rate of sale varies with time. In order to reduce the cost of production to meet this fluctuation, the manufacturer keeps the rate of production constant. The temporary surplus (production minus sale) is stored in a special warehouse at a cost of 2 cents per unit per day. The rate of sale can be represented as

$$10,000 \left[1 - \frac{1}{3} \sin 2\pi t \right]$$

and the rate of production is 10,000, where the unit of time t is the year, with $t = 0$ at the time when the volume of storage is zero but is increasing (see Fig. 3–10). The warehouse owner is paid every four months. How much should the first two payments be, at $t = 1/3$ and at $t = 2/3$?

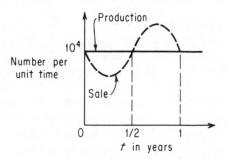

Fig. 3–10

3–11. A uniform elastic rod is attached to a ceiling. Show that the elongation of the rod under its own weight W is $(WL)/(2EA)$, where L is the length and A is the

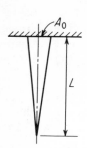

cross-sectional area of the rod, and E is Young's modulus of the material. If this rod is made of steel ($E = 30 \times 10^6$ lb per sq in.; weighing 490 lb per cu ft) and is 10 ft in length and 2 sq in. in cross section, find the elongation.

3–12. A slender rod in the shape of a right circular cone is attached to the ceiling, as shown in Fig. 3–11. Find an expression for the elongation of the rod under its own weight W.

Fig. 3–11

3–13. Find the reactions supporting the beams shown in Fig. 3–12(a), (b), (c), and (d).

Ans. (a) 4000 lb, 4000 lb; (b) 90 lb, 210 lb; (c) 250 lb, 500 lb; (d) 7500 ft-lb, 750 lb

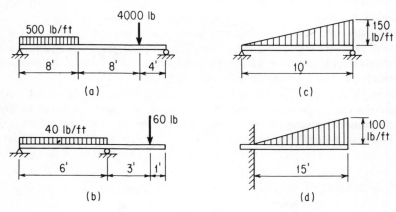

Fig. 3–12

3–3. Bending moments and shearing forces on beams

A beam is a structural member supporting lateral loads. In the design of beams, the engineer finds it convenient to deal with quantities known as bending moments and shearing forces on beams. This topic is discussed here, because it furnishes a simple example of obtaining a function by integration.

When a portion of a beam is taken as a free body, the external forces are balanced by the stresses at the cross section, as shown in Fig. 3–13(a). In a section of a beam with no longitudinal loads, the fibers on one side of the beam are stretched, while those on the other side are compressed. These tensile and compressive stresses form couples, the total moment of which is independent of the moment center used (see Problem 2–19). This moment M is called the *resisting moment* at this section. In addition to the tensile and compressive stresses, there are shearing stresses along the surface of the section to produce static equilibrium of the free body. The total force of the shearing stresses is called the *resisting shear force V* at this section. The values of M and V can be computed from the loads and reactions on either portion of the beam. Obviously, the values of M and V vary from section to section; i.e., M and V are functions of x along the beam. In design, the values of M and V are first computed from the external forces (see Fig. 3–13(b)), and the beam is then made strong enough to withstand the stresses required to produce these values of M and V at every section. Note that there is no net longitudinal force of the stresses, since there is no longitudinal load applied to the beam.

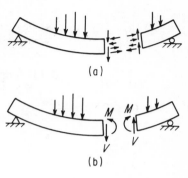

(a)

(b)

Fig. 3–13

Note that, in Fig. 3–13(b), the same resisting moment M is in the clockwise or the counterclockwise direction, depending on which portion, the right side or the left side, of the beam is taken as the free body. Thus, it is not convenient to describe the condition of bending with the direction of the moment M. It is the engineering convention to regard bending as positive if the top of the beam is being compressed. When the bottom of the beam is being compressed and the top stretched, the bending is regarded as negative (see Fig. 3–14). Similarly, the shear force V may be directed upward or downward, depending on which portion of the beam is used as the free body.

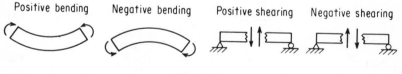

Fig. 3–14

It is the engineering convention to consider shearing as positive when V acts downward when the portion of the beam to the left of the section is taken as the free body. Positive shearing indicates a net upward load on this free body.

For equilibrium of either portion of the beam, the magnitude of the resisting moment M at a section is equal to the total moment of the other forces on either side of the beam about a moment center at this section. This total moment is called the *bending moment* and is numerically equal to the resisting moment M. It is the convention to call the bending moment positive when the bending is positive.

(a)

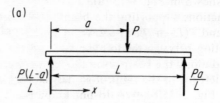

(b) For $0 < x < a$

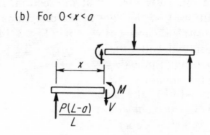

(c) For $a < x < L$

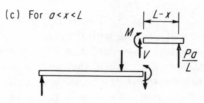

(d)

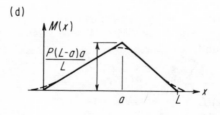

(e)

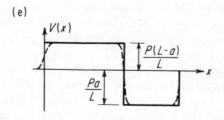

Fig. 3–15

Example 3–4. Find the bending moment $M(x)$ and the shearing force $V(x)$ for the beam shown in Fig. 3–15 (a).

First find the reactions supporting the beam. The reactions can easily be shown to be Pa/L and $P(L-a)/L$, as shown in Fig. 3–15(a).

Consider any section between the left support and the load; i.e., $0 < x < a$, where x is measured along the beam from the left support. Take the portion of the beam to the left (or to the right, if so desired) of this section as a free body, as shown in Fig. 3–15(b). We do not know the directions of the resisting moment M and the shear force V at the section. It is good practice to assume, in computation, that they act in the directions corresponding to positive bending and positive shearing, as shown in Fig. 3–14. If these assumed directions are incorrect, we will obtain negative values for the bending moment and shearing force, indicating that the bending and the shearing are negative. The useful equations of Statics are $\sum F_z = 0$ and $\sum M_y = 0$. Thus, for $0 < x < a$,

$$\sum F_z = \frac{P(L-a)}{L} - V = 0$$

giving $V = P(L-a)/L$; and, with moment center at the section,

$$\sum M_y = \frac{P(L-a)x}{L} - M = 0$$

giving $M = P(L-a)x/L$.

Similarly, for any section between the load and the right support (i.e., $a < x < L$), we have with the portion of the beam to the right of the section as a free body, as shown in Fig. 3–15(c),

$$\sum F_z = \frac{Pa}{L} + V = 0$$

giving $V = -Pa/L$; and, with moment center at the section,

$$\sum M_y = M - \frac{Pa}{L}(L-x) = 0$$

giving $M = Pa(L-x)/L$.

These functions, $M(x)$ and $V(x)$, are shown graphically in Fig. 3–15(d) and (e), respectively. The plot of M against x is known as the *moment diagram*, and the plot of V against x is known as the *shear diagram*. The discontinuities of $V(x)$ and the first derivative of $M(x)$ are caused by the idealization of the load and supports as "point loads." In reality, all applied forces are distributed over a finite area, however small. The actual $M(x)$ and $V(x)$ are better represented by the dashed lines in Fig. 3–15(d) and (e).

Example 3–5. Find the bending moment $M(x)$ and the shearing force $V(x)$ for the beam in Example 3–3.

First find the reactions supporting the beam. These reactions have been

(a)

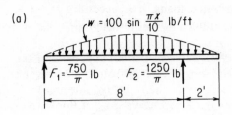

(b) For $0 < x_1 < 8'$

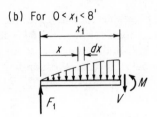

(c) For $8' < x_1 < 10'$

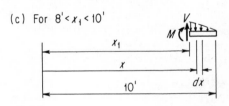

(d) V- diagram

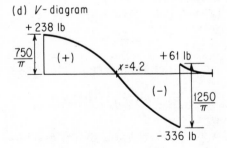

(e) M- diagram

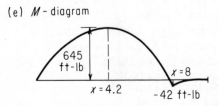

Fig. 3–16

found in Example 3–3 to have the values shown in Fig. 3–16(a). In this problem with distributed loads, it is necessary to let $x =$ distance in ft of a load from the left support, and $x_1 =$ distance in ft of a section from the left support.

For any section between the two supports, take the portion of beam to the left of the section as a free body, as shown in Fig. 3–16(b). Thus, for $0 < x_1 < 8$,

$$\sum F_z = F_1 - \lim_{\Delta x \to 0} \sum_{x=0}^{x_1} w \, \Delta x - V = 0$$

giving

$$V = F_1 - \int_0^{x_1} 100 \sin \frac{\pi x}{10} \, dx = \frac{750}{\pi} - \frac{1000}{\pi} \left(1 - \cos \frac{\pi x_1}{10} \right)$$

$$= \frac{250}{\pi} \left(4 \cos \frac{\pi x_1}{10} - 1 \right) \text{lb}$$

With moment center at the section,

$$\sum M_y = F_1 x_1 - \lim_{\Delta x \to 0} \sum_{x=0}^{x_1} (x_1 - x) w \, \Delta x - M = 0$$

giving

$$M = \frac{750}{\pi} x_1 - \int_0^{x_1} (x_1 - x) 100 \sin \frac{\pi x}{10} \, dx = \frac{250}{\pi} \left(-x_1 + \frac{40}{\pi} \sin \frac{\pi x_1}{10} \right) \text{ft-lb}$$

In these integrals, x_1, indicating a section, is a constant. The values of V and M are functions of x_1.

For any section to the right of the right support, take the portion of the beam to the right of the section as a free body, as shown in Fig. 3–16(c). Thus, for $8 < x_1 < 10$,

$$\sum F_z = V - \lim_{\Delta x \to 0} \sum_{x=x_1}^{10} w \, \Delta x = 0$$

giving

$$V = \int_{x_1}^{10} 100 \sin \frac{\pi x}{10} \, dx = \frac{1000}{\pi} \left(1 + \cos \frac{\pi x_1}{10} \right) \text{lb}$$

With moment center at the section,

$$\sum M_y = M + \lim_{\Delta x \to 0} \sum_{x=x_1}^{10} (x - x_1) w \, \Delta x = 0$$

giving

$$M = - \int_{x_1}^{10} (x - x_1) 100 \sin \frac{\pi x}{10} \, dx = \frac{1000}{\pi} \left(x_1 - 10 + \frac{10}{\pi} \sin \frac{\pi x_1}{10} \right) \text{ft-lb}$$

After integration, the subscript of x_1 can be dropped without causing confusion. With these expressions of $M(x)$ and $V(x)$, the moment diagram and the shear diagram can be constructed as shown in Fig. 3–16(d) and (e). We are interested in the maximum and minimum of these functions. For

example, the maximum positive moment between the two supports is located
at the value of x given by

$$\frac{dM}{dx} = \frac{d}{dx}\left[\frac{250}{\pi}\left(-x+\frac{40}{\pi}\sin\frac{\pi x}{10}\right)\right] = 0$$

or $\cos(\pi x/10)=1/4$, $\pi x/10=\pi(75.5°/180°)$; i.e., $x=4.2$ ft. Therefore, the
maximum positive moment is

$$\text{maximum } M = \frac{250}{\pi}\left(-4.2+\frac{40}{\pi}\sin 75.5°\right) = 645 \text{ ft-lb}$$

Other maxima and minima are located at the ends of the beam and at the
support, where the functions $M(x)$ and $V(x)$ or their derivatives are discontinuous. The occurrence of these maxima and minima has been discussed
in Art. 1–8.

Problems

3–14. Find the bending moment $M(x)$ and the shearing force $V(x)$ for the beams
shown in Fig. 3–17(a) and (b), and Fig. 3–12(b) and (d). Find the maximum
and minimum values of $M(x)$ for Fig. 3–12(b).   *Ans.* +101 and −180 ft-lb

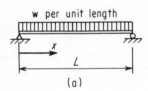
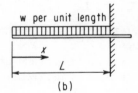

Fig. 3–17

3–4. Double integrals by iteration

Suppose it is necessary to compute the volume D of a hill, the height
$f(x, y)$ above a level ground, the x-y plane, being given as shown in
Fig. 3–18. An approximate value of the
volume can be obtained by dividing the
base area A into N small areas ΔA and

finding the sum $\sum\limits_{i=1}^{N} f_i \, \Delta A$, where f_i is the

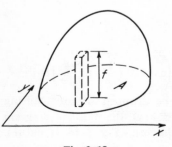

Fig. 3–18

value of a height f in the ith small area ΔA.
This value of the volume is not exact, because the height f is not constant over
each area ΔA. However, when each ΔA is
reduced in size, the variation of f over

each ΔA becomes small. When ΔA is made infinitesimally small, the variation of f over ΔA approaches zero as a limit. Thus

$$D = \lim_{\Delta A \to 0} \sum_{A} f(x, y) \, \Delta A$$

the summation being taken over A. The expression on the right-hand side of this equation is called a *double integral*, and is usually written as

$$\iint_A f(x, y) \, dA \equiv \lim_{\Delta A \to 0} \sum_{A} f(x, y) \, \Delta A \qquad (3\text{–}11)$$

where the area A is called the *region of integration*, corresponding to the interval of integration of the simple integral in Eq. (3–1). Note that the double integral has been defined in a manner entirely analogous to that for the simple integral. The only difference is that, in Eq. (3–11), the function f is a function of two variables and the integration is taken over a region in the plane of these variables.

The value of a double integral can be obtained very often by iteration; i.e., by repeated integration. First take a simple example: the base area A of a volume is bounded by the lines $x=0$, $x=5$, $y=0$, and $y=4$, as shown in

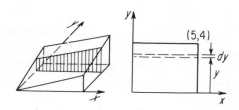

Fig. 3–19

Fig. 3–19; and the height $f(x, y)$ over the area A is $f(x, y)=0.2x+0.3y$. To obtain the volume, we can first find the cross-sectional area of a cut parallel to the x axis. The area of any such cut is $\int_{x=0}^{x=5} f(x, y) \, dx$, where y in $f(x, y)$ is a constant in this integral. In our example, this integral is

$$\int_{x=0}^{x=5} (0.2x+0.3y) \, dx = (0.1x^2+0.3xy) \Big|_0^5 = 2.5+1.5y$$

Note that this integral is a function of y. This means that the cross-sectional area depends on where the cut is. With the cross-sectional area known, the volume can be obtained:

$$\int_0^4 (2.5+1.5y) \, dy = 22$$

The same result can be obtained by first finding the cross-sectional area of a cut perpendicular to the x axis, as shown in Fig. 3–20. The area of any such cut is $\int_{y=0}^{y=4} f(x, y)\, dy$, where x in $f(x, y)$ is a constant in this integral. This integral is a function of x. In our example, it is

$$\int_0^4 (0.2x+0.3y)\, dy = (0.2xy+0.15y^2)\Big|_0^4 = 0.8x+2.4$$

The volume is therefore

$$\int_0^5 (0.8x+2.4)\, dx = 22$$

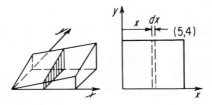

Fig. 3–20

Next, consider a region of integration A of arbitrary shape enclosed by a curve which is cut by any line parallel to the x or y axis in not more than two points. (Otherwise, the region A can be divided into subregions satisfying this requirement, and each subregion is treated separately.) In Fig. 3–21,

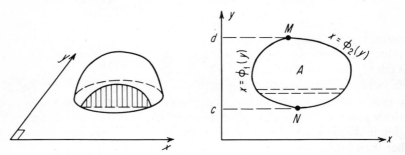

Fig. 3–21

let M and N be the points of maximum and minimum ordinates, respectively, of the curve enclosing region A. On the two branches of the curve separated by points M and N, let the abscissas be $x=\phi_1(y)$ and $x=\phi_2(y)$, as shown in Fig. 3–21. The double integral can be evaluated by first integrating in the direction of constant y, from the limit $x=\phi_1(y)$ to $x=\phi_2(y)$. This means that the limits of integration for the cross-sectional area of a cut perpendicular to the y axis depend on where the cut is. This first integral is

$$\int_{x=\phi_1(y)}^{x=\phi_2(y)} f(x, y)\, dx$$

with y considered as a constant in $f(x, y)$. This integral is a function of y. The value of the double integral is then obtained by integrating with respect to y between the limits c and d:

$$\iint_A f(x, y)\, dA = \int_c^d \left[\int_{x=\phi_1(y)}^{x=\phi_2(y)} f(x, y) \cdot dx \right] dy \qquad (3\text{--}12)$$

Similarly, the value of the double integral can be obtained by first integrating in the direction of constant x. In Fig. 3–22, let points P and Q be the points of maximum and minimum abscissas, respectively, of the curve enclosing region A, and let the two branches of the curve separated by P and Q be $y=\psi_1(x)$ and $y=\psi_2(x)$, respectively. First, integrate in the direction of constant x from the limit $\psi_1(x)$ to $\psi_2(x)$. This integral is

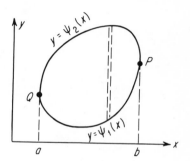

$$\int_{y=\psi_1(x)}^{y=\psi_2(x)} f(x, y)\, dy$$

with x considered as a constant in $f(x, y)$.

Fig. 3–22

This integral is a function of x. The value of the double integral is then obtained by integrating between the limits $x=a$ and $x=b$:

$$\iint_A f(x, y)\, dA = \int_a^b \left[\int_{y=\psi_1(x)}^{y=\psi_2(x)} f(x, y)\, dy \right] dx \qquad (3\text{--}13)$$

Equations (3–12) and (3–13) give the same value, but one of the two may involve less work of computation, depending on the nature of $f(x, y)$ and the curve enclosing the region of integration.

In introducing the double integral, an example of finding the volume above the region of integration A has been used. The definition in Eq. (3–11) is entirely general. The function $f(x, y)$ can be any function, and A can be any region in the x-y plane, even with the variables x and y representing quantities other than linear measurements.

When polar coordinates are used, the area ΔA in Eq. (3–11) can be expressed as $\rho\, \Delta\theta\, \Delta\rho$, and the function $f(x, y)$ is to be replaced by $F(\rho, \theta)$. Again, the double integral can be evaluated by iteration. Consider any region A which is enclosed by a curve that is not cut by any line of constant ρ or constant θ in more than two points. First, we have

$$\iint_A F(\rho, \theta)\, dA = \int_{\rho_1}^{\rho_2} \left[\rho \int_{\theta=\phi_1(\rho)}^{\theta=\phi_2(\rho)} F(\rho, \theta)\, d\theta \right] d\rho \qquad (3\text{--}14)$$

where ρ is considered as a constant in $F(\rho, \theta)$ in the first integration. The limits in the first integration must be valid for any value of ρ. The quantities ρ_1, ρ_2, ϕ_1, and ϕ_2 are shown in Fig. 3–23(a). We also have

$$\iint_A F(\rho, \theta)\, dA = \int_{\theta_1}^{\theta_2} \left[\int_{\rho=\psi_1(\theta)}^{\rho=\psi_2(\theta)} \rho F(\rho, \theta)\, d\rho \right] d\theta \qquad (3\text{–}15)$$

where θ is considered as a constant in $F(\rho, \theta)$ in the first integration. The limits in the first integration must be valid for any value of θ for the area A. The quantities θ_1, θ_2, ψ_1, and ψ_2 are shown in Fig. 3–23(b).

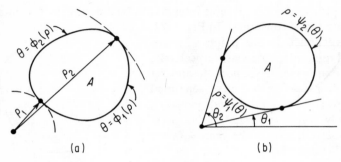

(a)　　　　　　　　　　　　　　　　(b)

Fig. 3–23

Double integration is used in the determination of centroids and second moments of areas, quantities frequently encountered in engineering practice. Sometimes, these integrals are difficult to evaluate. In the following two articles, alternative methods of computing these quantities are discussed.

Example 3–6. Find the area between the parabola

$$y = \frac{1}{2}x^2 - x - 2$$

and the line

$$y = \frac{1}{2}x + 3$$

To define the area A, find the intersection of the two lines by solving the two equations simultaneously. The intersections can be shown to be $(5, 11/2)$ and $(-2, 2)$. The enclosed area A is a double integral:

$$A = \iint_A dA = \iint_A dx \cdot dy$$

In using Eq. (3–13) with $f(x, y) = 1$, the first integration is performed in the direction of constant x (see Fig. 3–24(a)):

$$A = \int_{-2}^{5} \left[\int_{\frac{1}{2}x^2 - x - 2}^{\frac{1}{2}x + 3} dy \right] dx = \int_{-2}^{5} \left[\left(\frac{1}{2}x + 3 \right) - \left(\frac{1}{2}x^2 - x - 2 \right) \right] dx = 28 \frac{7}{12}$$

Note that the first integral is nothing other than the height of the enclosed area at any value of x. The area A is therefore the summation of the areas of the infinitesimal vertical strips.

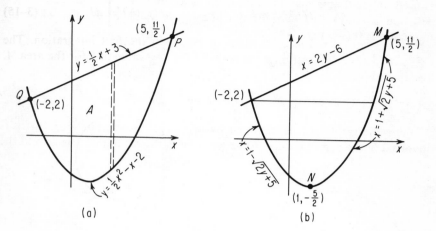

Fig. 3–24

The same value can be obtained by first integrating at constant y, according to Eq. (3–12), but more work is involved in the computation. The lowest point of the enclosing curve must first be found:

$$\frac{d}{dx}\left(\frac{1}{2}x^2 - x - 2\right) = 0$$

at the lowest point, i.e., at $x = 1$, and at

$$y = \frac{1}{2}x^2 - x - 2 = \frac{-5}{2}$$

In integrating along the direction of constant y first, the lower limit of the integration $\phi_1(y)$ in Eq. (3–12) is different for the intervals $11/2 > y > 2$ and $2 > y > -5/2$ (see Fig. 3–24(b)). Thus

$$A = \int_{-5/2}^{2}\left[\int_{1-\sqrt{2y+5}}^{1+\sqrt{2y+5}} dx\right] dy + \int_{2}^{11/2}\left[\int_{2y-6}^{1+\sqrt{2y+5}} dx\right] dy$$

$$= \int_{-5/2}^{2}[(1+\sqrt{2y+5})-(1-\sqrt{2y+5})] dy + \int_{2}^{11/2}[(1+\sqrt{2y+5})-(2y-6)] dy$$

$$= 28\frac{7}{12}$$

Example 3–7. Find the area enclosed by

$$\rho = a(1+\cos\theta)$$

Here, $A = \iint dA = \iint \rho \, d\theta \, d\rho$, i.e., $F(\rho, \theta) = 1$ in Eqs. (3–14) and (3–15). For convenience, we are going to evaluate half of the area. If Eq. (3–15) is used, the half area may be considered as enclosed by two curves, $\rho = \psi_1(\theta) = 0$ and $\rho = \psi_2(\theta) = a(1 + \cos \theta)$. The maximum value of θ is π, while the minimum is 0 (see Fig. 3–25(a)).

$$\frac{A}{2} = \int_0^\pi \left[\int_0^{a(1+\cos\theta)} \rho \cdot d\rho \right] d\theta$$

$$= \int_0^\pi \frac{1}{2} [a(1+\cos\theta)]^2 \, d\theta = \frac{a^2}{2} \left(\theta + 2\sin\theta + \frac{1}{2}\sin\theta\cdot\cos\theta + \frac{\theta}{2} \right) \Big|_0^\pi = \frac{3\pi a^2}{4}$$

The same result can be obtained by using Eq. (3–14), but more work is involved in the computation. In the latter case, the maximum ρ is $2a$ and the

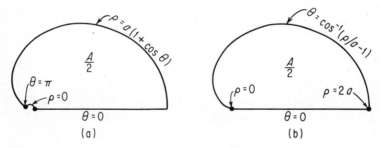

Fig. 3–25

minimum is 0. The half area is enclosed by the curves $\theta = \phi_1(\rho) = 0$, and $\theta = \phi_2(\rho) = \cos^{-1}\left(\frac{\rho}{a} - 1\right)$, as shown in Fig. 3–25(b). Thus

$$\frac{A}{2} = \int_0^{2a} \left[\int_0^{\cos^{-1}\left(\frac{\rho}{a}-1\right)} \rho \cdot d\theta \right] d\rho = \int_0^{2a} \rho \cdot \cos^{-1}\left(\frac{\rho}{a} - 1\right) \cdot d\rho$$

Example 3–8. Two circular cylinders with equal radii intersect perpendicularly. Find the volume at the intersection common to both cylinders.

In order to use Eq. (3–11) in computing a volume, first define the x–y plane, and find the height $f(x, y)$ above this plane. For convenience, we are going to compute half of the common volume, the perspective view of which is shown in Fig. 3–26(a). Put the x–y plane perpendicular to one of the cylinders with the y axis along the axis of the other cylinder. For $f(x, y)$, which gives the height for any (x, y), we have from Fig. 3–26(c)

$$f = \sqrt{R^2 - x^2}$$

Thus the half volume is

$$\frac{V}{2} = \lim_{\Delta A \to 0} \sum_{A} f \Delta A = \iint_{A} \sqrt{R^2 - x^2} \, dA$$

where A is a circle of radius R in the x–y plane.

$$\frac{V}{2} = \int_{-R}^{R} \left[\int_{-\sqrt{R^2-x^2}}^{\sqrt{R^2-x^2}} \sqrt{R^2 - x^2} \cdot dy \right] dx = \int_{-R}^{R} 2\sqrt{R^2 - x^2} \sqrt{R^2 - x^2} \cdot dx = \frac{8}{3} R^3$$

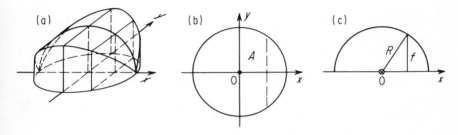

Fig. 3–26

Example 3–9. In a new flat pivot, before wear of the contacting surfaces has occurred, the pressure between them may be assumed to be uniform. If the coefficient of friction between the two contacting surfaces is μ, find the torque required to keep the pivot rotating against friction.

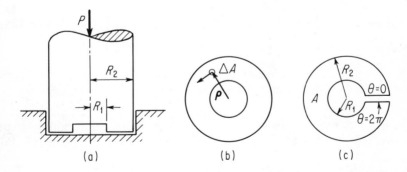

Fig. 3–27

For each small area ΔA of the base, the normal force is $p \, \Delta A$, where $p = P/A$, since p is assumed to be uniform. The frictional force on this ΔA is therefore $\mu p \, \Delta A$. Since frictional forces always act in the direction against the relative movement, this force acts in a perpendicular direction to the vector $\boldsymbol{\rho}$ locating this force relative to the center of the pivot, as shown in Fig. 3–27(b).

The moment of this frictional force on ΔA about the center is therefore $(\mu P/A)\rho\,\Delta A$. The total moment due to friction is therefore

$$M = \lim_{\Delta A \to 0} \sum_A \frac{\mu P}{A} \rho\,\Delta A = \frac{\mu P}{A} \int\int_A \rho\,dA = \frac{\mu P}{A} \int\int_A \rho^2\,d\theta\,d\rho$$

The annular base area may be considered as an area bounded by $\theta = \phi_1(\rho) = 0$ and $\theta = \phi_2(\rho) = 2\pi$, with maximum ρ equal to R_2 and minimum ρ equal to R_1, as shown in Fig. 3–27(c). Thus,

$$M = \frac{\mu P}{A} \int_{R_1}^{R_2} \left[\int_0^{2\pi} \rho^2\,d\theta \right] d\rho = \frac{2\pi\mu P}{3A} (R_2^3 - R_1^3)$$

Problems

3–15. Solve Problem 3–1 by using Eq. (3–12). Repeat by using Eq. (3–13).

3–16. Find the area enclosed by the lines $x = 3$, $y = 3$, and a circle of radius equal to 5 units with its center at the origin. See Fig. 3–28.   *Ans.* 56.7 sq units

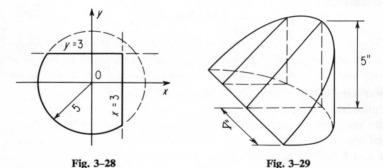

Fig. 3–28   Fig. 3–29

3–17. Find the volume of a wedge 5 inches high cut from a right circular cylinder of radius 4 inches by a plane through a diameter of the base. See Fig. 3–29.
Ans. 53.3 cu in.

3–18. Find the volume of a sphere of radius R by using (a) Eq. (3–12), (b) Eq. (3–14), and (c) Eq. (3–15).   *Ans.* $4\pi R^3/3$

3–5. Centroid of a plane area

Suppose it is necessary to support at one point a thin flat plate which is uniform in thickness t and in unit weight w. Let the plate lie in the x–y plane. The point of support must be so located that the plate is in static equilibrium. Let the proper location of this point be $(\bar{x}, \bar{y})$, as shown in Fig. 3–30. The plate is under the action of parallel gravitational forces. For a system of parallel forces in equilibrium in space, we have three useful equations from Statics: $\sum F_z = 0$, and, with the origin as the moment center, and (x, y) locating each force F_z,

$$\sum M_x = \sum F_z y = 0 \quad \text{and} \quad \sum M_y = \sum -F_z x = 0$$

From these three equations, we can determine the values of $\bar{x}, \bar{y}$ and the weight R of a given plate:

$$\sum F_z = R - \lim_{\Delta A \to 0} \sum_A wt \, \Delta A = 0 \quad \text{or} \quad R = wt \iint_A dA = wtA$$

$$\sum M_x = R\bar{y} - \lim_{\Delta A \to 0} \sum_A ywt \, \Delta A = 0 \quad \text{or} \quad \bar{y} = \frac{wt \iint_A y \cdot dA}{wtA} = \frac{1}{A} \iint_A y \cdot dA$$

$$\sum M_y = -R\bar{x} + \lim_{\Delta A \to 0} \sum_A xwt \, \Delta A = 0 \quad \text{or} \quad \bar{x} = \frac{1}{A} \iint_A x \cdot dA$$

The values of $\bar{x}$ and $\bar{y}$ can be obtained by evaluating the double integrals. The point $(\bar{x}, \bar{y})$ is the center of gravity of the uniform thin plate. However, the quantities $\bar{x}$ and $\bar{y}$ as defined by

$$\bar{x} = \frac{1}{A} \iint_A x \, dA \qquad (3\text{–}16)$$

$$\bar{y} = \frac{1}{A} \iint_A y \, dA \qquad (3\text{–}17)$$

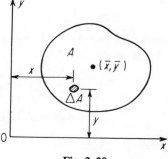

Fig. 3–30

appear very often in engineering problems, in connection with plane areas. The point in the plane of an area located by $(\bar{x}, \bar{y})$ is called the *centroid* of the area. The values of $\bar{x}$ and $\bar{y}$ depend not only on the shape of the area A, but also on the position of the x and y axes. However, it can easily be shown that the location of the centroid relative to the area is independent of the location of the coordinate axes. The centroid of a circular area is always located at its center, no matter where the area is relative to the axes.

In some cases, the centroid of an area can be located without integration. If a plane area is symmetrical with respect to a line, the centroid of the area lies on this line. This fact is evident, because the moments of the parts of the area on the opposite sides of the line are numerically equal but of opposite signs. Thus, the centroid of an elliptical area is located at the intersection of the major and minor axes, and the centroid of the area enclosed by an isosceles triangle is on the median bisecting the angle between the equal sides.

The centroids of many common figures can be found in engineering handbooks. When the centroids of some basic figures are known, the centroid of an area composed of these basic figures can be easily found, as follows. Let the area A be composed of subareas A_1, A_2, A_3, ... A_n, the centroids of which are located at $(\bar{x}_1, \bar{y}_1)$, $(\bar{x}_2, \bar{y}_2)$, $(\bar{x}_3, \bar{y}_3)$, ... $(\bar{x}_n, \bar{y}_n)$ respectively, as

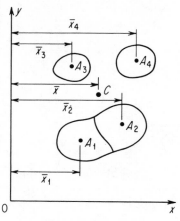

Fig. 3–31

shown in Fig. 3–31. According to Eq. (3–16), we have $\bar{x}$ of the entire area $A = (A_1 + A_2 + ... + A_n)$:

$$A\bar{x} = \iint_A x\,dA = \iint_{A_1} x\,dA + \iint_{A_2} x\,dA + \iint_{A_3} x\,dA + ... + \iint_{A_n} x\,dA$$

$$= A_1\bar{x}_1 + A_2\bar{x}_2 + A_3\bar{x}_3 + ... + A_n\bar{x}_n$$

Thus

$$\bar{x} = \frac{A_1\bar{x}_1 + A_2\bar{x}_2 + A_3\bar{x}_3 + ... + A_n\bar{x}_n}{A_1 + A_2 + A_3 + ... + A_n} = \frac{\displaystyle\sum_{i=1}^{n} A_i\bar{x}_i}{\displaystyle\sum_{i=1}^{n} A_i} \tag{3–18}$$

Similarly, according to Eq. (3–17) we have $\bar{y}$ of the entire area A:

$$\bar{y} = \frac{A_1\bar{y}_1 + A_2\bar{y}_2 + A_3\bar{y}_3 + ... + A_n\bar{y}_n}{A_1 + A_2 + A_3 ... + A_n} = \frac{\displaystyle\sum_{i=1}^{n} A_i\bar{y}_i}{\displaystyle\sum_{i=1}^{n} A_i} \tag{3–19}$$

Example 3–10. Find the centroid of the sector of a circle shown in Fig. 3–32.

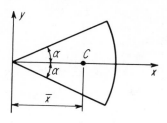

Fig. 3–32

Due to symmetry, the centroid must lie on the x axis, as shown. The distance is

$$\bar{x} = \frac{1}{A} \iint_A x \, dA = \frac{1}{r^2\alpha} \iint_A x \, dA$$

The double integral can be more easily evaluated by using polar coordinates.

$$\iint_A x \, dA = \iint_A \rho \cos\theta \cdot \rho \, d\theta \cdot d\rho = \int_{-\alpha}^{\alpha} \left[\int_0^r \rho^2 \cos\theta \cdot d\rho \right] d\theta = \int_{-\alpha}^{\alpha} \frac{r^3}{3} \cos\theta \cdot d\theta$$

$$= \frac{2}{3} r^3 \sin\alpha$$

Thus
$$\bar{x} = \frac{2r \sin\alpha}{3\alpha}$$

Example 3–11. Find the centroid of the *L*-shaped area minus a circular area, as shown in Fig. 3–33.

This area A may be considered to consist of three subareas: A_1 is a 3 in. by 4 in. rectangle with its centroid c_1 at $\bar{x}_1 = 7$ in. and $\bar{y}_1 = 1.5$ in.; A_2 is a 5 in. by 12 in. rectangle with its centroid c_2 at $\bar{x}_2 = 2.5$ in. and $\bar{y}_2 = 6$ in.; and A_3 is a *negative* 2-in. circular area with its centroid c_3 at $\bar{x}_3 = 3$ in. and $\bar{y}_3 = 10$ in. With $A_1 = 12$ sq in., $A_2 = 60$ sq in., and $A_3 = -\pi$ sq in. in Eqs. (3–18) and (3–19) for composite areas, we have the centroid c of the whole area A located by

$$\bar{x} = \frac{12 \times 7 + 60 \times 2.5 - \pi \times 3}{12 + 60 - \pi} = \frac{224.6}{68.86} = 3.26 \text{ in.}$$

$$\bar{y} = \frac{12 \times 1.5 + 60 \times 6 - \pi \times 10}{12 + 60 - \pi} = \frac{346.6}{68.86} = 5.04 \text{ in.}$$

Example 3–12. A *Theorem of Pappus*: if a plane area is revolved about an axis in its plane, and this axis does not cut this area, the volume of the

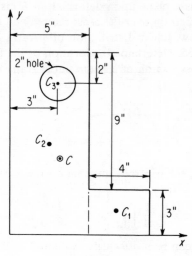

Fig. 3-33

solid of revolution thus generated is equal to the product of the plane area A and the distance travelled by the centroid of A in one revolution. Prove this theorem.

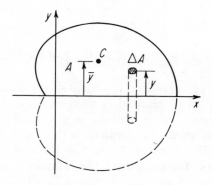

Fig. 3-34

Take a very small area ΔA of area A. In one revolution, the solid generated by ΔA is $2\pi y \cdot \Delta A$, where y is the distance of ΔA from the axis of revolution (see Fig. 3-34). The total volume is

$$V = \lim_{\Delta A \to 0} \sum_A 2\pi y \cdot \Delta A = 2\pi \iint_A y \cdot dA = 2\pi \bar{y} A$$

Q.E.D.

Example 3-13. In elementary analysis of beams, it is assumed that a plane cross section remains a plane upon deformation. This assumption leads to a linear distribution of strain over the cross section and therefore, for materials obeying Hooke's Law, linear distribution of stresses over the cross section, as shown in Fig. 3-35. Determine the location of the neutral axis (the line of no stress) of the cross section of a beam under transverse loads.

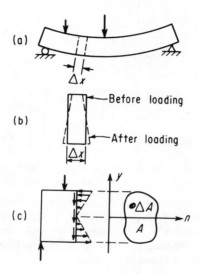

Fig. 3-35

Let the n axis be the neutral axis at a section and the y axis be perpendicular to it in the plane of the cross section. For equilibrium, we must have $\sum F_x = 0$, with any portion of the beam as a free body. Since there is no applied load in the longitudinal direction, we have

$$\sum F_x = \lim_{\Delta A \to 0} \sum s\, \Delta A = \iint_A s \cdot dA = 0$$

where s is the stress. The exact stress distribution can be found only by a much more complicated analysis. By assuming a linear distribution $s = ky$, we then have

$$\sum F_x = \iint_A ky \cdot dA = 0$$

Since k is a constant for the cross section, we have $\iint_A y \cdot dA = 0$, or $\bar{y} = 0$.

Thus, the centroid of the cross section is on the neutral axis. In other words, the neutral axis must pass through the centroid of the cross section if the stresses are linearly distributed.

Problems

3-19. The centroid of a triangular area is located at a distance equal to $h/3$ from any base, where h is the altitude of the triangle measured from this base. Verify this statement by finding $\bar{y}$ of the triangular area shown in Fig. 3-36.

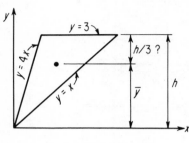 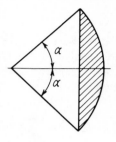

Fig. 3-36   Fig. 3-37

3-20. Locate the centroid of the segment of a circle. With $\alpha = \pi/2$ in Fig. 3-37, see if your result agrees with the result of Example 3-10 for a semicircle.

Ans. $\frac{2}{3}r \sin^3\alpha/(\alpha - \frac{1}{2}\sin 2\alpha)$

3-21. The cross section of a cast-iron flywheel is shown in Fig. 3-38. Find the weight of this flywheel. The unit weight of the cast iron is 450 lb per cubic ft. (Hint: make use of the theorem of Pappus. Use the result of Example 3-10 to locate the centroid of a sector of a circle.)

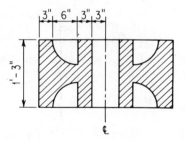

Fig. 3-38

3-6. The second moments of a plane area

In defining the centroid of a plane area, we have come across the integrals $\iint_A x \cdot dA$ and $\iint_A y \cdot dA$. These two integrals are sometimes called the *first moments* of the plane area A about the y and x axes, respectively. In dealing with plane areas in engineering problems, the following integrals are also very often encountered: $\iint_A y^2 \, dA$, $\iint_A x^2 \, dA$, $\iint_A \rho^2 \, dA$, and $\iint_A xy \, dA$. These integrals are to be discussed in this article. The dimensions of these integrals are $[L^4]$.

(a) The integral

$$I_x \equiv \lim_{\Delta A \to 0} \sum_A y^2 \, \Delta A = \iint_A y^2 \, dA \qquad (3\text{–}20)$$

is the *second moment* of the area A with respect to the x axis, and is often called the *moment of "inertia"* of A with respect to the x axis. The second moment with respect to any axis in the plane of the area can be defined in a similar manner; e.g.,

$$I_y \equiv \lim_{\Delta A \to 0} \sum_A x^2 \, \Delta A = \iint_A x^2 \, dA \qquad (3\text{–}21)$$

Obviously, the numerical values of I_x and I_y depend on the shape and size of the area and its location relative to the axes.

The second moments of many common figures are listed in engineering handbooks. When the second moment of an area with respect to a centroidal axis is known, its second moment with respect to a parallel axis can be easily computed. Let the x' axis be a centroidal axis parallel to the x axis. The distance between the two axes is $\bar{y}$, as shown in Fig. 3–39.

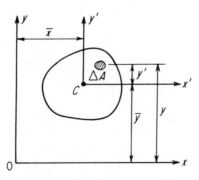

Fig. 3–39

$$I_x = \iint_A y^2 \, dA = \iint_A (y' + \bar{y})^2 \, dA$$

$$= \iint_A (y')^2 \, dA + 2\bar{y} \iint_A y' \, dA + \bar{y}^2 \iint_A dA$$

The integral $\iint_A y' \, dA$ is proportional to the distance from the centroid to the

x' axis (see Eq. 3–17). Since the x' axis is a centroidal axis, the integral must be equal to zero. Therefore

$$I_x = \bar{I}_{x'} + A\bar{y}^2 \tag{3-22}$$

in which $\bar{I}_{x'}$ is the second moment with respect to the centroidal axis x'. Similarly,

$$I_y = \bar{I}_{y'} + A\bar{x}^2 \tag{3-23}$$

Thus the *theorem of Parallel Axes*: the second moment of a plane area with respect to any axis is equal to the sum of its second moment with respect to a parallel centroidal axis and the product of the area and the square of the distance between the two axes.

For examples of computation and applications, the student can now study Examples 3–14 to 3–16.

(b) The *polar moment of "inertia"* of a plane area with respect to an axis z perpendicular to its plane is defined as

$$J_z \equiv \lim_{\Delta A \to 0} \sum_A \rho^2 \, \Delta A = \iint_A \rho^2 \, dA \tag{3-24}$$

where ρ is the distance of ΔA from the z axis (see Fig. 3–40). The polar

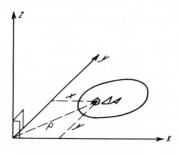

Fig. 3–40

moment of "inertia" of an area may be computed from Eq. (3–24), or by one of the following methods.

The value of J_z may be computed from I_x and I_y:

$$J_z = \iint_A \rho^2 \, dA = \iint_A (x^2 + y^2) \, dA = \iint_A x^2 \, dA + \iint_A y^2 \, dA$$

$$J_z = I_x + I_y \tag{3-25}$$

where the three axes are perpendicular to one another, and the area is in the x–y plane. In computation, the x and y axes should be so chosen that I_x and I_y can be most easily evaluated.

The theorem of parallel axes is also applicable in the case of the polar moments of "inertia" of plane areas. Let the z' axis pass through the centroid of area A in the x–y plane, and let the z' axis be parallel to and at a distance of L from the z axis (see Fig. 3–41).

$$J_z = \iint_A \rho^2 \, dA = \iint_A [(x'+\bar{x})^2 + (y'+\bar{y})^2] \, dA$$

$$= \iint_A (x'^2 + y'^2) \, dA + (\bar{x}^2 + \bar{y}^2) \iint_A dA + 2\bar{x} \iint_A x' \, dA + 2\bar{y} \iint_A y' \, dA$$

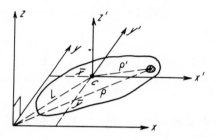

Fig. 3–41

Since the x', y', and z' axes here are centroidal axes, we have $\iint_A x' \, dA = 0$, and $\iint_A y' \, dA = 0$. With $x'^2 + y'^2 = \rho'^2$ and $x^2 + y^2 = L^2$, we have

$$J_z = \bar{J}_{z'} + AL^2 \qquad (3\text{–}26)$$

where L is the distance of the z axis from the centroidal z' axis, and $J_{z'}$ is the polar moment of "inertia" with respect to the centroidal z' axis. (The student can now study Example 3–17 below, and solve Problems 3–27 to 3–29.)

(c) The integral generally known as the *product of "inertia"* of a plane area with respect to two rectangular axes in its plane is

$$P_{xy} \equiv \lim_{\Delta A \to 0} \sum_A xy \, \Delta A = \iint_A xy \, dA \qquad (3\text{–}27)$$

Unlike the other integrals discussed in this article, the product of inertia of an area is not always positive, but may be negative or zero. It can easily be seen that, if one of the two axes is an axis of symmetry, the product of inertia of the area with respect to these axes is zero.

The theorem of parallel axes for products of inertia is slightly different from Eqs. (3–22) and (3–26). Let the x' and y' axes be two rectangular centroidal axes, parallel to the x and y axes, respectively, as shown in Fig. 3–42.

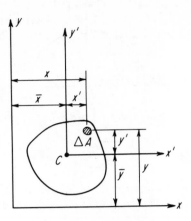

Fig. 3–42

The distance between the x and x' axes is $\bar{y}$, and the distance between the y and y' axes is $\bar{x}$. Then

$$P_{xy} = \iint_A (x' + \bar{x})(y' + \bar{y})\, dA$$

$$= \iint_A x'y'\, dA + \bar{x}\bar{y} \iint_A dA + \bar{y} \iint_A x'\, dA + \bar{x} \iint_A y'\, dA$$

Since each of the last two integrals is the first moment of the area with respect to a centroidal axis, each of them is equal to zero. Thus

$$P_{xy} = \bar{P}_{x'y'} + A\bar{x}\bar{y} \tag{3–28}$$

(The student can now study Examples 3–18 to 3–20, and solve Problem 3–30.)

Example. 3–14. Find the second moment of a circular area (a) with respect to a diameter, and (b) with respect to a tangent.

(a) Let the x' axis be one of the diameters, as shown in Fig. 3–43. Then

$$I_{x'} = \iint_A (y')^2\, dA$$

Using the polar coordinates, we have $y' = \rho \sin \theta$ and $dA = \rho\, d\theta \cdot d\rho$. Thus

$$I_{x'} = \int_0^{2\pi} \left[\int_0^R \rho^3 \sin^2 \theta \cdot d\rho \right] d\theta$$

$$= \int_0^{2\pi} \frac{R^4}{4} \sin^2 \theta \cdot d\theta = \frac{\pi}{4} R^4$$

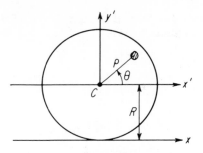

Fig. 3–43

(b) Since the second moment with respect to a centroidal axis is known, the second moment about a parallel tangent can be computed by the theorem of parallel axes:

$$I_x = I_{x'} + AR^2 = \frac{\pi}{4} R^4 + (\pi R^2) R^2 = \frac{5\pi}{4} R^4$$

Example 3–15. Find the second moment of the L-shaped area of Example 3–11 with respect to the centroidal axis parallel to the short arm. Make use of the results of Example 3–14 and the answer to Problem 3–22(b).

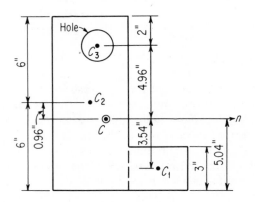

Fig. 3–44

The centroid c has been found in Example 3–14 to be located at 5.04 in. from the base, as shown in Fig. 3–44. The area is considered to consist of three subareas:

$A_1: A_1 = 3 \times 4 = 12$ in.²
    I about axis through c_1 parallel to n axis $= \frac{1}{12} \times 4 \times 3^3 = 9$ in.⁴ (see
        Problem 3–22(b))
    $I_n = 9 + 12 \times 3.54^2 = 159$ in.⁴ (by theorem of parallel axes)

A_2: $A_2 = 5 \times 12 = 60$ in.^{2}

$\quad$ I about axis through c_2 parallel to n axis $= \frac{1}{12} \times 5 \times 12^3 = 720$ in.^{4}

$\quad$ $I_n = 720 + 60 \times 0.96^2 = 775$ in.^{4}

A_3: $A_3 = \frac{\pi}{4} \times 2^2 = \pi$ in.^{2} *(negative)*

$\quad$ I about axis through c_3 parallel to n axis $= \frac{\pi}{4} \times 1^4 = \frac{\pi}{4}$ in.^{4} *(negative)*

$\quad$ $I_n = \frac{\pi}{4} + \pi \times 4.95^2 = 78$ in.^{3} *(negative)*

For the total area A, $I_n = 159 + 775 - 78 = 856$ in.^{4}
(The student can now solve Problems 3–22 to 3–24.)

Example 3–16. Find the longitudinal stresses at a cross section of a beam. The cross section of the beam is a circle with a radius of 5 in. The bending moment at this cross section is 10,000 in.-lb positive. There is no longitudinal load on the beam. The plane of loads passes the centroid of the section.

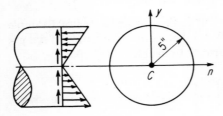

Fig. 3–45

Since there is no longitudinal load on the beam, the neutral axis n (see Fig. 3–45) passes through the centroid of the cross section (see assumptions involved in Example 3–13). With linear distribution of stresses over the cross section, we have the longitudinal stress s written as

$$s = ky$$

where k is an unknown constant for this cross section, the y axis is directed toward the top of the beam, and compressive stress is considered as positive. Thus, a positive bending moment (producing compression on top of the beam) corresponds to a positive value of k at the cross section. For equilibrium, the resisting moment of the longitudinal stresses must be equal to the bending moment at this section. With the origin of the n-y plane as moment center, we have, assuming that the n axis is perpendicular to the plane of loads,

$$\lim_{\Delta A \to 0} \sum_A ys \, \Delta A = M$$

or

$$k \iint_A y^2 \, dA = M$$

Thus

$$s = ky = \frac{My}{I_n} \tag{3-29}$$

This equation is often referred to as the *simple flexure formula*. The neutral axis has been assumed to be perpendicular to the plane of loads, in the derivation. This is not always the case. However, in this problem, the cross section is symmetrical about the plane of loads. By symmetry, the neutral axis must be perpendicular to this plane. (It can be shown that this is true also when the plane of loads contains a principal axis of the cross section. See Example 3–20 for the definition of principal axes.)

With $M = 10{,}000$ in.-lb and $I_n = \dfrac{\pi}{4} R^4 = \dfrac{\pi}{4} 5^4 = 491$ in.^{4},

$$s = \frac{10{,}000}{491}\, y = 20.4\, y \qquad (s \text{ in lb/in.}^2, \text{ and } y \text{ in in.})$$

At the top and bottom of the beam, where $y=5$ in. and $y=-5$ in. respectively, we have $s=102$ lb/in.^{2} and $s=-102$ lb/in.^{2} (i.e., tensile stress), respectively. (The student can now solve Problems 3–25 and 3–26.)

Example 3–17. In elementary study of twisting of circular cylindrical bars, it is assumed that a plane cross section remains a plane and all diameters of a cross section remain diameters. Find expressions for the shearing stresses and the angular deformation of the bar under torque T.

It will be seen presently that the elements of the bar are under shearing stresses. When an element is deformed by shearing stresses, the shearing strain $\epsilon/\Delta x$ is assumed to be related to the shearing stresses τ by

$$\tau = G\,\frac{\epsilon}{\Delta x}$$

where G is the modulus of rigidity of the material, and ϵ is the shear deformation (see Fig. 3–46(b)).

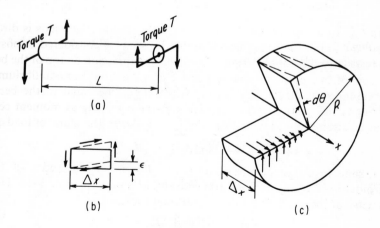

(a)

(b)

(c)

Fig. 3–46

Take a short length Δx of the bar, as shown in Fig. 3–46(c). The relative angular displacement of the two sections is $\Delta\theta$. The shearing deformation of the element at the surface of the bar is therefore $R\,\varDelta\theta$, and the shearing strain is therefore $R\,\varDelta\theta/\varDelta x$. The shearing stresses of this element are $GR\,\varDelta\theta/\varDelta x$. Since the shear deformation of an element is proportional to the distance of the element from the center of the cross section, the shearing strain, and therefore the stress, are also proportional to the distance from the center. Thus, for an element at distance ρ from the center, the shearing stress τ is

$$\tau = G\frac{\rho\,\varDelta\theta}{\varDelta x}$$

For equilibrium with the applied torque T, the shearing stresses at a cross section must produce a torque equal in magnitude to T. Thus

$$T = \lim_{\varDelta A\to 0}\sum_A \rho\tau\,\varDelta A = \frac{G\varDelta\theta}{\varDelta x}\iint_A \rho^2 dA = \frac{G\,\varDelta\theta}{\varDelta x}J$$

where J is the polar moment of inertia of the section about the axis of the bar. Thus

$$\tau = \frac{T}{J}\rho \tag{3-30}$$

The relative angular displacement of two sections at distance L apart, called the *twist angle*, is

$$\theta = \lim_{\varDelta x\to 0}\sum_L \frac{\varDelta\theta}{\varDelta x}\varDelta x = \lim_{\varDelta x\to 0}\sum_L \frac{T}{JG}\varDelta x = \int_0^L \frac{T}{JG}dx$$

For a uniform bar under constant T throughout its length,

$$\theta = \frac{TL}{JG} \tag{3-31}$$

Example 3–18. Find the product of inertia of the area shown in Fig. 3–47 with respect to the x and y axes.

$$P_{xy} = \iint_A xy\,dA = \iint_{A_1} xy\,dA + \iint_{A_2} xy\,dA$$
$$= \int_0^2 \left[\int_0^{12} xy\,dx\right] dy + \int_2^{10}\left[\int_0^4 xy\,dx\right] dy$$
$$= 144 + 384 = 528\text{ in.}^4$$

The same result can also be obtained as follows. Let x'-y' and x''-y'' be the centroidal axes of A_1 and A_2, respectively, as shown in Fig. 3–47. Due to symmetry of the areas about their centroidal axes, we have

$$\bar{P}_{x'y'}\text{ of }A_1 = 0\quad\text{and}\quad \bar{P}_{x''y''}\text{ of }A_2 = 0$$

By the theorem of parallel axes, we have

$$P_{xy}\text{ of }A_1 = 0 + (2\times 12)\times 1\times 6 = 144\text{ in.}^4$$
$$P_{xy}\text{ of A}_2 = 0 + (4\times 8)\times 2\times 6 = 384\text{ in.}^4$$

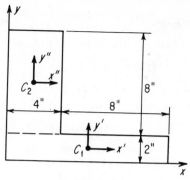

Fig. 3–47

For the total area A,

$$P_{xy} = 144 + 384 = 528 \text{ in.}^4$$

Example 3–19. Given I_x and I_y and P_{xy} of area A, find $I_{x'}$ and $I_{y'}$, where the x-y and x'-y' axes are in the plane of area A with the same origin, as shown in Fig. 3–48.

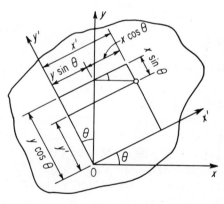

Fig. 3–48

Let θ be the angle between the x and the x' axes. From Example 2–8 or Fig. 3–48, $y' = y \cdot \cos \theta - x \cdot \sin \theta$,

$$I_{x'} = \iint_A (y')^2 dA = \iint_A (y \cos \theta - x \sin \theta)^2 dA$$

$$= \cos^2 \theta \iint_A y^2 dA + \sin^2 \theta \iint_A x^2 dA - 2 \sin \theta \cos \theta \iint_A xy \, dA$$

Thus

$$I_{x'} = I_x \cos^2 \theta + I_y \sin^2 \theta - 2P_{xy} \sin \theta \cos \theta \qquad (3\text{–}32)$$

Similarly, with $x' = y \sin \theta + x \cos \theta$,

$$I_{y'} = I_x \sin^2 \theta + I_y \cos^2 \theta + 2P_{xy} \sin \theta \cos \theta \qquad (3\text{--}33)$$

It can easily be verified that

$$I_{x'} + I_{y'} = I_x + I_y = J_z$$

For example, the second moment of an ellipse with respect to the x' axis which is at an angle of 30° with the major axis, the x axis (see Fig. 3–49), is

$$I_{x'} = I_x \cos^2 (30°) + I_y \sin^2 (30°) - 2P_{xy} \sin (30°) \cos (30°)$$

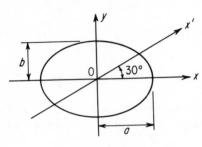

Fig. 3–49

It can be shown that $I_x = \dfrac{\pi}{4} ab^3$ (see Problem 3–22(c)), and $I_y = \dfrac{\pi}{4} a^3 b$. Since the ellipse is symmetrical with respect to the x and the y axes, $P_{xy} = 0$. Thus

$$I_{x'} = \frac{\pi}{4} ab^3 \left(\frac{\sqrt{3}}{2}\right)^2 + \frac{\pi}{4} a^3 b \left(\frac{1}{2}\right)^2 + 0 = \frac{\pi}{16} ab (a^2 + 3b^2)$$

Example 3–20. Given I_x, I_y and P_{xy} of an area A, find the x' axis, passing through the same origin and lying in the same plane as the x and y axes, such that $I_{x'}$ is the maximum or the minimum.

For any angle θ between the x' and x axes, we have from Eq. (3–32)

$$I_{x'} = I_x \cos^2 \theta + I_y \sin^2 \theta - 2P_{xy} \sin \theta \cos \theta$$

For maximum or minimum $I_{x'}$, $\dfrac{dI_{x'}}{d\theta} = 0$. With $\cos^2 \theta = \dfrac{1 + \cos 2\theta}{2}$ and $\sin^2 \theta = \dfrac{1 - \cos 2\theta}{2}$, we have maximum or minimum $I_{x'}$ when $\tan 2\theta = \dfrac{2P_{xy}}{I_y - I_x}$. There are two solutions of θ, at 90° apart, one giving the maximum and the other giving the minimum $I_{x'}$. These two positions of the x' axis are called the *principal axes* of the area with respect to the specified origin. Note that, if either one of the x and y axes is an axis of symmetry, they are principal axes, since P_{xy} is then equal to zero.

Problems

3–22. Determine the second moments of the plane areas shown in Fig. 3–50 with respect to the specified axes.

Ans. (a) $bh^3/12$, (b) $bh^3/12$, (c) $\pi ab^3/4$, (d) $17\pi a^3 b/4$

(a) A triangle with respect to one of its base

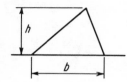

(c) An ellipse with respect to its major axis

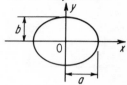

(b) A rectangle with respect to centroidal axis parallel to the base

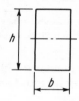

(d) An ellipse with respect to the m-axis located as shown

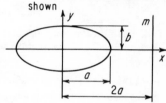

Fig. 3–50

3–23. In a circular plate 16 inches in diameter, there are drilled five 2-inch holes and one 4-inch hole, as shown in Fig. 3–51. Find the second moment of the remaining area with respect to the x axis.   *Ans.* 2965 in.^{4}

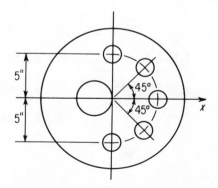

Fig. 3–51

3-24. The *third moment* of an area A in the x-y plane about the x axis is defined as

$$T_x = \iint_A y^3 dA. \text{ Show that}$$

$$T_x = \bar{T}_{x'} + A\bar{y}^3 + 3\bar{y}\bar{I}_{x'}$$

where $\bar{I}_{x'}$ and $\bar{T}_{x'}$ are the second and third moments of the area about its centroidal axis parallel to the x axis.

3-25. Find the maximum compressive and tensile stresses in the beam shown in Fig. 3-52.   *Ans.* 107 lb/in.^{2}, 213 lb/in.^{2}

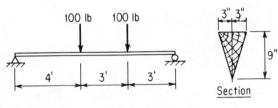

Fig. 3-52

3-26. If the beam in the previous problem is square in cross section, what must be the minimum size of the section so that the longitudinal stresses do not exceed 120 lb per sq in.   *Ans.* 6 in. by 6 in.

3-27. Given that the second moment of a circular area of radius R with respect to a diameter is $R^4/4$, find the polar moment of inertia of an annular area with an inner radius of 5 in. and outer radius of 10 in. about an axis passing through a point on the outer edge.   *Ans.* 38,250 in.^{4}

3-28. A hollow circular steel cylinder is 10 ft long. The inner radius of the cross section is 4 in. and the outer radius is 6 in. Estimate the maximum shearing stresses and the twist angle of the cylinder, when it is twisted in the manner shown in Fig. 3-53. (Modulus of rigidity of steel = 12,000,000 lb/in.^{2}.)

Ans. 44 lb/in.^{2}, 0.734×10^{-4} radian

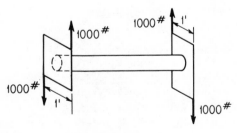

Fig. 3-53

3-29. To move a plate of area a over a thin layer of liquid at a velocity v, as shown in Fig. 3-54(a), the force F required is experimentally found to be equal to

$\mu av/h$, where h is the depth of the liquid, and μ is a constant for the liquid under the condition of the tests. Assuming that this relationship is valid for every small area ΔA of another plate shown in Fig. 3–54(b) which is circular and rotating, find an expression for the torque required to keep the circular plate of radius R rotating at an angular speed ω on the liquid surface.

Ans. $\pi\mu\omega R^4/2h$

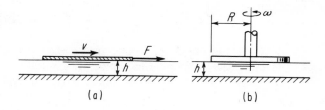

Fig. 3–54

3–30. Find an expression for θ in Fig. 3–55 to locate the principal axes of the right-angled triangular area through the point 0. Also, find the second moments of the area with respect to these principal axes when $a=b$.

Ans. $\tan 2\theta = ab/(a^2 - b^2)$, $a^4/8$, $a^4/24$

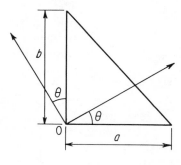

Fig. 3–55

3–7. Hydrostatic pressure on plane surfaces

A *fluid* (liquid or gas) is a material which cannot resist any shearing stress without being continuously deformed. When a fluid is at rest and is therefore not being deformed, there are no shearing stresses in it. For example, when a portion of a resting fluid is used as a free body, as shown in Fig. 3–56, the forces acting on each surface of the fluid are normal to the surface.

It will now be proved that, in a fluid at rest, the fluid pressure at a point is independent of the direction. Take a small volume around the point in question, as shown in Fig. 3–56. Let the mean pressure on the three surfaces be P_1, P_2, and P_3, as shown. Since the fluid element is in static equilibrium, we have

$$\sum F_x = P_2 \, \varDelta y \, \varDelta z - \left(P_1 \, \varDelta y \, \frac{\varDelta z}{\sin \theta} \right) \sin \theta = 0$$

giving $P_2 = P_1$; and

$$\sum F_z = P_3 \, \varDelta y \, \varDelta x - \left(P_1 \, \varDelta y \, \frac{\varDelta x}{\cos \theta} \right) \cos \theta - w \, \frac{\varDelta x \, \varDelta y \, \varDelta z}{2} = 0$$

giving $P_3 = P_1 + (w \, \varDelta z / 2)$. Letting $\varDelta z$ approach zero ($\varDelta x$ approaches zero at the same time, so as to maintain any desired value of θ), we have $P_1 = P_2 = P_3$

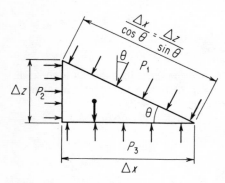

Fig. 3–56

at a point for any value of θ. Thus, the pressure at a point is shown to be independent of direction.

The pressure in a fluid varies from place to place. As a result, the density of the fluid is not uniform. As the density of a gas is very sensitive to changes in temperature and pressure, the variation of density must be considered, in dealing with gases, unless the variations of pressure and temperature are known to be very small. On the other hand, the density of a liquid is much less sensitive to such variations. In dealing with liquids, the density can be considered to be uniform, unless these variations are exceedingly large; e.g., in computing the pressure in a deep ocean. In this article, the pressure variation in a resting fluid in which density can be considered to be uniform is studied.

The variation of pressure along the vertical in a resting fluid of constant density can be obtained as follows. Take a vertical column of fluid as a free body, as shown in Fig. 3–57. Since for equilibrium, $\sum F_z = 0$, we have pressure P at point b:

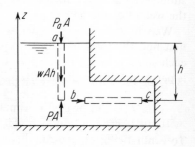

Fig. 3–57

$$P = wh + P_a = \rho g h + P_a \qquad (3\text{–}34)$$

where w and ρ are the unit weight and density of the fluid, respectively, h is the distance below the reference point a, and P_a is the pressure at a (e.g., the atmospheric pressure if point a is located at the open free surface of a liquid).

Differentiating this equation to find the rate of change of pressure with respect to depth, we have

$$\frac{dP}{dh} = w = \rho g$$

i.e., the pressure increases linearly with depth. This equation is usually called the *hydrostatic equation*.

It will be shown that Eq. (3–34) is applicable even when point b is not located directly under point a. Take a horizontal bar of fluid bc as free body, as shown in Fig. 3–57. For equilibrium, we have pressure at c equal to that at b. Since pressure at a point is independent of direction, the horizontal pressure at b is equal to the vertical pressure given by Eq. (3–34). Thus, Eq. (3–34) gives the pressure P for all points of the fluid at a level at distance h below the reference point a.

In engineering problems dealing with machines and structures in contact with liquid with a free open surface, the gage pressure (i.e., pressure above the atmospheric pressure) is used. For example, in the design of a dam, the net force on the dam is due to the gage pressure on the surface exposed to water. With p denoting gage pressure, i.e.

gage p = absolute P − atmospheric pressure

and placing point a at the free surface of the liquid, Eq. (3–34) is reduced to

$$p = wh = \rho gh \qquad (3\text{–}35)$$

where h now denotes the distance of the point below the level of the free surface. With Eq. (3–35), we will compute the forces from hydrostatic pressure on plane surfaces.

Example 3–21. Find the weight W required to keep a gate closed when submerged in water, as shown in Fig. 3–58. The gate is hinged at the top and the weight of the gate is negligible.

We will write the equations of Statics, using the gate as a free body. Let us first find the total force and moment of the hydrostatic (gage) pressure. On each small area ΔA of the gate, a hydrostatic force $p\,\Delta A$ is acting. This force is perpendicular to the flat gate. The total hydrostatic force is therefore

$$F = \lim_{\Delta A \to 0} \sum_A p\,\Delta A = \iint_A p\,dA$$

To evaluate this double integral, place the x-y plane in the plane of the gate. To have a simple expression for the integrand p, place the x axis on the free surface or its extension, as shown in Fig. 3–58. Then, $p = wh = w \sin\theta\, y$, and

$$F = w \sin\theta \iint_A y\,dA$$

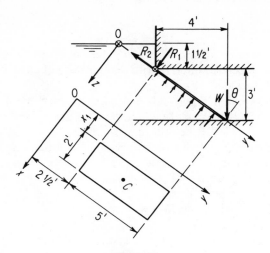

Fig. 3–58

The magnitude of the hydrostatic force can therefore be found by evaluating the double integral. The value of F can also be computed, as follows, if the location of the centroid of the area A is known. Note that the double integral is equal to $\bar{y}A$ and $\bar{y} \sin \theta$ is the distance h_c between the centroid c of area A and the free surface. Thus

$$F = wh_cA \qquad (3\text{–}36)$$

i.e., the mean hydrostatic pressure F/A on a flat submerged area is equal to the pressure wh_c at the centroid of the area.

In computing the moment of the hydrostatic force, it will be found convenient to use the origin on the free surface as the moment center. For each small area ΔA at y, the hydrostatic force is $w \sin \theta\, y\, \Delta A$, with a moment arm y. Thus, the total moment about the origin from hydrostatic pressure is

$$M_x = \lim_{\Delta A \to 0} \sum_A (w \sin \theta)\, y^2\, \Delta A = w \sin \theta \iint_A y^2\, dA$$

Consequently, the total moment can be found by evaluating this double integral. Note that this integral is the second moment I_x of the area A.

When W in Fig. 3–58 is just enough to keep the gate closed, there is no reaction from the floor. Let R_1 and R_2 be the two components of the reaction at the hinge. For equilibrium, we have

$$\sum F_y = W \sin \theta - R_2 = 0$$

$$\sum F_z = R_1 + W \cos \theta - w \sin \theta \iint_A y\, dA = 0$$

and, with moment center at the origin,

$$\Sigma M_x = w \sin \theta \iint_A y^2 \, dA - 2.5R_1 + 6W = 0$$

Evaluating the double integrals or using values of $\bar{y}$ and I_x from handbooks, we have, with $w = 62.4$ lb per cu ft, the forces in lb:

$$R_2 = 0.6 \, W$$
$$R_1 + 0.8 \, W = 1872$$
$$2.5R_1 + 6W = 10{,}110$$

Solving, we have $W = 1360$ lb, $R_1 = 780$ lb, and $R_2 = 816$ lb.

Problems

3–31. A vertical trapezoidal barrier is erected at the end of a flume, as shown in Fig. 3–59. The unit weight of water is 62.4 lb per cu ft. Starting from the fact that $p = wh$, i.e., without using Eq. (3–36), find the total hydrostatic force acting on the barrier.   *Ans.* 13,500 lb

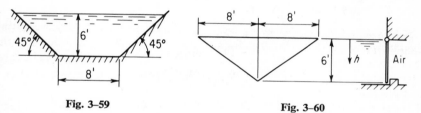

Fig. 3–59   Fig. 3–60

3–32. A vertical triangular gate is exposed to a static body of liquid on one side, as shown in Fig. 3–60. The liquid weighs 60 lb per cu ft. The gate is held in place by a hinge along the top and a key at the bottom. Starting from the fact that $p = wh$, find the reaction at the key.   *Ans.* 2880 lb

3–33. A circular gate 4 ft in diameter covers the entrance to a tunnel under water, as shown in Fig. 3–61. The gate is supported at the top and at the bottom by hinges. Find the reactions at these hinges.   *Ans.* 688 lb and 880 lb

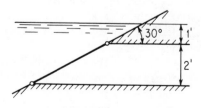

Fig. 3–61

3–34. A triangular plate is bolted to the end of a triangular channel, as shown in

Fig. 3–62. The channel is filled with water to the top of the plate. Find the tensile forces in the three bolts at the three corners of the plate.

Ans. 750 lb, 375 lb, and 375 lb

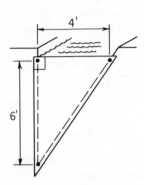

Fig. 3–62

3–8. Triple integrals by iteration

Suppose it is necessary to compute the weight of a solid of variable unit weight $f(x, y, z)$. Obviously, the total weight T is

$$T = \lim_{\Delta V \to 0} \sum_V f(x, y, z) \, \Delta V$$

where the summation is taken over the entire volume V of the solid. This sum is called a *triple integral*, and is usually written as

$$\iiint_V f(x, y, z) \, dV = \lim_{\Delta V \to 0} \sum_V f(x, y, z) \, \Delta V \tag{3–37}$$

Expressions in the form of Eq. (3–37) are encountered very often in engineering problems, with $f(x, y, z)$ being some quantity (not necessarily the unit weight) associated with the corresponding volume ΔV.

The triple integral can be evaluated by iteration in a manner analogous to Eqs. (3–12) to (3–15). Consider a volume V enclosed by a surface which is cut by any line parallel to the x, y, or z axis in not more than two points. (If the surface is such that this condition is not satisfied, the volume V can be divided into subvolumes satisfying this condition, and each subvolume is then treated separately.) Let C be the curve joining the points of the surface tangent to lines parallel to the z axis, and let A be the area enclosed by the projection of curve C on the x-y plane, as shown in Fig. 3–63. (Imagine a beam of light, from above, parallel to the z axis. The curve C is then the boundary between the bright and dark portions of the enclosing surface, and area A is the shadow of the volume on the x-y plane.) Let the two parts of the surface separated by curve C be $z = \zeta_1(x, y)$ and $z = \zeta_2(x, y)$. With $dV = dx\ dy\ dz$, the triple integral can be written as

$$\iiint_V f(x, y, z)\ dV = \int_{x_1}^{x_2} \left\{ \int_{y=\psi_1(x)}^{y=\psi_2(x)} \left[\int_{z=\zeta_1(x, y)}^{z=\zeta_2(x, y)} f(x, y, z)\ dz \right] dy \right\} dx$$

(3–38)

where the first integration with respect to z is performed with x and y held constant. The limits of this integration must be valid for any (x, y). If $f(x, y, z)$ is the unit weight of the solid mass, this first integration gives the weight of solid over unit area of A. This value is a function of x and y over the area A.

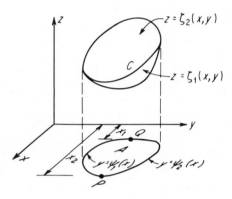

Fig. 3–63

Thus, when the first integration has been performed, the triple integral is reduced to a double integral over the region A, which can then be evaluated. Similar expressions can be written for the triple integral with the first integration performed at constant values of y and z, or at constant values of z and x.

Triple integrals are involved in the determination of such quantities as the center of gravity of masses, the moment of inertia of masses with respect to an axis, etc.:

(a) The *center of gravity* is the location of the resultant of the gravitational forces acting on the mass. The magnitude of this resultant is the weight W of the mass. With the z axis pointing upward, we have for the location $(\bar{x}, \bar{y}, \bar{z})$ of the center of gravity:

$$W\bar{x} = \iiint_V wx\ dV$$

(3–39)

and

$$W\bar{y} = \iiint_V wy\ dV$$

(3–40)

where w is the unit weight of the mass, and $W = \iiint_V w \cdot dV$. Similarly, with the x or y axis pointing upward, we have

$$W\bar{z} = \iiint_V wz \, dV \tag{3-41}$$

Obviously, when a mass is symmetrical about a plane, the center of gravity must lie on this plane. When there are two planes of symmetry, the center of gravity must lie on their line of intersection. When there are three planes of symmetry, the center of gravity is located at the intersection of these planes. An equation for the center of gravity of composite masses, analogous to Eq. (3–18), can also be written. When the total mass of volume V may be considered as the combination of several masses of volumes V_1, V_2, ..., V_n, the center of gravity of the whole mass is located at

$$W\bar{x} = \iiint_V wx \, dV = \iiint_{V_1} wx \, dV + \iiint_{V_2} wx \, dV + \ldots + \iiint_{V_n} wx \, dV$$

Thus

$$\bar{x} = \frac{W_1 \bar{x}_1 + W_2 \bar{x}_2 + \ldots + W_n \bar{x}_n}{W} \tag{3-42}$$

where W_i is the weight and $\bar{x}_i$ locates the center of gravity of V_i ($i = 1, 2, \ldots n$). Similar equations can be written for $\bar{y}$ and $\bar{z}$.

(b) The *moment of inertia* of a mass M with respect to an axis is defined as

$$I \equiv \lim_{\Delta M \to 0} \sum_M l^2 \, \Delta M = \iiint_V \frac{w}{g} l^2 \, dV \tag{3-43}$$

where l is the distance of ΔM from the axis, w is the unit weight of the material, g is the gravitational acceleration, and V is the volume of the mass M. The dimensions of I of mass M are (mass × length^2). In engineering units (force in lb, length in ft, and time in sec), mass is in slugs and I is expressed in slug-ft^2. In the cgs units (force in dynes), I is expressed in gm-cm^2. In evaluating the triple integral in Eq. (3–43), it is well to remember that the distance l of a point at (x, y, z) from the x, y or z axis is $\sqrt{y^2 + z^2}$, $\sqrt{z^2 + x^2}$, and $\sqrt{x^2 + y^2}$, respectively.

It follows, from Eq. (3–43), that the moment of inertia of a mass M which consists of several masses M_1, M_2, ..., M_n, is equal to the sum of I_1, I_2, ..., I_n with respect to the same axis. Also, in a manner entirely analogous to the derivation of Eq. (3–26), it can be shown that the theorem of parallel axes is also valid here:

$$I_n = \bar{I}_{n'} + ML^2 \tag{3-44}$$

where n and n' axes are parallel, the n' axis passes through the center of gravity of mass M, and L is the distance between the two axes.

Example 3–22. Locate the center of gravity of the pyramid shown in Fig. 3–64. Also find its moment of inertia with respect to the z axis. The unit weight w of the solid is uniform.

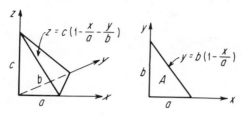

Fig. 3–64

First find the weight of the solid. According to Eq. (3–38),

$$W = \iiint_V w \, dV = w \iint_A \left[\int_0^{c\left(1-\frac{x}{a}-\frac{y}{b}\right)} dz \right] dA$$

where A is the area of the projection of the solid in the x-y plane. Thus

$$W = wc \int_0^a \left[\int_0^{b\left(1-\frac{x}{a}\right)} \left(1-\frac{x}{a}-\frac{y}{b}\right) dy \right] dx = \frac{wabc}{6}$$

To determine $\bar{x}$, we have

$$W\bar{x} = \iiint_V wx \, dV = w \iint_A \left[\int_0^{c\left(1-\frac{x}{a}-\frac{y}{b}\right)} x \, dz \right] dA = wc \iint_A x\left(1-\frac{x}{a}-\frac{y}{b}\right) dA$$

$$= wc \int_0^a \left[\int_0^{b\left(1-\frac{x}{a}\right)} x\left(1-\frac{x}{a}-\frac{y}{b}\right) dy \right] dx = \frac{wa^2bc}{24} = \frac{Wa}{4}$$

Thus $\bar{x} = a/4$. In a similar manner, we have $\bar{y} = b/4$, and $\bar{z} = c/4$.

To determinate I_z, we have from Eq. (3–43)

$$I_z = \iiint_M l^2 dM = \frac{w}{g} \iiint_V (x^2+y^2) \, dV = \frac{w}{g} \iint_A \left[\int_0^{c\left(1-\frac{x}{a}-\frac{y}{b}\right)} (x^2+y^2)dz \right] dA$$

$$= \frac{wc}{g} \int_0^a \left[\int_0^{b\left(1-\frac{x}{a}\right)} \left(1-\frac{x}{a}-\frac{y}{b}\right)(x^2+y^2)dy \right] dx = \frac{wabc}{60 \, g}(a^2+b^2)$$

Since $M = \dfrac{W}{g} = \dfrac{wabc}{6g}$, we can also write $I_z = M\dfrac{a^2+b^2}{10}$.

Example 3–23. Find the moment of inertia of a solid right circular cylinder with respect to axis n shown in Fig. 3–65. The density of the solid is uniform.

It is more convenient to find first I_z with respect to a centroidal axis, and then find I_n by using the theorem of parallel axes, Eq. (3–44).

$$I_z = \iiint_V \frac{w}{g} l^2 dV = \frac{w}{g} \iint_A \left[\int_0^H (x^2+y^2)dz \right] dA = \frac{wH}{g} \iint_A (x^2+y^2)\, dA$$

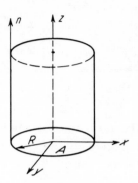

Fig. 3–65

where A is the circular base area. This double integral can be easily evaluated by using cylindrical coordinates

$$I_z = \frac{wH}{g} \int_0^R \left[\int_0^{2\pi} \rho^3 d\theta \right] d\rho = \frac{\pi}{2} \cdot \frac{w}{g} HR^4 = \frac{1}{2} MR^2$$

By the theorem of parallel axes,

$$I_n = I_z + MR^2 = \frac{1}{2} MR^2 + MR^2 = \frac{3}{2} MR^2$$

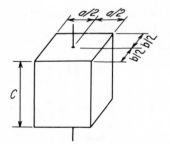   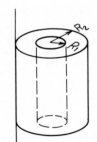

(a) A right parallelopiped.
(Use a triple integral.)

(b) A hollow circular cylinder. (Hint: Use the results of Example 2.23.)

Fig. 3–66

Problems

3–35. Find the moment of inertia of the masses, shown in Fig. 3–66, of homogeneous material with respect to the axis indicated in each case.

Ans. (a) $M(a^2 + b^2)/12$, (b) $M(3R_2^2 + R_1^2)/2$

3–9. Polar-cylindrical and polar-spherical coordinates

In evaluating double integrals, we have learned that, for a given function f and a particular shape of the region A of integration in Eq. (3–11), the work of computation is much less when a proper set of coordinate axes is used. For example, polar coordinates are sometimes used instead of the common rectangular coordinates. Similarly, a triple integral can often be more easily determined by using coordinates other than the rectangular coordinates. In this section, the polar-cylindrical coordinates and the polar-spherical coordinates are introduced. The choice of coordinates is governed by the shape of the volume V and the nature of the function f in the triple integral in Eq. (3–37).

(a) Polar-cylindrical coordinates:

The three coordinates in this system are ρ, θ, and z. ρ is measured radially from the z axis, and θ is the angle between this radial line and the x-z plane, as shown in Fig. 3–67. Surfaces of constant z are planes parallel to the x-y plane. Surfaces of constant θ are planes radial from the z axis and perpendicular to the x-y plane. Surfaces with constant values of ρ are circular cylindrical surfaces with the z axis as their common axis. This system of coordinates is most suitable when the volume V and the function f are symmetrical about an axis, the z axis.

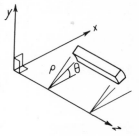

In using this system to evaluate a triple integral, we have for an elementary volume at (ρ, θ, z)

$$dV = \rho \, d\theta \, d\rho \, dz$$

Fig. 3–67

and coordinates x and y, if any, involved in the function f, should be replaced by ($\rho \cos \theta$) and ($\rho \sin \theta$), respectively. The triple integral is therefore reduced to

$$\iiint F(\rho, \theta, z) d\theta \, d\rho \, dz$$

which can be evaluated by iteration (see Example 3–24).

(b) Polar-spherical coordinates:

The three coordinates in this system are ρ, θ, and ϕ. The radial distance ρ is measured from the origin. Angle θ is measured from the z axis and angle ϕ is measured from x-z plane, as shown in Fig. 3–68. With the z axis representing the polar axis of the earth, the angle θ is equivalent to the colatitude, and a change in ϕ is equivalent to a change in longitude. Surfaces with constant values of ρ are spheres with their common center at the origin. Surfaces with

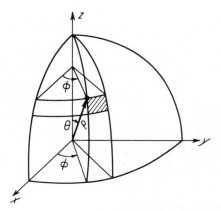

Fig. 3–68

constant values of θ are circular cones with their common apex at the origin and with the z axis as their common axis. Surfaces with constant values of ϕ are radial planes from the z axis.

In using this system to evaluate a triple integral, we have for an elementary volume at (ρ, θ, ϕ),

$$dV = (\rho \sin \theta \, d\phi) \cdot (\rho \, d\theta) \cdot d\rho$$

Coordinates x, y, and z, if any, involved in the function f, should be replaced by $x = \rho \sin \theta \cos \phi$, $y = \rho \sin \theta \sin \phi$, and $z = \rho \cos \theta$ (see Example 3–25).

Example 3–24. Find the weight and the moments of inertia I_z and I_x of the solid cone shown in Fig. 3–69. The unit weight increases linearly with z and ρ; i.e., $w = w_0(1 + az + b\rho)$, where w_0 is the unit weight at the apex of the cone, and a and b are constants.

In this problem, the most convenient coordinates to use are the polar-cylindrical coordinates.

For the weight W of the cone, we have

$$W = \iiint_V w \, dV = \iiint w_0(1 + az + b\rho)\rho \, d\theta \, d\rho \, dz$$

$$= w_0 \int_{z=0}^{z=H} \left\{ \int_{\rho=0}^{\rho=\frac{R}{H}z} \left[\int_{\theta=0}^{\theta=2\pi} (1 + az + b\rho)\rho \, d\theta \right] d\rho \right\} dz$$

$$= \frac{\pi}{3} R^2 H w_0 \left(1 + \frac{3a}{4} H + \frac{b}{2} R \right)$$

In the first integration with arbitrary constant values of ρ and z, the limits 0 and 2π of θ must be valid for any value of ρ or z. In the second integration with respect to ρ at arbitrary constant values of z, the limits 0 and Rz/H of ρ

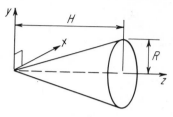

Fig. 3–69

must be valid for any value of z. (The value Rz/H is the radius of the cross-section at a distance z from the apex.) For the particular case of constant unit weight (i.e., $a=b=0$), we have $W=w_0\pi R^2 H/3$.

Similarly, for I_z we have with l in Eq. (3–43) equal to ρ,

$$I_z = \iiint_V \frac{w}{g}\rho^2 \, dV = \iiint \frac{w_0}{g}(1+az+b\rho)\rho^2 \, \rho \, d\theta \, d\rho \, dz$$

$$= \frac{w_0}{g}\int_{z=0}^{z=H}\left\{\int_{\rho=0}^{\rho=\frac{R}{H}z}\left[\int_{\theta=0}^{\theta=2\pi}(1+az+b\rho)\rho^3 \, d\theta\right]d\rho\right\}dz$$

$$= \frac{w_0\pi R^4 H}{10g}\left(1+\frac{5}{6}aH+\frac{2}{3}bR\right)$$

For the particular case of constant unit weight (i.e., $a=b=0$),

$$I_z = \frac{w_0\pi R^4 H}{10g} = \frac{3}{10}\cdot\frac{w_0\pi R^2 H}{3g}\cdot R^2 = \frac{3}{10}\cdot\frac{w}{g}R^2 = \frac{3}{10}MR^2$$

To compute I_x, we have to find an expression, in terms of ρ, θ, and z, for the distance l of an element at (ρ, θ, z) from the x axis:

$$l^2 = y^2+z^2 = (\rho \sin \theta)^2+z^2$$

$$I_x = \iiint_V \frac{w}{g}l^2 dV = \int_{z=0}^{z=H}\left\{\int_{\rho=0}^{\rho=\frac{Rz}{H}}\left[\int_{\theta=0}^{\theta=2\pi}\frac{w_0}{g}(1+az+b\rho)\cdot\right.\right.$$

$$\left.\left.(\rho^2 \sin^2 \theta+z^2)\rho \, d\theta\right]d\rho\right\} dz$$

$$= \frac{w_0\pi R^2 H^3}{3g}\left[\frac{3}{5}\left(1+\frac{R^2}{4H^2}\right)+\frac{aH}{2}\left(1+\frac{R^2}{4H^2}\right)+\frac{bR}{3}\left(1+\frac{3R^2}{10H^2}\right)\right]$$

Example 3–25. Find the weight of half of a spherical shell, shown in Fig. 3–70. The radius of the inner surface is R_1, and that of the outer surface is R_2. The unit weight w of the solid varies linearly with the distance z from the

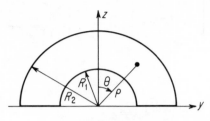

Fig. 3–70

base and with the distance ρ from the center of the sphere; i.e., $w = w_0$ $(1 + az + b\rho)$, where w_0, a and b are constants.

In this problem, the polar-spherical coordinates seem to be the most suitable. For the weight of the shell, we have

$$W = \iiint_V w \, dV$$

$$= \iiint w_0 (1 + a\rho \cos \theta + b\rho) (\rho \sin \theta \, d\phi) d\rho \, (\rho \, d\theta)$$

$$= w_0 \int_{\theta=0}^{\theta=\pi/2} \left\{ \int_{\rho=R_1}^{\rho=R_2} \left[\int_{\phi=0}^{\phi=2\pi} (1 + a\rho \cos \theta + b\rho)\rho^2 \sin \theta \, d\phi \right] d\rho \right\} d\theta$$

$$= w_0 \frac{2\pi}{3} \left[(R_2^3 - R_1^3) + \frac{3}{4} \left(\frac{a}{2} + b \right) (R_2^4 - R_1^4) \right]$$

In the first integration with respect to ϕ, the limits 0 and 2π for ϕ are valid for any constant values of ρ and θ. In the second integration with respect to ρ, the limits R_1 and R_2 are valid for any constant value of θ.

Problems

3–36. Locate the center of gravity of (a) a right circular cone of height H, and (b) a hemisphere of radius R. The material of these masses is homogeneous.

Ans. (a) $H/4$, (b) $3R/8$ from base

3–37. Find the moment of inertia of the masses of homogeneous material shown in Fig. 3–71 with respect to the axis indicated in each case. In case (b), first use polar-cylindrical coordinates, and then repeat by using polar-spherical coordinates. *Ans.* (a) $M(3R^2 + 4H^2)/12$, (b) $2MR^2/5$

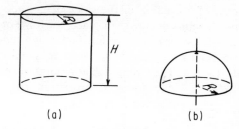

Fig. 3–71

3–38. The roof of an exhibition hall consists of several cylindrical concrete shells, as shown in Fig. 3–72. The length of each shell is 200 ft. The underside of each shell is half of a circular-cylindrical surface with a radius of 20 ft. The thickness t of the shell (measured radially, as shown) varies, being 24 inches at the bases and decreasing linearly with the angle θ to 12 inches at the top. Find the volume of each shell by using polar-cylindrical coordinates. (a) Integrate with respect to ρ first. (b) Repeat the problem by·integrating with respect to θ first.

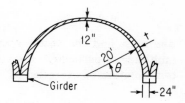

Fig. 3–72

Ans. 18,700 $\pi/3$ cu ft

3–10. Electrostatic field, magnetic field, etc.

Every particle of matter attracts every other particle with a certain force. According to Newton's law of universal gravitation, this force of attraction exerted by a particle of mass m on a particle of mass m' is (see Fig. 3–73)

$$F = -G\frac{mm'}{r^2}\,e_r \qquad (3\text{–}45)$$

where r is the distance between the particles, e_r is the unit vector directed

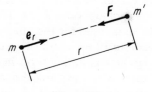

Fig. 3–73

from mass m to mass m', and G is the gravitational constant, the numerical value of which depends on the units used for the other quantities in the formula. In cgs units, $G = 6.67 \times 10^{-8}$ dyne-cm²/gm². (By the law of action and reaction, a force of attraction of the same magnitude is also exerted by mass m' on mass m.) As mass m' moves in space, the force of attraction exerted by mass m on mass m' varies in direction and magnitude. A gravitational field is said to have been set up in the space by mass m wherever a force of attraction towards it is felt. The strength E at a point of the field is defined as the force of attraction per unit mass of the attracted mass; i.e.,

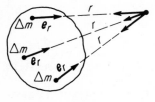

Fig. 3–74

$$E = -G \frac{m}{r^2} e_r \qquad (3\text{–}46)$$

where e_r is the unit vector directed from mass m to the point where the value of E exists. In Eqs. (3–45) and (3–46), the masses m and m' are masses of particles. In computing the force of attraction exerted by a mass of finite volume, one must find the vector sum of the forces of attraction exerted by the multitude of particles in the volume (see Fig. 3–74). The force of attraction can therefore be expressed as an integral:

$$E = \lim_{\Delta m \to 0} \sum_m -G \frac{\Delta m}{r^2} e_r = -G \int_m \frac{e_r}{r^2} \, dm \qquad (3\text{–}47)$$

Although the computation of gravitational attraction is not usually encountered in engineering practice, gravitation is mentioned here because of its similarity to many vector quantities encountered in engineering studies. Several examples of this type are given below.

When two particles with charges q and q' respectively are placed at a distance r apart, there is a force of attraction or repulsion between them. According to Coulomb's law, the force F acting on the charge q' is

$$F = +k \frac{qq'}{r^2} e_r \qquad (3\text{–}48)$$

where e_r is the unit vector directed from the charge q to the charge q'. The force is in the direction of e_r (i.e., repulsive) if q and q' are of the same sign, and attractive if q and q' are of opposite signs. The numerical value of the constant k depends on the units used for the other quantities in the formula, and the nature of the medium in which the two charges are placed. (With mechanical quantities in cgs system and charges in statcoulombs, $k = 1$ dyne-cm²/statcoulomb² in vacuum. With mechanical quantities in mks system and charges in coulombs, $k \doteq 9 \times 10^9$ newton-m²/coulomb² in vacuum, 1 newton being 10^5 dynes and 1 coulomb $= 3 \times 10^9$ statcoulombs.) When the charge q' is placed at various points in space, the force of attraction or repulsion varies in direction and in magnitude. An electrostatic field is said to have been set up in the space by the charge q. The intensity E at any point in the field is defined as the force exerted per unit charge of the charge q'; i.e.,

$$E = +k \frac{q}{r^2} e_r \qquad (3\text{–}49)$$

where e_r is the unit vector directed from the charge q to the point where the value of E exists. The force exerted by charges distributed in space is the vector sum of the forces exerted by the charges, and can therefore be expressed as an integral:

$$E = k \int_q \frac{e_r}{r^2} dq \qquad (3\text{–}50)$$

where the integration is to include all the charges q.

Another example is the velocity field set up by a source or sink in a potential fluid flow. Although this type of flow is only an idealization of actual fluid flow, it yields, under suitable conditions, very useful approximations to actual cases. A source is an imaginary point where fluid is supposedly being created continuously. When only one source is put in an infinite space filled with the fluid, the fluid created at the source is assumed to flow radially outward, evenly in all directions. (The student may imagine a source as an infinitesimally small spherical surface with infinite number of holes evenly distributed over the surface. This sphere is immersed in a fluid and the same kind of fluid is being sent out from the sphere, as shown in Fig. 3–75). If the volume created per unit time is Q, the velocity of the fluid at a distance r from the source is then

Fig. 3–75

$$v = \frac{Q}{4\pi r^2} e_r \qquad (3\text{–}51)$$

where Q (sometimes $Q/4\pi$) is called the strength of the source, and e_r is the unit vector directed from the source to the point where the value of v exists. A sink is a source with negative strength; i.e., a sink is a point where fluid is supposedly being continuously destroyed. With a negative value of Q, Eq. (3–51) gives the velocity field due to a sink. The velocity at a point in space due to the presence of distributed sources and sinks is the vector sum of the velocities due to the sources and sinks, according to Eq. (3–51); i.e.,

$$v = \frac{1}{4\pi} \int_Q \frac{e_r}{r^2} dQ \qquad (3\text{–}52)$$

where Q includes all the sources and sinks.

The integrals in Eqs. (3–47), (3–50), and (3–52) differ from those previously discussed in that these new integrals involve a vector function in the integrand.

Take for instance Eq. (3–47). For each elementary mass dm located at (x, y, z), not only is the distance r, from dm to the point where E is to be found, a function of the position (x, y, z), but also the direction of unit vector e_r from dm depends on (x, y, z). To evaluate this integral, it is convenient to express E and e_r in their components and deal with the components in the direction of one axis at a time. Write

$$E = \int A \, dm$$

Here, A can be written as

$$A = iA_x + jA_y + kA_z$$

Since i, j, and k are constant in magnitude and direction, we have

$$E = i \int A_x dm + j \int A_y dm + k \int A_z dm$$

The integrals may be simple integrals, double integrals, or triple integrals. For example, if electric charges are distributed along a line, the element dq in Eq. (3–50) can be expressed as $\sigma \, ds$, where ds is the length of an element along the line and σ is the charge per unit length. The integral then is an integral along a line. If masses are distributed over a volume, the element dm in Eq. (3–47) may be expressed as $\lambda \, dV$, with λ as the mass per unit volume (density). The integral is then a triple integral. For examples of evaluating these integrals, see Examples 3–26 to 3–28.

Another somewhat similar but not analogous phenomenon is the magnetic field of an electric current element. A magnetic field may be set up by moving electric charges. In a magnetic field, a magnetic pole or a moving electric charge will experience a force acting on it. Thus, in addition to the electrostatic force mentioned above, a moving charge q exerts a force on another moving charge q'. We are going to study the magnetic field set up by moving electric charges here. The most common case of moving charges, in practice, is that of a current in a conductor. According to Ampère's law or Biot's law, the intensity of the magnetic field dH (in proper units) due to a current element ds in length with a current i is

$$dH = \frac{1}{4\pi} (e_i \times e_r) \frac{i}{r^2} \, ds \tag{3–53}$$

where r is the distance from the current element to the point where this dH is set up, e_r is the unit vector in this direction, and e_i is the unit vector in the direction of the current. With i in amperes and lengths in meters, H is in amp/m. In other words, the magnitude of dH is

$$dH = \frac{1}{4\pi} \frac{\sin \theta \, i \, ds}{r^2} \tag{3–54}$$

The angle θ is in the plane of e_r and e_i, and dH is perpendicular to this plane, as shown in Fig. 3–76. The intensity of the magnetic field at a point due to a current in a conductor of finite length L is the vector sum of the dH due to all the current elements in the conductor:

$$H = \frac{1}{4\pi} \int_L \frac{(e_i \times e_r)}{r^2} \, i \cdot ds \tag{3-55}$$

For an example of evaluation of this integral, see Example 3–29.

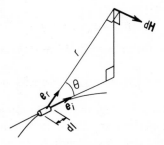

Fig. 3–76

Example 3–26. Find the force of attraction on a unit mass placed at (x_0, y_0) in the x-y plane, exerted by a uniform thin rod of length $2a$, as shown in Fig. 3–77.

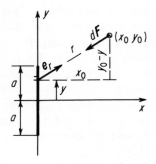

Fig. 3–77

Let σ be the mass per unit length of the rod. For an element dy in length, the mass is $dm = \sigma \, dy$, and the force exerted by dm on the unit mass is, according to Eq. (3–45),

$$dF = -G \frac{\sigma \, dy}{r^2} e_r$$

First, express r and the components of e_r in terms of the coordinates of dm.

Since the magnitude of e_r is unity, its x and y components can be seen to be x_0/r and $(y_0-y)/r$.

$$e_r = i\frac{x_0}{r}+j\frac{y_0-y}{r}$$

Also

$$r = \sqrt{x_0^2+(y_0-y)^2}$$

Thus

$$dF = -G\sigma\left(i\frac{x_0}{r^3}+j\frac{y_0-y}{r^3}\right)dy$$

Since

$$dF = i\,dF_x+j\,dF_y$$

we have

$$dF_x = -G\sigma x_0\frac{dy}{r^3}$$

and

$$dF_y = -G\sigma\frac{(y_0-y)dy}{r^3}$$

Thus

$$F_x = \int dF_x = -G\sigma x_0\int_{-a}^{a}\frac{dy}{[x_0^2+(y_0-y)^2]^{3/2}} = -G\sigma x_0\left.\frac{-(y_0-y)}{x_0^2\sqrt{x_0^2+(y_0-y)^2}}\right|_{-a}^{a}$$

$$= -\frac{G\sigma}{x_0}\left[\frac{y_0+a}{\sqrt{x_0^2+(y_0+a)^2}}-\frac{y_0-a}{\sqrt{x_0^2+(y_0-a)^2}}\right]$$

$$F_y = \int dF_y = -G\sigma\int_{-a}^{a}\frac{(y_0-y)dy}{[x_0^2+(y_0-y)^2]^{3/2}} = -G\sigma\left.\frac{1}{\sqrt{x_0^2+(y_0-y)^2}}\right|_{-a}^{a}$$

$$= -\frac{G\sigma}{x_0}\left[\frac{x_0}{\sqrt{x_0^2+(y_0-a)^2}}-\frac{x_0}{\sqrt{x_0^2+(y_0+a)^2}}\right]$$

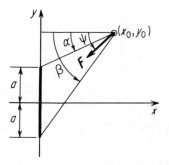

Fig. 3–78

The problem is now solved. However, the following result is also interesting. With the angles α and β measured from the line normal to the rod from the point (x_0, y_0), as shown in Fig. 3–78, these results can also be written as

$$F_x = -\frac{G\sigma}{x_0}(\sin \beta - \sin \alpha)$$

$$F_y = -\frac{G\sigma}{x_0}(\cos \alpha - \cos \beta)$$

and

$$\tan \psi = \frac{F_y}{F_x} = \frac{\cos \alpha - \cos \beta}{\sin \beta - \sin \alpha} = \tan \frac{\alpha + \beta}{2}$$

i.e., the resultant of the forces of attraction bisects the angle $(\beta - \alpha)$ subtended by the rod at the point (x_0, y_0). In general, the line of action of this resultant does not pass through the center of the attracting rod.

Example 3–27. Show that the gravitational field strength inside a spherical shell of a homogeneous mass is zero. In other words, show that the net force of attraction exerted by this shell on a mass placed inside is zero.

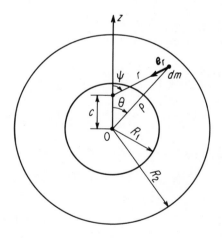

Fig. 3–79

Let λ be the mass per unit volume, R_1 be the radius of the inner surface, and R_2 be the radius of the outer surface. Let a unit mass be placed at a distance c off the center of the shell. Let the z axis pass through the center and the unit mass, as shown in Fig. 3–79. Since the shell with the unit mass is symmetrical about the z axis, the net force of attraction on the unit mass, if any, must act in the z direction. Therefore, it is sufficient to show that the z component of the net force is zero.

For any element dm of the shell, the attraction exerted on the unit mass is

$$d\mathbf{F} = -G \frac{dm}{r^2} \mathbf{e}_r = -G\lambda \frac{dV}{r^2} \mathbf{e}_r$$

Using polar-spherical coordinates, we first express r and $\mathbf{e}_r$ in terms of the coordinates (ρ, θ, ϕ) of dm:

$$r^2 = (\rho \cos \theta - c)^2 + (\rho \sin \theta)^2 = c^2 + \rho^2 - 2c\rho \cos \theta$$

Since the z component of $\mathbf{e}_r$ is $-\cos \psi$ or $-(\rho \cos \theta - c)/r$,

$$dF_z = G \frac{\lambda \, dV}{r^2} \cos \psi = G\lambda \frac{dV}{r^2} \cdot \frac{(\rho \cos \theta - c)}{r}$$

With $dV = \rho^2 \sin \theta \, d\phi \, d\theta \, d\rho$, we have

$$F_z = \int_{\rho=R_1}^{\rho=R_2} \left\{ \int_{\theta=0}^{\theta=\pi} \left[\int_{\phi=0}^{\phi=2\pi} \frac{G\lambda(\rho \cos \theta - c)\rho^2 \sin \theta}{(c^2 + \rho^2 - 2c\rho \cos \theta)^{3/2}} \, d\phi \right] d\theta \right\} d\rho$$

$$= 2\pi G\lambda \int_{\rho=R_1}^{\rho=R_2} \rho^2 \left\{ \int_{\theta=0}^{\theta=\pi} \frac{(\rho \cos \theta - c) \sin \theta}{(c^2 + \rho^2 - 2c\rho \cos \theta)^{3/2}} \, d\theta \right\} d\rho$$

It can be shown that

$$\int_{\theta=0}^{\theta=\pi} \frac{c \sin \theta \, d\theta}{(c^2 + \rho^2 - 2c\rho \cos \theta)^{3/2}} = \frac{-1}{\rho\sqrt{c^2 + \rho^2 - 2c\rho \cos \theta}} \Big|_0^\pi$$

and

$$\int_{\theta=0}^{\theta=\pi} \frac{\rho \cos \theta \sin \theta \, d\theta}{(c^2 + \rho^2 - 2c\rho \cos \theta)^{3/2}} = \left| \frac{-\cos \theta}{c\sqrt{c^2 + \rho^2 - 2c\rho \cos \theta}} - \frac{1}{c^2\rho} \sqrt{c^2 + \rho^2 - 2c\rho \cos \theta} \right|_0^\pi$$

Here $\sqrt{c^2 + \rho^2 - 2c\rho \cos \theta}$ is the distance r, which is always positive. For $\theta = 0$, we have

$$r = \sqrt{c^2 + \rho^2 - 2c\rho \cos \theta} = \sqrt{c^2 + \rho^2 - 2c\rho} = \sqrt{(\rho - c)^2} \quad \text{or} \quad \sqrt{(c - \rho)^2}$$

In this problem, ρ is always greater than c. The value $(\rho - c)$ should be used for r. Thus

$$\int_{\theta=0}^{\theta=\pi} \frac{(\rho \cos \theta - c) \sin \theta}{(c^2 + \rho^2 - 2c\rho \cos \theta)^{3/2}} \, d\theta$$

$$= \left[\frac{1}{c(\rho + c)} - \frac{\rho + c}{c^2\rho} + \frac{1}{\rho(\rho + c)} \right] - \left[\frac{-1}{c(\rho - c)} - \frac{\rho - c}{c^2\rho} + \frac{1}{\rho(\rho - c)} \right] = 0.$$

Therefore

$$F_z = 0$$

From this result, many interesting conclusions can be drawn. The net attraction exerted by a homogeneous solid sphere on a particle within the sphere at a distance c from the center can be seen to be equal to the attraction exerted by the spherical core of radius c. Due to the analogy between Eqs. (3–47) and (3–50), the electrostatic field intensity inside a spherical shell with uniformly distributed charges on the surface can be seen to be zero. Similarly, due to the analogy between Eqs. (3–47) and (3–52), the velocity of the fluid inside a spherical shell due to sources (or sinks) evenly distributed on the surface can also be seen to be zero.

Example 3–28. A narrow annular surface, with inner radius R_1 and outer radius R_2, is assumed to be uniformly charged with σ charges per unit area. Find the electrostatic field intensity at the point $(0, 0, c)$, as shown in Fig. 3–80.

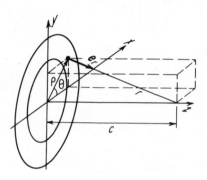

Fig. 3–80

The electrostatic field intensity E can be computed with Eq. (3–50): $E = k \int (e_r/r^2)dq$. For any elementary area dA at $(x, y, 0)$ or $(\rho, \theta, 0)$ we have $dq = \sigma\, dA$. Using polar-cylindrical coordinates, we first express r and the components of e_r in terms of the coordinates (ρ, θ) of dA

$$r^2 = \rho^2 + c^2$$

$$e_r = i\left(\frac{-\rho \cos \theta}{r}\right) + j\left(\frac{-\rho \sin \theta}{r}\right) + k\left(\frac{c}{r}\right)$$

Thus

$$dE = i\, dE_x + j\, dE_y + k\, dE_z = k\sigma\left[i\left(\frac{-\rho \cos \theta}{r^3}\right) + j\left(\frac{-\rho \sin \theta}{r^3}\right) + k\left(\frac{c}{r^3}\right)\right]dA$$

First compute the z component,

$$E_z = \int dE_z = k\sigma \iint_A \frac{c}{r^3} dA = k\sigma c \int_{R_1}^{R_2}\left[\int_0^{2\pi} \frac{1}{(\rho^2 + c^2)^{3/2}}\,\rho\, d\theta\right]d\rho$$

$$= 2\pi k\sigma c\left[\frac{1}{\sqrt{R_1^2 + c^2}} - \frac{1}{\sqrt{R_2^2 + c^2}}\right]$$

It can be shown that $E_x = 0$ and $E_y = 0$. Therefore, $E = kE_z$. (The student can now solve Problems 3–35 to 3–39.)

Example 3–29. Find the intensity of the magnetic field at the point $(0, 0, c)$ due to a current i in the rectangular loop shown in Fig. 3–81.

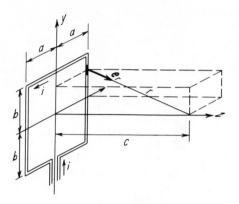

Fig. 3–81

According to Eq. (3–53), for each current element ds in length,

$$dH = \frac{i}{4\pi} \cdot \frac{e_i \times e_r}{r^2} \, ds$$

First express r, e_i and e_r in terms of the coordinates (x, y) of ds. For a current element ds at $(x, y, 0)$,

$$r^2 = x^2 + y^2 + c^2$$

and the unit vector e_r directed from the element to the point $(0, 0, c)$ is

$$e_r = \left(\frac{-x}{r}\right) i + \left(\frac{-y}{r}\right) j + \left(\frac{c}{r}\right) k$$

The contribution of each straight portion of the loop to H_z at $(0, 0, c)$ is first to be computed:

(i) For the portion at $x = a$, with i in the positive y direction:

$$e_r = \left(\frac{-a}{r}\right) i + \left(\frac{-y}{r}\right) j + \left(\frac{c}{r}\right) k$$

$$e_i = j$$

$$e_i \times e_r = \begin{vmatrix} i & j & k \\ 0 & 1 & 0 \\ \dfrac{-a}{r} & \dfrac{-y}{r} & \dfrac{c}{r} \end{vmatrix} = \left(\frac{c}{r}\right) i + \left(\frac{a}{r}\right) k$$

Therefore

$$dH = \frac{i}{4\pi}\left(i\frac{c}{r^3}+k\frac{a}{r^3}\right)ds$$

$$dH_z = \frac{i}{4\pi}\cdot\frac{a}{r^3}\,ds = \frac{i}{4\pi}\cdot\frac{a}{(a^2+y^2+c^2)^{3/2}}\,ds$$

With s measured along the current in the positive y direction, we have $ds=dy$. Therefore,

$$H_z = \frac{ia}{4\pi}\int_{-b}^{b}\frac{dy}{(y^2+a^2+c^2)^{3/2}} = \frac{ia}{4\pi}\cdot\frac{y}{(a^2+c^2)\sqrt{y^2+a^2+c^2}}\bigg|_{-b}^{b}$$

$$= \frac{iab}{2\pi(a^2+c^2)\sqrt{a^2+b^2+c^2}}$$

(ii) For the straight portion at $x=-a$, with i in the negative y direction:

$$e_r = \left(\frac{a}{r}\right)i+\left(\frac{-y}{r}\right)j+\left(\frac{c}{r}\right)k$$

$$e_i = -j$$

$$e_i \times e_r = \begin{vmatrix} i & j & k \\ 0 & -1 & 0 \\ \dfrac{a}{r} & \dfrac{-y}{r} & \dfrac{c}{r} \end{vmatrix} = \left(\frac{-c}{r}\right)i+\left(\frac{a}{r}\right)k$$

Therefore,

$$dH_z = \frac{i}{4\pi}\cdot\frac{a}{r^3}\,ds = \frac{i}{4\pi}\cdot\frac{a}{(a^2+y^2+c^2)^{3/2}}\,ds$$

Here, s along the current is measured along the negative y direction from $y=b$ to $y=-b$. With $ds=-dy$,

$$H_z = \frac{ia}{4\pi}\int_{b}^{-b}\frac{-dy}{(y^2+a^2+c^2)^{3/2}} = \frac{iab}{2\pi(a^2+c^2)\sqrt{a^2+b^2+c^2}}$$

(iii) In similar manner, it can be shown that the z component of the field intensity at $(0, 0, c)$ due to each of the two portions of the loop parallel to the x axis is

$$H_z = \frac{iab}{2\pi(b^2+c^2)\sqrt{a^2+b^2+c^2}}$$

Thus, the z component of the magnetic field intensity due to the current through the whole loop is

$$H_z = 2\frac{iab}{2\pi(a^2+c^2)\sqrt{a^2+b^2+c^2}}+2\frac{iab}{2\pi(b^2+c^2)\sqrt{a^2+b^2+c^2}}$$

$$= \frac{iab}{\pi\sqrt{a^2+b^2+c^2}}\left(\frac{1}{a^2+c^2}+\frac{1}{b^2+c^2}\right)$$

It can be shown that, for the entire loop, $H_x=0$ and $H_y=0$. Thus, $\mathbf{H}=H_z\,\mathbf{k}$.

Problems

3–39. Sources are uniformly distributed along a straight line which is infinitely long. The volume of fluid created per foot of this line source is 2 cubic feet per second. By integrating Eq. (3–52), find the velocity of the fluid at a point 5 feet from the line source. Also solve this problem with the aid of the solution of Example 3–26.   *Ans.* $1/5\pi$ fps

3–40. Sources are distributed uniformly along four straight lines forming a square. If the strength of the line source is 2 cubic feet per second per foot length of line, find the velocity at the point P located at a distance of 4 feet from the plane of the square, as shown in Fig. 3–82.   *Ans.* 0.105 fps

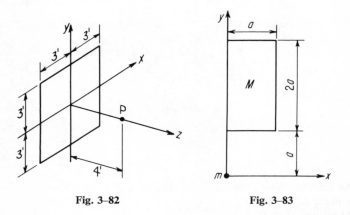

Fig. 3–82   Fig. 3–83

3–41. A thin uniform plate of mass M and a particle m are shown in Fig. 3–83. Find one component of the gravitational attraction between them.

3–42. Show that the force of attraction exerted by a spherical shell of a homogeneous material on a unit mass placed outside the shell at a distance c from its center is equal to GM/c^2, where G is the gravitational constant and M is the mass of the shell. (Hint: compare this problem with Example 3–27.)

3–43. Find the attraction exerted by a right circular cylinder of a homogeneous

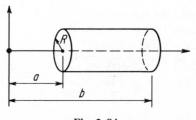

Fig. 3–84

matter on a unit mass placed on its axis at a distance a from one end of the cylinder. The other dimensions are shown in Fig. 3–84.

$$Ans. \ \frac{2GM}{R^2} \left(1 - \frac{\sqrt{R^2+b^2} - \sqrt{R^2+a^2}}{b-a} \right)$$

3–44. Find the magnetic field intensity at a point at a distance c from an infinitely long wire carrying a current i.   *Ans.* $i/2\pi c$

3–45. Find the magnetic field intensity set up by a current through a circular loop of radius R (a) at the center of the loop, and (b) at a point on its axis at a distance c from the plane of the loop. (Hint: for ds located at θ, the x component of e_i is $-\sin \theta$. See Fig. 3–85.)

Ans. (a) $i/2R$, (b) $iR^2/2(R^2+c^2)^{3/2}$

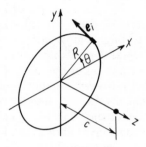

Fig. 3–85

3–46. An infinitely long cable carries a current i. The equation of its curve in the x-y plane is $y = x^2/2$. Set up the integral for the z component of the magnetic field created at $(0, 0, 1)$ by the current.

3–11. Line integrals and potentials

In Fig. 3–86 is shown the path along which a particle moves from A to B. Let force F be one of the forces acting on the particle. Very often, a force may vary from place to place (e.g., the gravitational force exerted by a mass). We want to express the work done by F when it varies along the path with $F_x(x, y, z)$, $F_y(x, y, z)$, and $F_z(x, y, z)$. During an infinitesimal displacement ds, the variation of F approaches zero. Thus, by definition, the work done by F in the displacement ds is $F \cdot ds$. The total work done by F along the path C is therefore $\int_C F \cdot ds$. This integral is called a

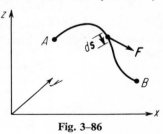

Fig. 3–86

line integral. In general, an integral along a curve C in the form $\int_C A \cdot ds$ is called a line integral, where A is a vector whose magnitude and direction may vary from place to place. Line integrals are very often encountered in engineering problems; e.g., in the study of fluid mechanics, electromagnetic theory, etc. In this book, it suffices to use the work done by a varying force as a physical example.

In evaluating a line integral, it is often convenient to use the rectangular coordinates. From Eq. (2–21), we have

$$\int_C \boldsymbol{F} \cdot d\boldsymbol{s} = \int_C [F_x(x, y, z)\, dx + F_y(x, y, z)\, dy + F_z(x, y, z)\, dz] \quad (3\text{–}56)$$

To evaluate each of the three parts of the integral, the integrand and the differential (for example, F_x and dx) can first be reduced to involve only one independent variable (x, y, or z, or even a coordinate other than x, y and z; e.g., θ in polar coordinates) by using the equation of the curve C. The line integral is thus reduced to three simple integrals (see Example 3–30).

The value of a line integral depends not only on how F varies from place to place, but also on the equation of the curve C between its two terminals, A and B (see Example 3–30). However, under a special condition which is met in many engineering problems, the line integral between two points is independent of the path between them. This fact greatly simplifies the evaluation of the line integral, since any conveniently chosen curve between the two ends may then be used in the calculation. The sufficient condition for the line integral to be independent of the path is the existence of a single-valued function $\phi\,(x, y, z)$ in the region, such that

$$F_x = -\frac{\partial \phi}{\partial x} \qquad F_y = -\frac{\partial \phi}{\partial y} \qquad F_z = -\frac{\partial \phi}{\partial z} \quad (3\text{–}57)$$

The function ϕ is called the *potential function*. The negative signs are used to conform with the convention that the vector $\boldsymbol{F}$ is directed in the direction of decreasing potential. For example, for the gravitational force on a mass m near the earth's surface, we may write $\phi = mgz$ with the z axis pointing upward, giving $F_x = 0$, $F_y = 0$, and $F_z = -mg$. Here, ϕ increases with elevation z, while $\boldsymbol{F}$ is directed toward decreasing ϕ (i.e., downward). Generally, ϕ may not be a measurable physical quantity but a mathematical function which describes a vector $\boldsymbol{F}$ according to Eqs. (3–57). When Eq. (3–57) is satisfied, Eq. (3–56) becomes

$$\int_C \boldsymbol{F} \cdot d\boldsymbol{s} = -\int_C \left[\frac{\partial \phi}{\partial x}\, dx + \frac{\partial \phi}{\partial y}\, dy + \frac{\partial \phi}{\partial z}\, dz \right]$$

According to Eq. (1–32), this becomes

$$\int_C \boldsymbol{F} \cdot d\boldsymbol{s} = -\int_C d\phi = -(\phi_B - \phi_A) = \phi_A - \phi_B \quad (3\text{–}58)$$

where ϕ_A and ϕ_B are the values of ϕ at the beginning and the end, respectively, of curve C. Thus, the line integral is equal to the decrease of potential along the curve, and is independent of the path C, when ϕ is single-valued. For example, the work done by the force of potential $\phi = mgz$ in any motion beginning at point A and ending at point B is equal to $mg(z_A - z_B)$ and is independent of the path taken in the motion. To find out whether Eqs. (3–57) are satisfied for given $F_x(x, y, z)$, $F_y(x, y, z)$, and $F_z(x, y, z)$ (i.e., whether ϕ exists), we make use of the relations that

$$\frac{\partial^2 \phi}{\partial x\, \partial y} = \frac{\partial^2 \phi}{\partial y\, \partial x} \qquad \text{etc.}$$

A potential ϕ exists if and only if

$$\frac{\partial F_x}{\partial y} = \frac{\partial F_y}{\partial x}, \frac{\partial F_y}{\partial z} = \frac{\partial F_z}{\partial y} \quad \text{and} \quad \frac{\partial F_z}{\partial x} = \frac{\partial F_x}{\partial z} \tag{3–59}$$

When these conditions are satisfied, a potential $\phi(x, y, z)$ exists and can be found by integrating Eqs. (3–57), as shown in Example 3–31.

Example 3–30. The magnitude and direction of force F vary with its location:

$$F = (3x^2 + 4y - z^3)i + (x - 2y^2 - xz)j + yk$$

Find the work done by F along the path C_1 in the x-y plane from point A at the origin to point B at $(2, 0, 0)$, as shown in Fig. 3–87. The equation of path C_1 is $y = 4x - 2x^2$. Also find the work done by F along another path C_2.

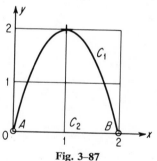

Fig. 3–87

Here, the components of the force are given. From Eq. (3–56), we have

$$\int_{C_1} F \cdot ds = \int_{C_1} [F_x dx + F_y dy + F_z dz]$$

$$= \int_{C_1} [(3x^2 + 4y - z^3)dx + (x - 2y^2 - xz)dy + y\, dz]$$

Consider the first part, $\int F_x dx$. While F_x is given as a function of x, y, and z in general, its value on the curve C_1 depends on one variable only, say x, since y and z of every point of this curve are determined by its coordinate x.

Thus, on the curve C_1 where $y = 4x - 2x^2$ and $z = 0$,

$$\int_{C_1} F_x dx = \int_{C_1} (3x^2 + 4y - z^3) dx = \int_0^2 (16x - 5x^2) dx = 18 \frac{2}{3}$$

Similarly for $\int F_y dy$, we have, from the equation of C_1, $x = 1 \pm \sqrt{1 - (y/2)}$ and $z = 0$. Here x is double-valued, with the negative sign for $0 \leqslant x \leqslant 1$ and the positive sign for $1 \leqslant x \leqslant 2$. Because of this change of sign, the integral $\int F_y dy$ must be performed in two parts:

$$\int_{C_1} F_y dy = \int_{C_1} (x - 2y^2 - xz) dy$$

$$= \int_0^2 \left(1 - \sqrt{1 - \frac{y}{2}} - 2y^2\right) dy + \int_2^0 \left(1 + \sqrt{1 - \frac{y}{2}} - 2y^2\right) dy = -2 \frac{2}{3}$$

This value of $\int F_y dy$ can also be obtained by integrating with respect to x. With $y = 4x - 2x^2$, $z = 0$, and $dy = (4 - 4x) dx$

$$\int_{C_1} F_y dy = \int_{C_1} (x - 2y^2 - xz) dy = \int_{x=0}^{x=2} [x - 2(4x - 2x^2)^2] (4 - 4x) dx = -2 \frac{2}{3}$$

Note that, although there is no net displacement in the y direction, $\int F_y dy$ is not zero.

Finally, we have $\int F_z dz = 0$, since $dz = 0$ everywhere along the path. Thus

$$\int_{C_1} \mathbf{F} \cdot d\mathbf{s} = 18 \frac{2}{3} - 2 \frac{2}{3} + 0 = 16$$

For the work done along path C_2 by the same force field $\mathbf{F}$, we have, with $y = z = 0$ and $dy = dz = 0$ everywhere along the path,

$$\int_{C_2} \mathbf{F} \cdot d\mathbf{s} = \int_{C_2} F_x dx = \int_{C_2} (3x^2 + 4y - z^3) dx = \int_0^2 3x^2 dx = 8$$

Note that, in this case, the line integrals between the same points along two different paths are different.

Example 3–31. Force $\mathbf{F}$ varies with its location:

$$\mathbf{F} = \frac{y}{x^2 + y^2} \mathbf{i} - \frac{x}{x^2 + y^2} \mathbf{j}$$

Find the work done by F between point A at $(1, 0, 0)$ and point B at $(0, 1, 0)$ along the path C_1 which is described by the equations $y = 1 - x$ and $z = 0$. Also see if a potential function ϕ exists for F.

From Eq. (3–56),

$$\int_{C_1} F \cdot ds = \int_{C_1} \left(\frac{y}{x^2 + y^2} \, dx - \frac{x}{x^2 + y^2} \, dy \right)$$

Using the equation of the path C_1: $y = 1 - x$, $dy = -dx$,

$$\int_{C_1} F \cdot ds = \int_1^0 \left(\frac{1 - x}{2x^2 - 2x + 1} + \frac{x}{2x^2 - 2x + 1} \right) dx = \tan^{-1}(2x - 1) \Big|_1^0 = -\frac{\pi}{2}$$

With the given F, Eqs. (3–59) are satisfied with

$$\frac{\partial}{\partial y} \left(\frac{y}{x^2 + y^2} \right) = \frac{\partial}{\partial x} \left(\frac{-x}{x^2 + y^2} \right)$$

Thus, there is a potential ϕ which can be found by integrating Eqs. (3–57) as follows:

$$\frac{\partial \phi}{\partial x} = -F_x = \frac{-y}{x^2 + y^2}$$

$$\frac{\partial \phi}{\partial y} = -F_y = \frac{x}{x^2 + y^2} \qquad\qquad (3\text{–}60)$$

$$\frac{\partial \phi}{\partial z} = -F_z = 0$$

Integrating each of these equations with respect to x, y, and z, respectively, we have three equations for ϕ:

$$\phi = -\tan^{-1}\left(\frac{x}{y} \right) + f_1(y, z) + c_1$$

$$\phi = \tan^{-1}\left(\frac{y}{x} \right) + f_2(z, x) + c_2 \qquad\qquad (3\text{–}61)$$

$$\phi = f_3(x, y) + c_3$$

Note that, since the derivatives in Eqs. (3–60) are partial derivatives, the other variables must be considered as constants in the integration. Instead of only a constant of integration, there can be a function of these other variables. For example, the first of Eqs. (3–61) is obtained with y and z treated as constants, and $f_1(y, z)$ can appear with the constant of integration c_1. We must now find $\phi(x, y, z)$ such that all three of Eqs. (3–61) are satisfied. To satisfy the third equation, z should not appear in the equation. Thus, in the first two equations, we have $f_1 = f_1(y)$ and $f_2 = f_2(x)$, which must not contain z. Realizing that $\tan^{-1}(x/y) = (\pi/2) - \tan^{-1}(y/x)$, we have from Eqs. (3-61)

$$\phi = \tan^{-1}\left(\frac{x}{y}\right) + f_1(y) + c_1 - \frac{\pi}{2}$$

$$\phi = \tan^{-1}\left(\frac{y}{x}\right) + f_2(x) + c_2$$

$$\phi = f_3(x, y) + c_3$$

To satisfy the first equation, $f_2(x)$ must be zero. To satisfy the second equation, $f_1(y)$ must be zero. Thus, the three equations are satisfied with

$$\phi = \tan^{-1}\left(\frac{y}{x}\right) + c$$

or, in cylindrical coordinates,

$$\phi = \theta + c$$

where c is an arbitrary constant. Here ϕ is multi-valued if we do not specify the region of operation. For example, at $x=1$ and $y=1$, $\phi - c = \tan^{-1} 1 = \frac{\pi}{4}$, $\frac{9\pi}{4}$, ... Thus Eq. (3-58) would not be useful, unless we can make ϕ single-valued by specifying the region of operation. This can be done by putting up a barrier at $\theta = \pi$, as shown in Fig. 3-88, thus making $-\pi \leqslant \phi - c \leqslant \pi$, and

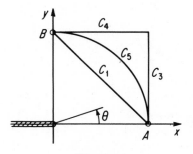

Fig. 3-88

therefore ϕ single-valued. Equation (3-58) is then useful. The line integral from A to B along any path (not crossing the barrier) then has the same value $(\phi_A - \phi_B)$. With $\phi_B = (\pi/2) + c$, and $\phi_A = c$, we have $\int_{C_1} \mathbf{F} \cdot d\mathbf{s} = -\pi/2$.

Once the fact is established that a single-valued potential for $\mathbf{F}$ exists, one can also easily find the line integral, without first finding the potential ϕ. Since the line integral is then independent of the path (as long as it does not cross the barrier), it can be evaluated along any convenient path other than the given path C_1. Take for example the path C_2, consisting of C_3 and C_4, as shown in Fig. 3–88.

$$\int_{C_1} \mathbf{F} \cdot d\mathbf{s} = \int_{C_2} \mathbf{F} \cdot d\mathbf{s} = \int_{C_3} (F_x dx + F_y dy) + \int_{C_4} (F_x dx + F_y dy)$$

$$= \int_0^1 -\frac{1}{1+y^2} \, dy + \int_1^0 \frac{1}{x^2+1} \, dx = -\frac{\pi}{2}$$

It is also instructive to consider the circular path C_5. Using polar-cylindrical coordinates, the equation of C_5 is $\rho = 1$. With $x = \rho \cos \theta$ and $y = \rho \sin \theta$, the given components of $\mathbf{F}$ are $F_x = (\rho \sin \theta)/\rho^2$, and $F_y = (-\rho \cos \theta)/\rho^2$. On C_5, these become $F_x = \sin \theta$ and $F_y = -\cos \theta$. Also on C_5,

$$dx = -\rho \sin \theta \, d\theta + \cos \theta \, d\rho = -\sin \theta \, d\theta$$
$$dy = \rho \cos \theta \, d\theta + \sin \theta \, d\rho = \cos \theta \, d\theta$$

Thus

$$\int_{C_1} \mathbf{F} \cdot d\mathbf{s} = \int_{C_5} \mathbf{F} \cdot d\mathbf{s} = \int_{C_5} (F_x dx + F_y dy)$$

$$= \int_{C_5} [\sin \theta \, (-\sin \theta \, d\theta) + (-\cos \theta) \cos \theta \, d\theta] = \int_0^{\pi/2} -d\theta = \frac{-\pi}{2}$$

In this example, the line integral along C_1 has been evaluated in three different manners: (a) by integrating along C_1, (b) by finding the potential and using Eq. (3–58), and (c) by showing the existence of a potential and integrating along other paths like C_2 and C_5. The choice of these methods depends on the problem.

Problems

3–47. A horizontal force of constant magnitude F acts at the end of a crank in its plane of motion. The length of the crank is R. It is originally in a vertical position. Find the work done by F on the crank in turning it through 90° to a horizontal position.

3–48. Show that, for the constant force in the previous problem, there exists a potential. Find this potential and solve the previous problem by using Eq. (3–58).

3–49. A force field is given as

$$\mathbf{F} = 2xy\mathbf{i} + (x^2 + y)\mathbf{j}$$

Find the work done by this force between the origin and the point (0, 2, 0) along (a) the y axis, and (b) along a straight line from the origin to the point (2, 2, 0) and then to (0, 2, 0). Are the two results the same? Show that a potential exists for $\mathbf{F}$, and find the potential. Find the work done from the potential.

Ans. Work = 2 units

3–50. A particle m placed at the origin creates a gravitational force field in accordance with the inverse-square law in Eq. (3–46). Express the three rectangular components of the force field in terms of the coordinates x, y, and z. Show that, for this force field, there exists a potential.

3–12. Integration by means of infinite series—elliptic integrals

The student must have learned from experience that integrals are sometimes difficult to evaluate. In fact, many simple-looking indefinite integrals are not even representable by a combination of a finite number of elementary functions. In such cases, the integrals can often be evaluated by means of infinite series.

In Chapter 1, it has been shown that a function $f(x)$ can be represented by a uniformly convergent infinite Taylor's series, within a certain range of the variable x. This is an example of representing a function with an infinite series. There are other ways of expanding a function into a series. For example, we have the binomial series which is derived from Newton's binomial theorem:

$$(a \pm b)^n = a^n \pm na^{n-1}b + \frac{n(n-1)}{2!} a^{n-2}b^2 \pm \frac{n(n-1)(n-2)}{3!} a^{n-3}b^3 + \ldots \quad (3\text{--}62)$$

for any real exponent n, where $b < a$ if n is not a positive integer. If n is a positive integer, this series contains $(n+1)$ terms. If n is not a positive integer but a real number, this series contains an infinite number of terms, and is therefore an infinite series. For example, the function $1/(1+x)$ with $|x| < 1$ can be expanded as

$$f(x) = (1+x)^{-1} = 1 - x + x^2 - x^3 + \ldots \quad (|x| < 1)$$

Although this series can also be obtained by Taylor's expansion, the work involved in binomial expansion is usually less. On the other hand, the application of Taylor's expansion is not limited to this particular type of functions. Another simple method of obtaining a series is by simple division, as illustrated by the following example. For $1/(1-x^4)$ with $|x| < 1$, we have

$$\frac{1}{1-x^4} = 1 + x^4 + x^8 + \ldots, \quad (|x| < 1)$$

When a function $f(x)$ is faithfully represented by a uniformly convergent infinite series within a certain range of the variable x, it is not unreasonable to speculate that the integral of $f(x)$ within this range is also faithfully represented by the integral of the series, term by term. In fact, it can be proved that this is correct if the series is uniformly convergent within the range of interest. (This condition is a sufficient condition. It is not a necessary condition because the integral of a series which is divergent for some values of x within the range of integration can sometimes be correct.)

In evaluating the integral $\int_a^b f(x)dx$ by means of an infinite series, the function $f(x)$ is to be replaced by a uniformly convergent infinite series (not necessarily a power series):

$$f(x) = \phi_1(x) + \phi_2(x) + \phi_3(x) + \dots$$

such that $\int \phi_1(x)dx$, $\int \phi_2(x)dx$, etc. can be expressed in terms of elementary functions. For practical reasons, this series should be rapidly convergent, so that only a few terms need to be used in computation. The technique of reducing $f(x)$ to a suitable series varies from problem to problem, and can only be learned through experience (see Example 3–33).

Several definite integrals which cannot be evaluated by using an indefinite integral are encountered so often in analysis that they have been computed by means of infinite series and tabulated. Among these tabulated integrals are the elliptic integrals. The integral

$$F(k, \phi_1) = \int_0^{\phi_1} \frac{d\phi}{\sqrt{1 - k^2 \sin^2 \phi}} \qquad (k < 1) \tag{3–63}$$

is called an incomplete *elliptic integral* of the first kind, and its value depends on the parameter k and the upper limit of integration ϕ_1. This integral can be evaluated by means of a series, as shown in Example 3–34. When the upper limit ϕ_1 is $\pi/2$, the integral is called a complete elliptic integral of the first kind, and is usually denoted by $K(k)$:

$$K(k) = \int_0^{\pi/2} \frac{d\phi}{\sqrt{1 - k^2 \sin^2 \phi}} \qquad (k < 1) \tag{3–64}$$

The integral

$$E(k, \phi_1) = \int_0^{\phi_1} \sqrt{1 - k^2 \sin^2 \phi} \, d\phi \qquad (k < 1) \tag{3–65}$$

is called an incomplete elliptic integral of the second kind. When the upper limit ϕ_1 is $\pi/2$, it is called a complete elliptic integral of the second kind. This integral can also be integrated by means of a series. Tabulated values of elliptic integrals can be found in Peirce and Foster's *A Short Table of Integrals*, Ginn, 1956, and Jahnke and Emde's *Tables of Functions*, Dover, 1951.

Example 3–32. A flexible cable is attached to two points at the same elevation. It will be shown in Example 4–22 that, if the load on the cable per unit horizontal distance is uniform (the weight of the cable being negligible compared to the load), the equation for the curve of the

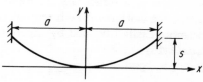

Fig. 3–89

cable is $y = sx^2/a^2$, where s is the sag and a is the half-span of the cable, as shown in Fig. 3–89. Find the length L of the cable for given values of s and a, where s is smaller than $a/2$.

For a short horizontal distance Δx, the length ΔL of the cable is

$$\Delta L = \sqrt{(\Delta x)^2 + (\Delta y)^2} = \sqrt{1 + \left(\frac{\Delta y}{\Delta x}\right)^2}\, \Delta x$$

Thus

$$L = \lim_{\Delta x \to 0} \sum_{x=-a}^{x=a} \sqrt{1 + \left(\frac{\Delta y}{\Delta x}\right)^2}\, \Delta x = \int_{-a}^{a} \sqrt{1 + \left(\frac{dy}{dx}\right)^2}\, dx = \int_{-a}^{a} \sqrt{1 + \left(\frac{2sx}{a^2}\right)^2}\, dx$$

This integral can be found in the usual manner to be

$$L = a\sqrt{1 + \left(\frac{2s}{a}\right)^2} + \frac{a^2}{2s} \log_e \left[\frac{2s}{a} + \sqrt{1 + \left(\frac{2s}{a}\right)^2}\right]$$

However, a simpler approximate solution can be obtained by the use of an infinite series. Since $(x/a) < 1$ and $(2s/a) < 1$, as specified, we have, according to the binomial theorem in Eq. (3–62):

$$\sqrt{1 + \left(\frac{2sx}{a^2}\right)^2} = 1 + \frac{1}{2}\left(\frac{2sx}{a^2}\right)^2 - \frac{1}{8}\left(\frac{2sx}{a^2}\right)^4 + \cdots$$

Therefore

$$L = \int_{-a}^{a} \sqrt{1 + \left(\frac{2sx}{a^2}\right)^2} \cdot dx = \int_{-a}^{a} dx + \frac{1}{2}\left(\frac{2s}{a^2}\right)^2 \int_{-a}^{a} x^2 dx - \frac{1}{8}\left(\frac{2s}{a^2}\right)^4 \int_{-a}^{a} x^4 dx + \cdots$$

$$= 2a\left[1 + \frac{2}{3}\left(\frac{s}{a}\right)^2 - \frac{2}{5}\left(\frac{s}{a}\right)^4 + \cdots\right]$$

For cases with $s \leqslant 0.4a$, L is given within 1% by the simple formula

$$L \doteq 2a\left[1 + \frac{2}{3}\left(\frac{s}{a}\right)^2\right]$$

since the error is about $4a(s/a)^4/5$.

Example 3–33. Evaluate $\int_0^1 \dfrac{e^x - e^{-x}}{x}\, dx$.

This integral cannot be evaluated in the usual manner. If, in integrating by means of a series, the integrand is expanded as a whole into a Taylor's series, the work involved is tedious and the result is complicated. A series can be more easily obtained by expanding e^x and e^{-x} separately. We have from Eq. (1–15)

$$e^x = 1 + x + \frac{x^2}{2!} + \frac{x^3}{3!} + \frac{x^4}{4!} + \frac{x^5}{5!} + \cdots$$

and

$$e^{-x} = 1 - x + \frac{x^2}{2!} - \frac{x^3}{3!} + \frac{x^4}{4!} - \frac{x^5}{5!} + \cdots$$

Thus

$$\frac{e^x - e^{-x}}{x} = 2\left(1 + \frac{x^2}{3!} + \frac{x^4}{5!} + \cdots\right)$$

and

$$\int_0^1 \frac{e^x - e^{-x}}{x}\, dx = 2\left[1 + \frac{1}{3(3!)} + \frac{1}{5(5!)} + \cdots\right]$$

Example 3–34. A pendulum is swinging in a vertical plane through an angle 2β $(\beta < \pi)$ as shown in Fig. 3–90. It will be shown in Example 4–29

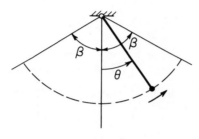

Fig. 3–90

that the time taken by the pendulum to travel through an angle θ_1 $(0 < \theta_1 < \beta)$ from its lowest position is

$$t = \sqrt{\frac{L}{2g}} \int_0^{\theta_1} \frac{d\theta}{\sqrt{\cos\theta - \cos\beta}} \tag{3–66}$$

Find the time required for the completion of one quarter of the oscillation (i.e., find t for $\theta_1 = \beta$).

With the following substitution, the integral in Eq. (3–66) can be reduced to Eq. (3–63), which is an elliptic integral of the first kind. With

$$\cos\theta = 1 - 2\sin^2\left(\frac{\theta}{2}\right)$$

and

$$\cos\beta = 1 - 2\sin^2\left(\frac{\beta}{2}\right)$$

we have

$$\cos\theta - \cos\beta = 2\left[\sin^2\left(\frac{\beta}{2}\right) - \sin^2\left(\frac{\theta}{2}\right)\right]$$

Change the variable θ to ϕ by setting

$$\sin\left(\frac{\theta}{2}\right) = \sin\left(\frac{\beta}{2}\right)\sin\phi$$

Thus, in terms of the new variable ϕ

$$\cos\theta - \cos\beta = 2\sin^2\left(\frac{\beta}{2}\right)(1 - \sin^2\phi) = 2\sin^2\left(\frac{\beta}{2}\right)\cos^2\phi.$$

For $d\theta$ in terms of ϕ, we have by differentiating,

$$\frac{1}{2}\cos\left(\frac{\theta}{2}\right)d\theta = \sin\left(\frac{\beta}{2}\right)\cos\phi\,d\phi$$

$$d\theta = \frac{2\sin\left(\frac{\beta}{2}\right)\cos\phi\,d\phi}{\cos\left(\frac{\theta}{2}\right)} = \frac{2\sin\left(\frac{\beta}{2}\right)\cos\phi\,d\phi}{\sqrt{1 - \sin^2\left(\frac{\beta}{2}\right)\sin^2\phi}}$$

Equation (3–66) can therefore be rewritten as

$$t = \sqrt{\frac{L}{g}}\int_0^{\phi_1}\frac{d\phi}{\sqrt{1 - \sin^2\left(\frac{\beta}{2}\right)\sin^2\phi}} \tag{3–67}$$

where the lower limit of integration is zero and the upper limit is

$$\phi_1 = \sin^{-1}\left[\frac{\sin\left(\frac{\theta_1}{2}\right)}{\sin\left(\frac{\beta}{2}\right)}\right]$$

The integral in Eq. (3–67), with $\sin(\beta/2) = k$ (which is less than unity, since β is less than π), is an elliptic integral of the first kind. In the absence of a table of integrals, this integral can be evaluated by means of a series. Since $k\sin\phi < 1$, we have from the binomial theorem,

$$(1 - k^2\sin^2\phi)^{-1/2} = 1 + \frac{1}{2}k^2\sin^2\phi + \frac{3}{8}k^4\sin^4\phi + \frac{5}{16}k^6\sin^6\phi + \ldots$$

The integral can then be evaluated by integrating term by term. In this problem, θ_1 is equal to β. The limit ϕ_1 in Eq. (3–67) is therefore $\pi/2$, and the integral is a complete elliptic integral of the first kind, $K(k)$:

$$
\begin{aligned}
K(k) &= \int_0^{\pi/2}\frac{d\phi}{\sqrt{1 - k^2\sin^2\phi}} \\
&= \int_0^{\pi/2}\left(1 + \frac{1}{2}k^2\sin^2\phi + \frac{3}{8}k^4\sin^4\phi + \frac{5}{16}k^6\sin^6\phi + \ldots\right)d\phi \\
&= \left|\phi + \frac{1}{2}k^2\cdot\frac{1}{2}(\phi - \sin\phi\cos\phi) + \frac{3}{8}k^4\left[\frac{3}{8}(\phi - \sin\phi\cos\phi)\right.\right. \\
&\qquad\qquad\qquad\qquad \left.\left. - \frac{1}{4}\sin^3\phi\cos\phi\right] + \ldots\right|_0^{\pi/2} \\
&= \frac{\pi}{2}\left[1 + \frac{1}{4}k^2 + \frac{9}{64}k^4 + \frac{25}{256}k^6 + \ldots\right]
\end{aligned}
$$

If the amplitude β is 60°, we have $k = \sin(\beta/2) = 1/2$. Thus

$$K\left(\frac{1}{2}\right) = \frac{\pi}{2}\left[1 + \frac{1}{4}\left(\frac{1}{2}\right)^2 + \frac{9}{64}\left(\frac{1}{2}\right)^4 + \frac{25}{256}\left(\frac{1}{2}\right)^6 + \ldots\right] = \frac{\pi}{2}(1.073)$$

Thus, we have the quarter period t for $\beta = 60°$:

$$t = \sqrt{\frac{L}{g}}\,K\left(\frac{1}{2}\right) = \frac{\pi}{2}\sqrt{\frac{L}{g}}\cdot(1.073)$$

which is about 7% larger than the value for small amplitudes.

Example 3–35. Find the magnetic field intensity set up by a current i along a circular loop at a point P in the plane of the loop at a distance m from the center c of the loop, as shown in Fig. 3–91. The distance m is less than the radius a of the loop.

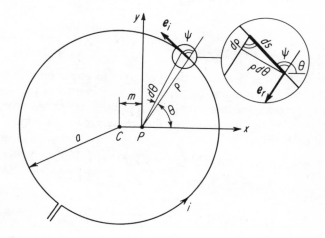

Fig. 3–91

In this problem, it is convenient to use point P as the origin. According to Eq. (3–53), the contribution to the field intensity at P of a current element ds is

$$dH = \frac{i}{4\pi}\cdot\frac{e_i \times e_r}{r^2}\cdot ds$$

To integrate, first express e_i, e_r, r and ds in terms of the coordinates (ρ, θ) of ds. Let ψ be the angle between the radius vector and the tangent of the loop. It can be seen from Fig. 3–91 that

$$ds = \frac{\rho\,d\theta}{\sin\psi}$$

$$r = \rho$$

$$e_i = i\cos(\psi + \theta) + j\sin(\psi + \theta)$$

and

$$e_r = -i \cos \theta - j \sin \theta$$

(The angle ψ is to be expressed in terms of coordinates (ρ, θ) of ds, if necessary. Note that, in Fig. 3–91, the two radial lines at $d\theta$ apart appear as parallel lines in the enlarged view of ds. This is so because ds is infinitesimally small and, therefore, point P is at infinite distance away in the enlarged view. Note also that all curved lines appear as straight lines. See discussion in Art. 1–9 in connection with Fig. 1–31.) Thus

$$e_i \times e_r = \begin{vmatrix} i & j & k \\ \cos(\psi+\theta) & \sin(\psi+\theta) & 0 \\ -\cos\theta & -\sin\theta & 0 \end{vmatrix} = k\,[\sin(\psi+\theta)\cos\theta - \sin\theta\cos(\psi+\theta)]$$

$$= k \sin[(\psi+\theta)-\theta] = k \sin\psi$$

Therefore,

$$H = \int dH = k\,\frac{i}{4\pi} \int \frac{\sin\psi}{\rho^2} \cdot \frac{\rho\,d\theta}{\sin\psi} = k\,\frac{i}{4\pi} \int \frac{d\theta}{\rho}$$

(Note that, so far, the derivation is applicable to any loop, as long as the loop and the point P lie in one plane, and point P is used as the origin.)

In order to evaluate the integral above, it is necessary to have the equation $\rho(\theta)$ of the loop. With $\theta = 0$ along the line cP as shown, the equation of the loop in this problem is

$$(\rho \sin\theta)^2 + (\rho\cos\theta + m)^2 = a^2$$

$$\rho^2 + (2m\cos\theta)\,\rho - (a^2 - m^2) = 0$$

or

$$\rho = -m \cdot \cos \pm \sqrt{m^2\cos^2\theta + (a^2 - m^2)}$$

Here, the positive sign must be used with the radical, since the distance ρ is always positive. Thus

$$H = k\,\frac{i}{4\pi} \int_0^{2\pi} \frac{d\theta}{-m\cdot\cos\theta + \sqrt{m^2\cos^2\theta + (a^2 - m^2)}}$$

To rationalize the denominator, multiply it and the numerator by $[\sqrt{m^2\cos^2\theta + (a^2-m^2)} + m\cos\theta]$. Upon simplifying,

$$H = k\,\frac{i}{4\pi(a^2 - m^2)} \left[a\int_0^{2\pi} \sqrt{1 - \left(\frac{m}{a}\right)^2 \sin^2\theta}\; d\theta + m\int_0^{2\pi} \cos\theta\, d\theta \right]$$

The last integral is equal to zero. In the first integral, the integrand is similar in the four quadrants. Thus

$$H = k\,\frac{ia}{\pi(a^2 - m^2)} \int_0^{\pi/2} \sqrt{1 - \left(\frac{m}{a}\right)^2 \sin^2\theta}\; d\theta$$

This integral is an elliptic integral of the second kind $E(k, \phi_1)$ in Eq. (3–65). The value of the integral depends on the values of the constant $k(=m/a$ here) and the upper limit of integration (equal to $\pi/2$ here). If $m=a/2$, we have $k=\frac{1}{2}$. From tables of elliptic integrals, $E\left(\frac{1}{2}, \frac{\pi}{2}\right)=1.4675$. Thus

$$H = k \frac{ia}{\pi(a^2-m^2)} E\left(\frac{1}{2}, \frac{\pi}{2}\right) = k\, 0.622\, \frac{i}{a}$$

Problems

3–51. Find by means of infinite series the following integrals:

$$\int_0^1 \sin(x^2)\cdot dx \quad \text{and} \quad \int_0^{1/3} e^x \cdot \log_e(1+x)\cdot dx$$

Ans. 0.310, 0.0629

3–52. From the relation $\int \dfrac{dx}{\sqrt{1-x^2}} = \sin^{-1}x + C$, we have $\int_0^u \dfrac{dx}{\sqrt{1-x^2}} = \sin^{-1}u$.

(a) Obtain a series expansion of $\sin^{-1}u$ by evaluating this integral by means of an infinite series. State the condition under which your expansion is valid.
(b) Remembering that $\sin^{-1}(1/2)=\pi/6$, compute π by using your series.

Ans. $u+\dfrac{1}{6}u^3+\dfrac{3}{40}u^5+\dfrac{5}{112}u^7+\ \cdots$

3–53. Find the length of the curve $y=\sin x/2$ between $x=0$ and $x=\pi/2$ by integration by means of an infinite series.

3–54. In measurements, errors (not mistakes) large and small are unavoidable. For equally trustworthy measurements of some quantity, the Gaussian law of errors states that the probability P for an error to have a magnitude between x_1 and x_2 is

$$P = \int_{x_1}^{x_2} \phi(x)\, dx \quad \text{where } \phi(x) = \frac{h}{\sqrt{\pi}}\, e^{-h^2x^2}$$

as shown in Fig. 3–92, and h is the precision constant of the measurements. (In measuring a distance, too large a reading will give a negative error. The error x has a dimension, in this case, of a length L. The dimension of h is then $1/L$.) Show that the probability that an error may fall within the interval $-0.4769/h \leqslant x \leqslant 0.4769/h$ is equal to 1/2. This magnitude $0.4769/h$ is called the *probable error* of the measurements.

3–55. Sources of total discharge Q are uniformly distributed along the y axis for a distance of $2a$, as shown in Fig. 3–93. Find a series solution for the velocity at a point P on the x axis, for cases with $c>a$. (Hint: this problem is analogous to Example 3–26. Evaluate the integral involved by means of an infinite series.) Also, find, from this series solution, an approximate expression for the velocity accurate to 1% for cases with $c \geqslant 2a$.

Ans. $\dfrac{Q}{4\pi c^2}\left[1-\dfrac{1}{2}\left(\dfrac{a}{c}\right)^2+\dfrac{3}{8}\left(\dfrac{a}{c}\right)^4-\ \cdots\right]$

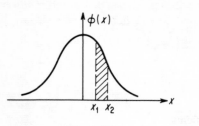

Fig. 3–92   Fig. 3–93

3–56. Show that the length L of a quarter of the ellipse in Fig. 3–49 is given by

$$L = \int_0^a \sqrt{\frac{a^2 - k^2 x^2}{a^2 - x^2}} \, dx$$

where $k = \sqrt{a^2 - b^2}/a$. Also show that $L = a \cdot E\left(k, \frac{\pi}{2}\right)$, where E is an elliptic integral of the second kind. (Hint: let $x = a \cdot \sin \phi$.) Also, supposing $b = a\sqrt{3}/2$, evaluate L by integrating the elliptic integral by means of an infinite series.

Ans. 1.47a

3–13. Numerical integration

In engineering practice, the function to be integrated is sometimes unknown, except for a few discrete values. For example, the distance traveled by a car can be obtained by integrating the speed $f(t)$, the values of which are read from the speedometer from time to time. Thus, the integrand $f(t)$ is unknown, except for values at some particular values of time t. In such cases, a definite integral can be evaluated by numerical integration. This method can also be used in cases where the integrand is known, but the evaluation of the integral is too tedious or cannot be performed by elementary methods. In these cases, computed values of the function to be integrated are used in numerical integration. The result of numerical integration is of course only approximate, but is often of sufficient accuracy for engineering purposes.

In Fig. 3–94, the known values of the integrand $f(x)$ at equal intervals of $\Delta x = b$ are shown by dots. This discussion will be confined to cases with equal intervals of the variable x. It is believed that the student will be able to handle cases with unequal intervals without further instruction. In deriving formulas for numerical integration, it is assumed that the function $f(x)$ can be approximated by a smooth curve passing the known points as represented by

$$f(x) \doteq c_0 + c_1 x + c_2 x^2 + \ldots + c_n x^n \tag{3–68}$$

where n is the number of intervals (for $n + 1$ known values of the function). The $(n + 1)$ c's are constants to be determined from the $(n + 1)$ known values of $f(x)$. Suppose two values of $f(x)$ are known: f_0 at $x=a$ and f_1 at $x=a+b$, as shown in Fig. 3–95. With $n=1$, Eq. (3–68) becomes

$$f(x) \doteq c_0 + c_1 x \qquad \text{(for } a \leqslant x \leqslant a+b)$$

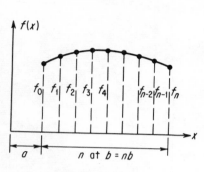

Fig. 3–94   Fig. 3–95

Since this equation must be satisfied at the two known points, we have two equations for the determination of the two constants c_0 and c_1:

$$f_0 = c_0 + c_1 a$$
$$f_1 = c_0 + c_1(a+b)$$

From these two equations, we have the constants c_0 and c_1 in terms of the known quantities f_0, f_1, a, and b:

$$c_1 = \frac{f_1 - f_0}{b} \quad \text{and} \quad c_0 = f_0 - \frac{a}{b}(f_1 - f_0)$$

Thus we have

$$f(x) \doteq f_0 - \frac{a}{b}(f_1 - f_0) + \frac{f_1 - f_0}{b} x$$

(This is the equation of a straight line passing through the two known points. This approximation is reasonable, since it is not known whether the curve of the actual function $f(x)$ is concave upward or downward.) Thus

$$\int_a^{a+b} f(x)\, dx \doteq \int_a^{a+b} \left[f_0 - \frac{a}{b}(f_1 - f_0) + \frac{f_1 - f_0}{b} x \right] dx = \frac{b}{2}(f_0 + f_1) \quad (3\text{–}69)$$

This is called the *trapezoidal rule* for computing the approximate integral between two known values of the integrand. The mean ordinate of the function $f(x)$ in the interval is taken to be $(f_0 + f_1)/2$.

Similarly, for the case with three known values f_0, f_1, and f_2 spaced at equal intervals of the independent variable, as shown in Fig. 3–96, we assume

$$f(x) \doteq c_0 + c_1 x + c_2 x^2 \qquad (a \leqslant x \leqslant a+2b)$$

With the three known values of $f(x)$, we have for the determination of the three constants:

$$f_0 = c_0 + c_1 a + c_2 a^2$$
$$f_1 = c_0 + c_1(a+b) + c_2(a+b)^2$$
$$f_2 = c_0 + c_1(a+2b) + c_2(a+2b)^2$$

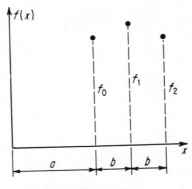

Fig. 3–96

from which the c's can be determined in terms of the known quantities f_0, f_1, f_2, a, and b. With these values of the c's, one can then show

$$\int_a^{a+2b} f(x)\, dx \doteq \frac{b}{3}(f_0 + 4f_1 + f_2) \tag{3–70}$$

This is called *Simpson's rule* for numerical integration over two equal intervals. The mean value of $f(x)$ of these two intervals is taken to be

$$(f_0 + 4f_1 + f_2)/6$$

Similarly, formulas for cases with more known values of $f(x)$ can be derived. For example, for four known values f_0, f_1, f_2 and f_3 spaced at equal intervals, we have

$$\int_a^{a+3b} f(x)\, dx \doteq \frac{3}{8} b\, (f_0 + 3f_1 + 3f_2 + f_3) \tag{3–71}$$

This is called Simpson's rule for numerical integration over three equal intervals. With more and more known values of $f(x)$, the formulas obtained according to this procedure become more and more complicated. Since the known values of the function $f(x)$ are subject to errors in practice, and the assumed form of $f(x)$ in Eq. (3–68) is only approximate, this procedure of fitting a curve through all the known values is not followed when there are four or more known values of $f(x)$. Instead, Eq. (3–69) or (3–70) is used repeatedly. Thus, when there are $(n+1)$ known values of $f(x)$

spaced at n equal intervals, as shown in Fig. 3–94, we have by the trapezoidal rule:

$$\int_a^{a+nb} f(x)\,dx = \frac{b}{2}(f_0+f_1)+\frac{b}{2}(f_1+f_2)+ \dots +\frac{b}{2}(f_{n-2}+f_{n-1})+\frac{b}{2}(f_{n-1}+f_n)$$

$$= b\left(\frac{f_0}{2}+f_1+f_2+ \dots +f_{n-1}+\frac{f_n}{2}\right) \tag{3-72}$$

Similarly, by Simpson's rule in Eq. (3–70), we have for even number of intervals n,

$$\int_a^{a+nb} f(x)\,dx \doteq \frac{b}{3}(f_0+4f_1+f_2)+\frac{b}{3}(f_2+4f_3+f_4)+ \dots +\frac{b}{3}(f_{n-2}+4f_{n-1}+f_n)$$

$$= \frac{b}{3}(f_0+4f_1+2f_2+4f_3+2f_4+ \dots +2f_{n-2}+4f_{n-1}+f_n) \tag{3-73}$$

When the number of intervals is odd, the integral over the first or the last interval is computed according to the trapezoidal rule. The accuracy of Eqs. (3–72) and (3–73) can be increased by using more known values at smaller intervals. For an example of application, see Example 3–36.

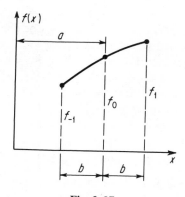

Fig. 3–97

There are several sources of errors in numerical integration. One of these is the use of a finite interval of the independent variable, instead of an infinitesimal interval, according to the definition of an integral in Eq. (3–1). This error can be estimated as follows. Take, for example, Simpson's rule for two equal intervals. As long as the actual integrand $f(x)$ can be expanded into a Taylor's series about the point 0 (see Fig. 3–97) over the interval of integration,

$$f(x) = f_0+f_0'(x-a)+\frac{f_0''}{2!}(x-a)^2+\frac{f_0'''}{3!}(x-a)^3+\frac{f_0^{iv}}{4!}(x-a)^4+ \dots$$

$$(a-b \leqslant x \leqslant a+b)$$

we have

$$\int_{a-b}^{a+b} f(x)\,dx = \int_{a-b}^{a+b} \left[f_0 + f_0'(x-a) + \frac{f_0''}{2!}(x-a)^2 + \frac{f_0'''}{3!}(x-a)^3 + \frac{f_0^{iv}}{4!}(x-a)^4 \right.$$
$$\left. + \dots \right] dx$$

$$= 2f_0 b + \frac{2f_0''}{3!}b^3 + \frac{2f_0^{iv}}{5!}b^5 + \dots$$

But with three known values of $f(x)$, we can express up to the second derivative at point 0 in terms of these three known values and higher derivatives at 0 (see Eqs. (1–24) and (1–27)). From Eq. (1–27) we have

$$f_0'' = \frac{f_{-1}-2f_0+f_1}{b^2} - \frac{f_0^{iv}}{12}b^2 - \dots$$

Thus

$$\int_{a-b}^{a+b} f(x)\cdot dx = 2f_0 b + \frac{2b^3}{3!}\left[\frac{f_{-1}-2f_0+f_1}{b^2} - \frac{f_0^{iv}}{12}b^2 - \dots \right] + \frac{2f_0^{iv}}{5!}b^5 + \dots$$

$$= \frac{b}{3}(f_{-1}+4f_0+f_1)\left[1 - \frac{f_0^{vi}}{30(f_{-1}+4f_0+f_1)}b^4 - \dots \right]$$

The percentage error of Simpson's rule can therefore be seen to be approximately proportional to b^4. (This error may also be considered to have come from the use of a truncated series, i.e., a series with higher-order terms neglected, and is sometimes called a *truncation error*.) The error of the integral can therefore be expressed approximately as kAb^4, where A is the value of the integral and k depends mainly on the properties of the integrand at the center 0 of the interval of integration. This approximate relationship can be used for estimating the truncation error of the integral in Eq. (3–73) according to Simpson's rule, as follows.

Let it be required to find the definite integral $\int_{a}^{a+L} f(x)\,dx$, where the range of integration L is given. If n is the number of intervals used in numerical integration according to Simpson's rule, we have $b=L/n$. Let A_i be the integral over the ith pair of intervals. Then, the error of this integral can be expressed as $k_i A_i (L/n)^4$, where k_i depends mainly on the properties of the integrand at the center of the ith pair of intervals. The total error of the result according to Eq. (3–73), is therefore

$$e_n \doteq k_1 A_1 \left(\frac{L}{n}\right)^4 + k_2 A_2 \left(\frac{L}{n}\right)^4 + \dots = (k_1 A_1 + k_2 A_2 + \dots)\cdot\left(\frac{L}{n}\right)^4 = \frac{K_n L^4}{n^4}$$
$$(3\text{–}74)$$

where K_n depends on the integrand and the number n. Similarly, when m intervals are used, we have the error

$$e_m \doteq \frac{K_m L^4}{m^4} \qquad\qquad (3\text{–}75)$$

From the definitions of e_n and e_m, we have

$$e_n = I - I_n \tag{3-76}$$

$$e_m = I - I_m \tag{3-77}$$

where I is the unknown true value of the integral, I_n is the result by Simpson's rule with n intervals, and I_m is that with m intervals. By assuming that

$$K_m \doteq K_n \tag{3-78}$$

we have altogether five approximate equations, from which the five unknowns e_n, e_m, K_n, K_m and I can be estimated. Although, due to the approximations involved, the value of I cannot be accurately determined in this manner, these equations a:e useful for estimating the small errors. Let $n > m$, so that $e_n < e_m$. The value of e_n can be estimated as follows. From Eqs. (3–76) and (3–77), $e_m - e_n = I_n - I_m$. From Eqs. (3–74) and (3–75), with the approximation from Eq. (3–78), $e_m/e_n \doteq (n/m)^4$. Therefore

$$e_n \doteq \frac{I_n - I_m}{\left(\dfrac{n}{m}\right)^4 - 1} \tag{3-79}$$

With the value of e_n closely estimated, the actual value of the integral I can then be more accurately determined from Eq. (3–76), as shown in Example 3–37. For similar result for the trapezoidal rule, see Problem 3–59.

Another source of error in numerical integration is the inaccuracy of the data of $f(x)$. If the known values of $f(x)$ are observed values, random errors are unavoidable. In Fig. 3–98, let the actual $f(x)$ be represented by the full line, and the observed values with random errors be represented by the dots. By numerical integration, we find the area under a dashed curve passing through the known points, while the actual integral is represented by the area under the full line. It can be seen that, due to the compensating effect of the random errors, the error of the mean ordinate obtained by numerical integration is less than the average magnitude of the errors of the data of $f(x)$. This is in strong contrast to what occurs with numerical differentiation, where the percentage error of the derivative can be very large for relatively small errors of the data of $f(x)$, as indicated by the difference between the slopes of the

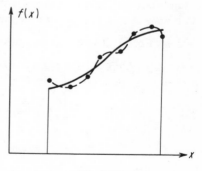

Fig. 3–98

dashed line and the full line in Fig. 3–98. These effects of integration and differentiation on the magnitude of errors are not limited to the numerical methods. Whenever an approximation is involved, such as in the use of a truncated series to represent $f(x)$, these effects are always present.

Another source of error is the assumption that the integrand $f(x)$ can be represented by a smooth function. This may not be the case. To reduce this type of error, the values of $f(x)$ at the discontinuities should be found, if possible. Errors of this type also tend to cancel one another, since it is likely that the actual values of $f(x)$ are higher than the assumed values in some parts of the range of integration, and less in other parts of the range, as shown in Fig. 3–99.

Equations (3–69) and (3–70), derived above, can also be used for numerical evaluation of double integrals such as $\iint f(x, y)\, dx\, dy$, where x and y need not be linear measurements. Suppose nine values $f_1, \ldots, f_9$ of the integrand are known at the nine points shown in Fig. 3–100. Remembering that double

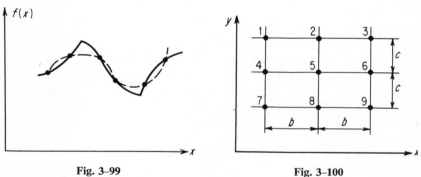

Fig. 3–99   Fig. 3–100

integration can be performed by iteration (see Art. 3–7), one can integrate with respect to x first at three constant values of y. Thus, by using Simpson's rule in Eq. (3–70), we have three values of $\int f(x, y)\, dx$: $b(f_1+4f_2+f_3)/3$, $b(f_4+4f_5+f_6)/3$, and $b(f_7+4f_8+f_9)/3$. With these values in Eq. (3–70), we have for the region shown in Fig. 3–100:

$$\iint f(x, y)\, dx\, dy \doteq \frac{c}{3}\left[\frac{b}{3}(f_1+4f_2+f_3)+4\frac{b}{3}(f_4+4f_5+f_6)+\frac{b}{3}(f_7+4f_8+f_9)\right]$$

$$= \frac{bc}{9}[f_1+f_3+f_7+f_9+4(f_2+f_4+f_6+f_8)+16f_5] \qquad (3\text{–}80)$$

Similarly, using Eq. (3–69) for the region bounded by points 1, 2, 4, and 5, we have

$$\iint f(x, y)\, dx\, dy \doteq \frac{bc}{4}(f_1+f_2+f_4+f_5) \qquad (3\text{–}81)$$

Example 3–36. A dam is to be built across a valley, the contour map of which is shown in Fig. 3–101. Find the storage volume of the reservoir formed behind the dam with the water surface at El. 150 ft above the mean sea level.

Let x=elevation in feet above the mean sea level, and $A(x)$=area in sq ft bounded by the dam and the contour line of elevation x. Then, the volume of storage is

$$v = \int_{105}^{150} A(x)\, dx$$

This integral is to be evaluated, by the trapezoidal rule with the values of $A(x)$ measured from the map (with, say, a planimeter) at 10-ft intervals. These

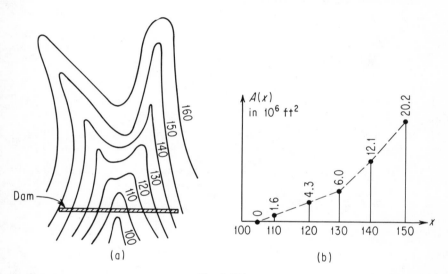

Fig. 3–101

values of $A(x)$ are shown in Fig. 3–101(b). According to the trapezoidal rule, Eq. (3–72),

$$\int_{110}^{150} A(x)\, dx \doteq 10\left(\frac{1.6}{2}+4.3+6.0+12.1+\frac{20.2}{2}\right) \times 10^6 = 333 \times 10^6 \text{ ft}^3$$

$$\int_{105}^{110} A(x)\, dx \doteq 5\left(0+\frac{1.6}{2}\right) \times 10^6 = 10^6 \text{ ft}^3$$

Thus, $V \doteq (333+4) \times 10^6 = 337$ million cu ft. (The student can now solve Problems 3–53 and 3–54.)

Example 3–37. Five values of a certain function $f(x)$ are given in Fig. 3–102 at intervals of $\pi/8$. Find the integral $\int_{0}^{\pi/2} f(x)\, dx$ by Simpson's rule. Also estimate the error of the result with Eq. (3–79).

First, use two intervals of $\pi/4$ each. According to Simpson's rule, the integral is

$$I_2 = \frac{(\pi/4)}{3}(0 + 4 \times 0.70711 + 1.00000) = 1.00228$$

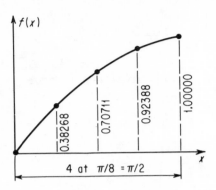

Fig. 3–102

Next, use four intervals of $\pi/8$ each. According to Simpson's rule, the integral is

$$I_4 = \frac{(\pi/8)}{3}(0 + 4 \times 0.38268 + 2 \times 0.70711 + 4 \times 0.92388 + 1.00000) = 1.00014$$

The error of I_4 is, according to Eq. (3–79),

$$e_4 \doteq \frac{I_4 - I_2}{\left(\frac{4}{2}\right)^4 - 1} = -0.00014$$

Thus, the integral I is $(I_4 + e_4) = 1.00000$. This value of the integral is accurate at least to four decimal places. (The values given above for $f(x)$ have been taken from a table of sin x. The actual integral is exactly equal to unity.)

Problems

3–57. From the data obtained by surveying, the cross-sectional areas of a proposed railroad embankment are computed for cross sections at 100 ft apart, and are shown in Fig. 3–103. Find the required volume of fill by the trapezoidal rule, and then by Simpson's rule.   *Ans.* 212,470 cu ft; 225,937 cu ft

3–58. Three known values of $f(x)$ are spaced at unequal intervals b and c, as shown in Fig. 3–104. Show that the integral of $f(x)$ over these two intervals is approximately equal to $\frac{1}{6bc}[f_2b\,(2c^2 + bc - b^2) + f_1\,(b+c)^3 + f_0c\,(2b^2 + bc - c^2)]$. Since the integral is independent of the location of these two intervals along the x axis, you may assume that $x = 0$ when $f(x) = f_0$.

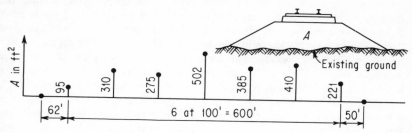

Fig. 3–103

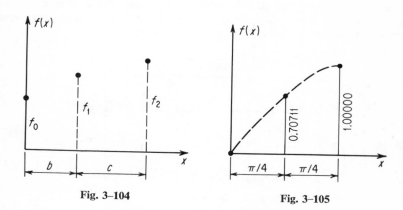

Fig. 3–104   Fig. 3–105

3–59. (a) Show that the percentage error of the result obtained by the trapezoidal rule is approximately proportional to b^2, where b is the interval of the independent variable. (b) A definite integral is first evaluated by the trapezoidal rule with m intervals, and then with n intervals. Let I_m denote the former result and I_n the latter. Show that the error of I_n is approximately equal to

$$\frac{I_n - I_m}{\left(\dfrac{n}{m}\right)^2 - 1}$$

(Hint: see the derivation of Eq. (3–79) for Simpson's rule.) (c) Given three values of a certain function $f(x)$ at intervals of $\pi/4$, as shown in Fig. 3–105, try to evaluate the integral $\int_0^{\pi/2} f(x)\, dx$ as closely as possible, and state how accurate your answer is.

3–60. In Example 3–37, five values of $\sin x$ are given, accurate to five decimal places. By Simpson's rule with four intervals of $\pi/8$ each, it has been shown that the integral $\int_0^{\pi/2} \sin x\, dx \doteq 1.00014$, with an error of -0.00014 due to the use of finite intervals in the integration. The error of the mean ordinate is therefore equal to $-0.00014/(\pi/2)$. To see the effect of random errors, add an error factor to the values given in Example 3–37, as follows. Open a telephone book (or any other large volume) five times at random. Read off the last two digits of the page number, multiply by 10^{-5} and consider this your random "observation error." Determine the sign of each error by flipping a coin, say, heads for a positive sign and tails for a negative sign. (For example, if when you open the book the third time, the page number is 467, and you get a head when you flip the coin, the random error for the third value of sin x is $+0.00067$. Your "observed" value is therefore $0.70711 - (+0.00067) = 0.70644$. Note that your errors are thus limited by ± 0.00099.) Compute the integral by Simpson's rule with four intervals, using your "observed" values. Compute the mean ordinate from this result. What is the additional error of the mean ordinate due to the presence of random errors? (Note that the magnitude of this error is much less than 0.00099, the possible maximum error of the individual "observed" value.)

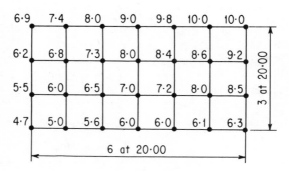

Fig. 3–106

3–61. To find the earthwork involved in excavating for the foundation of a building, the depths of excavation are determined by surveying at points 20 ft apart, as shown in Fig. 3–106, where the depths are given in feet. Compute the yardage of earthwork.   *Ans.* 1951 to 1967 cu yd

CHAPTER 4

ORDINARY DIFFERENTIAL EQUATIONS

4-1. Definitions

In many problems, the controlling equation involves the derivatives of an unknown function or functions. For example, in the study of growth of population, suppose that we have the following law of growth under suitable conditions. The instantaneous rate of growth (in number per year) of a population P is numerically equal to 1/10 the population P. This statement can be expressed as

$$\frac{dP}{dt} = 0.1P \tag{4-1}$$

where t is time in years. This equation involves the derivative of the unknown function $P(t)$. Such equations are called *differential equations*. A *solution* of a differential equation is a function which, together with its derivatives, satisfies the equation. For example,

$$P(t) = Ce^{0.1t} \quad (C \text{ being a constant}) \tag{4-2}$$

is a solution of Eq. (4-1) since, according to Eq. (4-2),

$$\frac{dP}{dt} = 0.1Ce^{0.1t} = 0.1P$$

Note that, for a given differential equation, there can be an infinite number of solutions, as, in this case, the constant C can be of any constant value. This should not be surprising, since Eq. (4-1) is applicable to all communities following this law of growth. For a particular community, say Baltimore City, additional information must be available to determine the constant C; e.g., $P=10^6$ at $t=0$ (at the beginning of 1960). Substituting into Eq. (4-2), $10^6 = Ce^0 = C$. Thus, for Baltimore

$$P(t) = 10^6 e^{0.1t} \tag{4-3}$$

This equation is good for all time in Baltimore, as long as Eq. (4-1) remains valid. Suppose that we want to know the population at the beginning of 1970. At $t=10$, Eq. (4–3) gives $P=10^6 e^{0.1 \times 10} = 2.72 \times 10^6$.

In general, there exists to a differential equation, under suitable conditions, a solution which represents an infinite number of solutions, such as Eq. (4–2). Such solutions are called *general solutions*. For a particular case, one of the solutions described by the general solution is chosen according to known conditions in this particular case. These conditions are called *initial conditions*, or *boundary conditions*. The solution thus chosen is called a *particular solution*. Equation (4–3) is a particular solution of Eq. (4–1), according to the condition that $P=10^6$ at $t=0$.

As integrals are sometimes difficult to obtain, the solutions of differential equations are often equally difficult to find. However, there are several types of equations for which general methods of solution have been established. To introduce some of these methods, it is necessary to give several definitions. (1) An *ordinary differential equation* is one which contains only total derivatives, such as Eq. (4–1). An equation containing partial derivatives is called a *partial differential equation*. (2) The *order* of a differential equation is the order of the highest derivative involved in the equation. Equation (4–1) is a first-order equation, since only a first derivative occurs in the equation. (3) A *linear differential equation* is one in which none of the terms involves products of the unknown function or its derivatives after radicals and fractions have been removed. Equation (4–1) is linear, because terms with P^2, $P(dP/dt)$, $(dP/dt)^2$, etc., are not involved. Otherwise, the equation is called a *nonlinear equation*. (4) The *degree* of a differential equation is the power of the highest derivative in the equation when fractions and radicals have been removed. The equation

$$\frac{dy}{dx} = \frac{\sqrt{y^2 - a^2}}{x}$$

is a second-degree equation since, upon removal of the radical, it becomes

$$\left(\frac{dy}{dx}\right)^2 = \frac{y^2 - a^2}{x^2}$$

which involves the second power of the (highest) derivative dy/dx. An equation with a degree higher than one is necessarily a nonlinear equation.

4–2. First-order ordinary differential equations of first degree

The general form of a first-order ordinary differential equation is

$$\frac{dy}{dx} = f(x, y) \tag{4–4}$$

Equation (4–1) is such an equation. From Eq. (4–2), we have seen that for such an equation there can be a general solution which contains one arbitrary constant. We have also seen from Eq. (4–3) that, for a particular case, the particular solution is obtained from the general solution with one known condition. We have yet to find whether there are solutions other than those represented by the general solution.

We shall interpret Eq. (4–4) and its solutions graphically. A solution $y(x)$ is a curve in the x–y plane and is called an *integral curve*. According to Eq. (4–4), we are seeking an integral curve or curves whose slope at any point (x, y) is equal to the given $f(x, y)$. Suppose we start arbitrarily from a point P at (x_0, y_0) in Fig. 4–1. Knowing the slope $f(x_0, y_0)$ at this point, we can locate a point on the same integral curve very close to P. (To be strictly correct, these two points can only be an infinitesimal distance apart.) With a new slope at this second point, we can locate a third point. This process may be continued to establish the whole integral curve passing through P. Similarly, we can obtain other integral curves by starting from other points such as Q. Thus, we have demonstrated graphically that, for Eq. (4–4), we can have an infinite number of integral curves (i.e., solutions). To

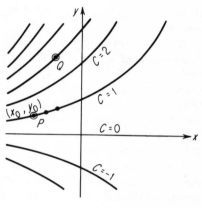

Fig. 4–1

determine which of these curves is the solution for a particular case, we must know one point on the curve, such as P. It is also apparent that we can specify one and only one arbitrary point for each curve. We cannot require an integral curve to pass through two arbitrary points, such as P and Q, and yet obey the differential equation. For example, in the case of Eq. (4–1), we cannot require the Baltimore population to be 10^6 in 1960 and 5×10^6 in 1961 without violating the law of growth specified by Eq. (4–1).

The above discussion suggests that, for first-order ordinary differential equations, there is a general solution containing one arbitrary constant. The general solution represents a family of infinite number of integral curves, with the arbitrary constant taking one particular value for each curve. A particular solution is obtained by determining the constant in the general solution with one known condition in a particular case. However, that this is always true has not been proved by the consideration above. In fact, this is not true in many cases. For example, there may not be any solution to a differential equation; e.g., $|\,dy/dx\,| + 1 = 0$. On the other hand, there may be more than one integral curve passing through a given point; e.g., $dy/dx = \sin^{-1} x$, where $\sin^{-1} x$ has multiple values for a given x. Since the purpose of engineering analysis is to seek the solution to a particular problem, we are naturally interested in the existence and uniqueness of a solution. The conditions under which we are assured of a solution of a certain type are given by what is called an *existence theorem*. The conditions under which a solution is the only possible solution are given by a *uniqueness theorem*. The proof of the existence and uniqueness of a solution has long been a challenge to mathematicians. For first-order first-degree ordinary differential equations, we have the following theorem which is stated here without proof:

Theorem: If $f(x, y)$ in Eq. (4–4) is continuous and single-valued, and $\partial f/\partial x$ and $\partial f/\partial y$ exist and are continuous in a region in the x–y plane, there is one and only one integral curve passing through each point in the region.

This theorem is both an existence theorem and a uniqueness theorem. It is an existence theorem in that we are assured of a particular solution for each given condition. It is a uniqueness theorem in that it states that there is only one particular solution for each case. Since Eq. (4–1) satisfies the conditions of the theorem, Eq. (4–3) is the only particular solution for the population of Baltimore. Equation (4–2), which gives one and only one particular solution for each case, is called the general solution. The general solution of a first-order ordinary differential equation contains one arbitrary constant.

Since there is one and only one particular solution under the specified conditions, how it is obtained is immaterial. If a solution with one arbitrary constant is found, by any method including guessing, and this solution gives one particular solution for each case, this solution is the general solution of the differential equation. (The student should appreciate the practical importance of mathematical theorems!) However, it should be mentioned that the general solution may appear in several forms. For example, the solution in Eq. (4–2) may be written as $\log_e P = 0.1t + C_1$. Sometimes, it is necessary to use more than one form in order to include all particular solutions. For example, the general solution of the differential equation

$$\frac{dy}{Ix} = \frac{y(y-2)}{x}$$

may be written as, among many other forms,

$$x^2 y - C_1(y-2) = 0$$

or

$$C_2 x^2 y - (y-2) = 0$$

It can be easily verified that, among many others, $y=0$ and $y=2$ are particular solutions of the differential equation. To include both of these particular solutions, it is necessary to use both forms of the general solution, with $C_1 = 0$ to obtain $y=0$, and with $C_2 = 0$ to obtain $y=2$.

While a general solution exists under suitable conditions, there are no definite methods of obtaining it. However, there are several types of first-order ordinary differential equations which can be treated by some general methods:

(1) Equations with variables separable. When an equation can be reduced to the form

$$f_1(x)f_2(y)\,dx + f_3(x)f_4(y)\,dy = 0 \tag{4–5}$$

where each function contains only one variable, the general solution may be obtained by separating the variables and integrating:

$$\int \frac{f_1(x)}{f_3(x)}\,dx + \int \frac{f_4(y)}{f_2(y)}\,dy + C = 0 \tag{4–6}$$

where the constant C is the combination of the two constants of integration. This is the general solution, since it contains one arbitrary constant C, giving one particular solution for each case. (An amazing number of engineering problems can be solved by this simple method. The student can now study the examples and physical problems following this article.)

(2) Homogeneous equations. A first-order equation is called *homogeneous* when each term of $f_1(x, y)$ and $f_2(x, y)$ in the equation

$$f_1(x, y)\,dx + f_2(x, y)\,dy = 0$$

is of the same degree of x and y; e.g.,

$$(x^2 - y^2)\,dx + (x^2 - xy)\,dy = 0$$

Homogeneous equations can be reduced to equations with separable variables by letting $y = vx$, where v is a new variable. For example, the equation above is thus changed into

$$(x^2 - v^2x^2)\,dx + (x^2 - vx^2)(v\,dx + x\,dv) = 0$$

or

$$\frac{1}{x}\,dx + \frac{1 - v}{1 + v - 2v^2}\,dv = 0$$

(3) Exact equations. The equation

$$f_1(x, y)\,dx + f_2(x, y)\,dy = 0 \tag{4–7}$$

is called an *exact equation* if there is a function $F(x, y)$ such that

$$\left.\begin{aligned} f_1(x, y) &= \frac{\partial F}{\partial x} \\[1em] f_2(x, y) &= \frac{\partial F}{\partial y} \end{aligned}\right\} \tag{4–8}$$

Then the differential equation is

$$\frac{\partial F}{\partial x}\,dx + \frac{\partial F}{\partial y}\,dy = dF = 0$$

The general solution is therefore

$$F(x, y) = C \tag{4–9}$$

Since for continuous derivatives $\partial^2 F/\partial y\,\partial x = \partial^2 F/\partial x\,\partial y$, the necessary and sufficient condition for Eq. (4–8) to be true is

$$\frac{\partial f_1}{\partial y} = \frac{\partial f_2}{\partial x} \tag{4–10}$$

for example, the equation

$$(x^2 - y)\,dx + (4 - x)\,dy = 0$$

is exact, since $\partial(x^2 - y)/\partial y = \partial(4 - x)/\partial x$. To find $F(x, y)$, we have from Eq. (4–8)

$$\frac{\partial F}{\partial x} = x^2 - y \qquad \text{and} \qquad \frac{\partial F}{\partial y} = 4 - x$$

Integrating

$$F = \frac{x^3}{3} - xy + \phi(y) + C_1$$

$$F = 4y - xy + \psi(x) + C_1$$

To satisfy both of these two equations, we must have

$$F = \frac{x^3}{3} - xy + 4y + C_1$$

Thus the solution, according to Eq. (4–9) is

$$\frac{x^3}{3} - xy + 4y = C$$

An equation may be reduced to an exact equation by multiplying the equation by a function called an *integrating factor*. For example, the equation

$$y\,dx - x\,dy = 0$$

can be reduced to an exact equation

$$\frac{y}{x^2}\,dx - \frac{1}{x}\,dy = 0$$

by multiplying the equation by $1/x^2$. Unfortunately, integrating factors are usually not easy to find.

(4) Linear equations. The general form of a first-order linear equation is

$$\frac{dy}{dx} + P(x)y = Q(x) \tag{4–11}$$

where $P(x)$ and $Q(x)$ are known functions of the independent variable x. This equation is linear, because only the first power of unknown y or dy/dx appears in the equation. The general solution of Eq. (4–11) may be obtained by multiplying the equation with the integrating factor $e^{\int P\,dx}$:

$$\frac{dy}{dx}\,e^{\int P\,dx} + e^{\int P\,dx}\,P(x)y = Q(x)e^{\int P\,dx}$$

Then

$$\frac{d}{dx}(ye^{\int P\,dx}) = Q(x)e^{\int P\,dx} \tag{4-12}$$

Thus, the general solution is

$$ye^{\int P\,dx} = \int Q(x)e^{\int P\,dx}\,dx + C \tag{4-13}$$

For example, take the equation

$$\frac{dy}{dx} + \frac{1}{x}y = x^2$$

Upon multiplication with $e^{\int dx/x} = x$, it becomes $d(xy)/dx = x^3$. The solution is therefore $xy = (x^4/4) + C$.

Some nonlinear equations can be reduced to a linear equation. For example, the *Bernoulli equation*

$$\frac{dy}{dx} + P(x)y = y^n Q(x) \tag{4-14}$$

can be reduced to a linear equation by a change of variable, with $v = y^{-n+1}$.

Example 4-1. Radium decomposes at a rate proportional to the amount present. Solve the following two separate cases.

(a) The rate of decomposition in grams per year is numerically equal to 0.0004 times the amount in grams present. Find how much is left of 2 gm of radium in 100 years.

Let t = time in years, and $R(t)$ = amount of radium in gm present at t. The differential equation controlling the decomposition is specified as

$$\frac{dR}{dt} = -0.0004R$$

(The negative sign is necessary because R is decreasing with t.) The initial condition for this particular piece of radium is $R = 2$ at $t = 0$.

The general solution of this equation may be obtained by separating the variables:

$$\frac{dR}{R} = -0.0004\,dt$$

Integrating both sides,

$$\log_e R = -0.0004t + \log_e C$$

where $\log_e C$ is the combination of the two constants of integration. This form for the arbitrary constant is chosen for the convenience of reducing this result to the following form:

$$R = Ce^{-0.0004t}$$

This solution has one arbitrary constant C, and is therefore the general solution of the differential equation. For the determination of C for a particular case, we need one known condition. In this case, we have $R=2$ at $t=0$. Therefore, the value of C must be such that

$$2 = Ce^0 = C$$

The particular solution for this particular piece of radium is therefore

$$R = 2e^{-0.0004t}$$

This solution is shown graphically in Fig. 4–2. When $t=100$,

$$R = 2e^{-0.04} = 1.92 \text{ gm}$$

Note that, although we are only interested in R at $t=100$, we first obtain a function $R(t)$ valid for any t. This "inefficiency" is necessary because the

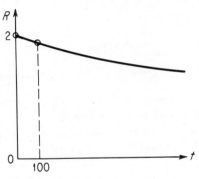

Fig. 4–2

controlling equation is a differential equation, the solution of which is a function.

(b) The rate of decomposition is proportional to the amount present, the constant of proportionality being unknown. A 2-gm piece of radium is found to have been reduced to 1.90 gm in 100 years. Find the half-life of this piece.

Here we have

$$\frac{dR}{dt} = -kR$$

where k is the unknown constant of proportionality. The general solution is

$$R = C_1 e^{-kt}$$

We need two known conditions to determine the two unknowns C_1 and k. While there is still only one arbitrary constant in the general solution, there is an unknown in the original differential equation. Only one of the two needed conditions should be considered as the initial condition, while the other condition serves to free the original differential equation of the unknown k. With $R=2$ at $t=0$ and $R=1.90$ at $t=100$, we have

$$2 = C_1 e^0 = C_1$$

and

$$1.90 = C_1 e^{-100k}$$

From these equations, we have $C_1=2$ and $k=0.000513$. Thus, the particular solution is

$$R = 2e^{-0.000513t}$$

The half-life is the time taken to become half disintegrated; i.e., when R becomes 1 gm.

$$1 = 2e^{-0.000513t}$$

$$t = \frac{\log_e 2}{0.000513} = 1350 \text{ yrs}$$

Example 4-2. The rate of evaporation (in volume per unit time) of a mothball is assumed to be proportional to its instantaneous surface area. Given the initial radius r_0, and $r=r_0/2$ at $t=1$ year, find the total time taken by the mothball to disappear completely.

Let t be time in years, $r(t)$ be the radius, $S(t)$ be the surface area $=4\pi r^2$, and $V(t)$ be the volume $=\frac{4}{3}\pi r^3$. According to the assumed rate of evaporation,

$$\frac{dV}{dt} = -kS$$

where k is an unknown constant. Since V and S are both functions of r, this equation can be reduced to a differential equation with the unknown function $r(t)$:

$$\frac{d}{dt}\left(\frac{4}{3}\pi r^3\right) = -k(4\pi r^2)$$

$$\frac{dr}{dt} = -k$$

$$r = -kt+C$$

This is the general solution containing one arbitrary constant C. To determine C and k, we have the conditions: $r=r_0$ at $t=0$; and $r=r_0/2$ at $t=1$. It can be easily shown that $C=r_0$ and $k=r_0/2$. Thus, the particular solution is

$$r = r_0\left(1-\frac{t}{2}\right)$$

For $r=0$, $t=2$; i.e., the mothball will disappear in two years.

Example 4-3. With given natural resources and economic facilities, there is a limit L to which a population P can grow. Assuming that the rate of growth at any time is jointly proportional to the instantaneous population P and to the difference between P and L, find an expression for $P(t)$.

According to the assumed rate of growth,

$$\frac{dP}{dt} = kP(L-P) \tag{4–15}$$

where k and L are constants. (Note that, when P is very small compared with

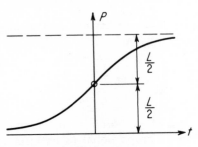

Fig. 4–3

L, $(L-P)$ is approximately constant, and this equation becomes Eq. (4–1). When P approaches L, the rate of growth approaches zero. See Fig. 4–3.) Separating the variables, we have

$$\frac{1}{L}\left(\frac{1}{P}+\frac{1}{L-P}\right) dP = k \cdot dt$$

$$\log_e \frac{P}{L-P} = kLt + C$$

To determine C, we must choose the origin for t. Choosing $t=0$ when $P=L/2$, we have $C=\log_e 1=0$. Solving for $P(t)$, we have

$$P = \frac{L}{1+e^{-kLt}}$$

This integral curve is usually referred to as the *logistic curve* in population studies.

Example 4–4. A solid dissolves in a liquid at a rate jointly proportional to the amount undissolved and to the difference between the saturation concentration and the instantaneous concentration of solution. The saturation concentration is known to be 25 lb of solid in 100 lb of liquid. When 40 lb of solid is put into 200 lb of liquid, it is found that the concentration becomes 1 lb in 20 lb in one hour. Find the amount of solid left undissolved in 10 hrs.

Let $t=$ time in hours, $x(t)=$ amount of undissolved solid in lb, $c(t)=$ concentration in lb of solid in lb of liquid, and c_s = saturation concentration. The rate of dissolving (i.e., rate of decrease of x) is given as

$$\frac{dx}{dt} = -kx(c_s-c)$$

where k is an unknown constant of proportionality. The unknowns, $x(t)$ and $c(t)$, are related as follows: at any time t, the amount of solid in solution is $(40-x)$ lb. Therefore

$$c = \frac{40-x}{200}$$

With this and the given c_s, the differential equation becomes

$$\frac{dx}{dt} = -kx\left(\frac{25}{100}-\frac{40-x}{200}\right) = -\frac{kx}{20}\left(1+\frac{x}{10}\right)$$

$$\left(\frac{1}{x}-\frac{1}{10+x}\right)dx = -\frac{k}{20}dt$$

Integrating, we have

$$\log_e \frac{x}{10+x} = -\frac{k}{20}t + C$$

For determining k and C, we have two conditions: $x=40$ at $t=0$; and $(40-x)/200=c=1/20$ (i.e., $x=30$) at $t=1$. It can be shown that $C=\log_e(4/5)$ and $-k/20=\log_e(15/16)$. Thus, the particular solution is

$$\frac{5x}{4(10+x)} = \left(\frac{15}{16}\right)^t$$

At $t=10$,

$$\frac{5x}{4(10+x)} = \left(\frac{15}{16}\right)^{10} = 0.524$$

$$x = 7.21 \text{ lb undissolved}$$

Problems

4–1. The general solution of the equation $dy/dx=x/y$ is $x^2-y^2=C$. Sketch curves in the x-y plane for the particular solutions with $C=-2, -1, 0, 1$ and 2. Also determine from the general equation the value of C for the particular solution with the following condition: $x=\sqrt{5}$ and $y=2$. Indicate this condition and the particular solution on your graph.   *Ans.* 1

4–2. Find the general solution of each of the following equations:

(a) $\dfrac{dy}{dx} = xy^2-x$ *Ans.* $x^2 = C+\log_e\left|\dfrac{y-1}{y+1}\right|$

(b) $(x^3+y^3)\,dx-3xy^2dy = 0$ *Ans.* $2y^3 = x^3-Cx$

(c) $y(2xy+1)dx+(y-x)dy = 0$ (Hint: multiply by $1/y^2$)

$$\text{*Ans.* } x^2+\frac{x}{y}+\log_e y = C$$

(d) $\dfrac{dy}{dx} + \dfrac{2y}{x+1} - (x+1)^3 = 0$ *Ans.* $y = \frac{1}{6}(x+1)^4 + C(x+1)^{-2}$

(e) $3\dfrac{dy}{dx} + y - (1-2x)y^4 = 0$ *Ans.* $y^3(Ce^x - 2x - 1) = 1$

4–3. The population $P(t)$ of a certain city was observed to be one million at the beginning of 1940, and 2 millions at the beginning of 1960. (a) Assuming that the instantaneous rate of growth is proportional to the population, find the function $P(t)$. (b) The differential equation involved is a first-order equation. It is said that its general solution involves only one arbitrary constant. Why is it necessary to have the two conditions in 1940 and 1960 in finding the particular $P(t)$? (c) Compute the population at the beginning of 1980. Is the increase in P from 1960 to 1980 the same as that from 1940 to 1960? (d) When will the population become 3 millions?   *Ans.* (c) 4 millions

4–4. In a chemical process, a substance is transformed at a rate proportional to the amount left unchanged. If 4 gm of this substance is left after one hour, and 1 gm is left after another hour, find the initial amount at the beginning of the reaction.   *Ans.* 16 gm

4–5. When the engine of a car is shut off, it is observed that the speed of the car is reduced to one half in one minute. Assuming that the rate of decrease of speed is proportional to the air resistance, which is assumed to be proportional to the second power of the speed, find the time taken to come to a full stop. How would you interpret your answer?   *Ans.* $t = \infty$

4–6. According to Newton's law of cooling, the temperature of a solid body drops at a rate proportional to the instantaneous difference between the temperature of the body and the temperature of the surrounding moving air. The temperature of a body is observed to be 140°F at $t=0$, 100°F at $t=1$, and 80°F at $t=2$, where t is time in hours. Assuming that the room temperature remains unchanged during the cooling, find the room temperature. Why is it necessary to specify three known conditions (at $t=0$, 1, and 2) in this problem?   *Ans.* 60°F

4–7. The rate of drop of pressure in an automobile tire due to slow leakage may be assumed to be proportional to $(p^2 - p_a^2)$, where p is the instantaneous absolute pressure in the tire, and p_a is the atmospheric pressure. If p_a is 14.7 lb/in.², and the gauge pressure in the tire is found to drop from 30 to 25 lb/in.² in ten days, when will it be 20 lb/in.²? (Hint: absolute pressure = gauge pressure plus atmospheric pressure.)   *Ans.* Another 13.4 days

4–8. In planning to meet future demand for water, gas and electricity in a city, it is necessary to estimate the population in the future. The population at present is 3 millions, was 2 millions 25 years ago, and one million 50 years ago. Estimate the population 25 years from now by assuming that the growth of population follows Eq. (4–15). (Ignore the result in Example 4–3 and solve the problem independently.)   *Ans.* 3.60 millions

4–9. The concentration at saturation of sulphur in benzol is given as 10 lb of sulphur in 100 lb of benzol. Sulphur dissolves in benzol at a rate proportional jointly to the amount undissolved and to the difference between the saturation concentration and the instantaneous concentration. If 15 lb of sulphur is put into 100 lb of benzol, half of it is found to have dissolved in 3 hrs. Find the time when 95% saturation is reached. *Ans.* Another 5.62 hrs

4–3. Setting up differential equations

From the examples and problems of the previous article, the student has gained some experience in setting up differential equations. In setting up a differential equation for a given problem, the law governing the phenomenon must first be known. A decision must then be made as to which quantity is the dependent variable and which is the independent variable. Symbols for these quantities are then chosen and their units specified, if necessary. In many problems, as those shown in the previous article, the differential equation can be written down immediately according to the law governing the phenomenon. In this article, several examples are given involving geometrical relations (see Examples 4–5 to 4–7). In the next article, examples are given where the differential equations must be derived by considering differential elements.

In setting up differential equations, we may sometimes obtain first an equation involving indefinite integrals. These integrals can be eliminated by differentiating the equation term by term. The student will recall, from Eq. (3–7),

$$\frac{d}{dx_1}\int_a^{x_1} f(x)\,dx = \lim_{\Delta x_1 \to 0} \frac{\int_a^{x_1+\Delta x} f(x)\,dx - \int_a^{x_1} f(x)\,dx}{\Delta x}$$

$$= \lim_{\Delta x_1 \to 0} \frac{\int_{x_1}^{x_1+\Delta x} f(x)\,dx}{\Delta x_1}$$

$$= \frac{f(x_1)\,\Delta x_1}{\Delta x_1} = f(x_1) \tag{4–16}$$

and

$$\frac{d}{dx_1}\int_{x_1}^{a} f(x)\,dx = \frac{d}{dx_1}\left[-\int_a^{x_1} f(x)\,dx\right] = -f(x_1) \tag{4–17}$$

A differential equation can thus be obtained and solved (see Examples 4–8 and 4–9). It should be mentioned, however, that a solution of the differential equation may not be a solution of the original equation with the integrals (see Example 4–9). The reason for this is that, upon differentiation, some constants in the original equation may not appear in the differential equation, and can therefore exert no influence on the solution of the differential equation. It is therefore necessary to test such a solution by substituting it in the original equation.

Example 4–5. In many problems, two families of curves perpendicular to each other are encountered. These two families of curves are called *orthogonal trajectories*. (For example, in the flow of electricity in a thin plate, the lines of flow are perpendicular to the lines of constant voltage. In the flow of heat in a thin plate, the lines of flow are perpendicular to the lines of constant temperature.) Given the general equation of one family:

$$x^2 - ky^2 = 1$$

where k is a constant for each curve of the family, find the general equation of the other family. In particular, find the equation of the curve of the latter family passing $(1, 2)$.

Let the first family be called family A and the second be called family B. The general equation of family A being given, we are seeking the general equation of family B. Since the two families are orthogonal, we have at any point

$$\left(\frac{dy}{dx}\right) \text{ of } B = -\frac{1}{\left(\dfrac{dy}{dx}\right) \text{ of } A} \qquad (4\text{–}18)$$

From this relationship, we can obtain a differential equation for family B.

For family A, we are given

$$x^2 - ky^2 = 1$$

where k is constant along a curve. The slope of a curve with a particular value of k is therefore obtained by differentiating this equation with k as a constant:

$$2x - 2ky\frac{dy}{dx} = 0$$

However, in Eq. (4–18) we want dy/dx of the whole family A, not just that of one of the curves. Since the value of k varies from one curve to another over the x–y plane, we must find k as a function of x and y. We can obtain $k(x, y)$ from the given equation of family A: $k = (x^2-1)/y^2$. Thus, for family A in general,

$$\frac{dy}{dx} = \frac{x}{ky} = \frac{xy}{x^2-1}$$

According to Eq. (4–18), we have for family B:

$$\frac{dy}{dx} = -\frac{x^2-1}{xy}$$

By separating the variables and integrating, we obtain the general equation of family B:

$$y^2 = \log_e x^2 - x^2 + C$$

where C is an arbitrary constant (see Fig. 4–4). For the particular curve

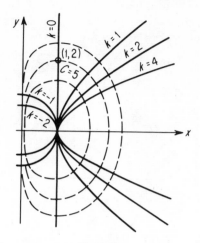

Fig. 4-4

of this family that passes through point (1, 2), the constant C must be such that

$$2^2 = \log_e 1^2 - 1^2 + C$$

or $C = 5$. Thus, the equation of this particular curve is

$$y^2 = \log_e x^2 - x^2 + 5$$

(The student can now solve Problems 4–10 and 4–11.)

Example 4–6. Find the orthogonal trajectories of the curves represented by

$$\rho = a + \cos \theta$$

where a is constant for each curve.

This problem is similar to the previous one, except that the general equation of family A is expressed in polar coordinates. In this case, we make use of the tangent of the angle ψ between the radius vector and the curve, as shown in Fig. 4–5. (Compare with the case with rectangular coordinates, in the previous example, where we make use of the tangent of the angle between a line parallel to the x axis and the curve; i.e., dy/dx.) The value of $\tan \psi$ can be seen to be

$$\tan \psi = \frac{\rho \, d\theta}{d\rho} = \frac{\rho}{\left(\dfrac{d\rho}{d\theta}\right)} \tag{4-19}$$

Let ψ_A be the angle between the radius vector and a curve of family A, and ψ_B be that between the radius vector and a curve of family B at the same

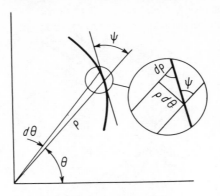

Fig. 4–5

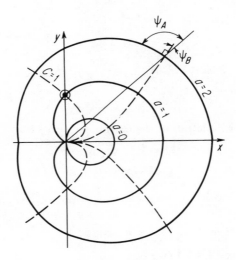

Fig. 4–6

point, as shown in Fig. 4–6. Since the two families are orthogonal to each other (i.e., the difference between ψ_A and ψ_B is 90°), we have $\tan \psi_A = -1/\tan \psi_B$, or

$$\frac{-\left(\dfrac{d\rho}{d\theta}\right)}{\rho} \text{ of family } B = \frac{\rho}{\left(\dfrac{d\rho}{d\theta}\right)} \text{ of family } A \qquad (4\text{–}20)$$

A differential equation for family B can thus be obtained.

For family A, we have

$$\rho = a + \cos \theta$$

where a is constant along each curve of the family. The value of $d\rho/d\theta$ of a particular curve can be obtained by differentiation with a as a constant.

$$\frac{d\rho}{d\theta} = -\sin\theta$$

Therefore

$$\frac{\rho}{\left(\dfrac{d\rho}{d\theta}\right)} = -\rho\cos\theta$$

Although this expression has been obtained for one particular curve, it can be used for the whole family, because the constant a identifying this particular curve does not appear in the expression. (Should the constant a appear in this expression, it would be necessary to eliminate a in a manner similar to the elimination of k in the previous example.)

According to Eq. (4–20), we have for family B

$$\frac{d\rho}{d\theta} = \rho^2 \csc\theta$$

The general solution of this equation is

$$\frac{1}{\rho} = C - \log_e(\csc\theta - \cot\theta)$$

where C is an arbitrary constant. For a particular curve of family B, say the curve passing the point $\rho = 1$ and $\theta = \pi/2$, the value of C is such that

$$\frac{1}{1} = C - \log_e(1-0)$$

i.e., $C = 1$. The equation of this particular curve is therefore

$$\frac{1}{\rho} = 1 - \log_e(\csc\theta - \cot\theta)$$

(The student can now solve Problems 4–12 and 4–13.)

Example 4–7. A river of width L flows with speed V, and a boat sails with speed v relative to the water. The boat starts from point A and tries to get to point B directly opposite on the other bank. Find the path of the boat if it is always heading towards B.

First try to use rectangular coordinates, as shown in Fig. 4–7(a). Let $y(x)$ be the path of the boat. The tangent at any point (x, y) of the path is in the direction of the absolute velocity $(v + V)$ of the boat. Thus, we have at any point (x, y) on the path,

$$\frac{dy}{dx} = \tan\theta = \frac{v\sin\phi}{V - v\cos\phi}$$

With

$$\sin \phi = \frac{L-y}{\sqrt{x^2+(L-y)^2}} \quad \text{and} \quad \cos \phi = \frac{x}{\sqrt{x^2+(L-y)^2}}$$

we have

$$\frac{dy}{dx} = \frac{v(L-y)}{V\sqrt{x^2+(L-y)^2}-vx}$$

However, this equation is difficult to integrate.

Next, try to use polar coordinates as shown in Fig. 4–7(b). Let $\rho(\theta)$ be the path of the boat. We try to express $\tan \psi$ as a function of ρ and θ because,

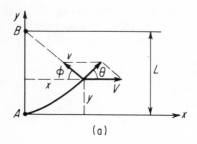
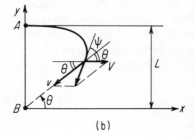

(a) (b)

Fig. 4–7

with $\tan \psi = \rho \, d\theta/d\rho$, we have then an equation for $\rho(\theta)$. From Fig. 4–7(b), for any point (ρ, θ) on the path

$$\tan (\psi+\theta) = \frac{v \sin \theta}{v \cos \theta - V}$$

Since

$$\tan (\psi+\theta) = \frac{\tan \psi+\tan \theta}{1-\tan \theta \cdot \tan \psi}$$

or

$$\tan \psi = \frac{\tan (\psi+\theta)-\tan \theta}{1+\tan \theta \cdot \tan (\psi+\theta)}$$

we have by substituting

$$\rho \frac{d\theta}{d\rho} = \tan \psi = \frac{V \sin \theta}{v - V \cos \theta}$$

Integrating

$$\log_e \rho = \frac{v}{V} \log_e \tan \frac{\theta}{2} - \log_e \sin \theta + \log_e C$$

With the initial condition $\rho = L$ at $\theta = \pi/2$, we have $C = L$. Thus, the path of the boat is

$$\rho = L \csc \theta \cdot \left(\tan \frac{\theta}{2}\right)^{v/V}$$

(The student can now solve Problems 4–14 and 4–15.)

Example 4–8. A weight W is suspended by a slender rod of a uniform material weighing w per unit volume, as shown in Fig. 4–8. Find the shape of the rod such that the tensile stress is equal to a constant value k throughout its length.

To write an expression for the stress, let $x =$ distance measured from the lower end of the rod, and $A(x) =$ the unknown cross-sectional area. Then the weight of the rod below a section at x_1 is $\int_0^{x_1} wA(x)\, dx$, and the tensile strength at this section is

$$\frac{\int_0^{x_1} wA(x)\, dx + W}{A(x_1)}$$

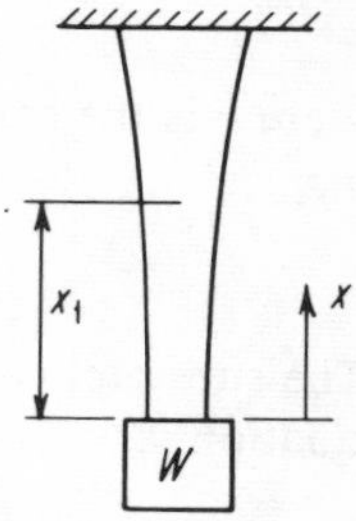

It is required that the tensile stress be constant $(=k)$, independent of x_1. Therefore

$$\int_0^{x_1} wA(x)\, dx + W = kA(x_1) \qquad (4\text{–}21)$$

Both sides of this equation are functions of x_1. This equation can be reduced to a differential equation by differentiating both sides with respect to x_1. According to Eq. (4–16), we have

$$wA(x_1) = k\, \frac{d}{dx_1} A(x_1) \qquad (4\text{–}22)$$

Fig. 4–8

(The subscript can now be omitted without creating confusion.) The general solution of this equation is

$$A(x) = C \exp\left(\frac{w}{k} x\right)$$

where $\exp(wx/k)$ is another way of writing $e^{wx/k}$. For determining the arbitrary constant C, we have the following condition: at the section at $x=0$, $A = W/k$. Therefore

$$\frac{W}{k} = C \exp(0) = C$$

Thus, the rod should have the following shape:

$$A(x) = \frac{W}{k} \exp\left(\frac{w}{k} x\right)$$

This is a particular solution of the differential equation Eq. (4–22). It is necessary to verify if this is also the solution of Eq. (4–21). Upon substituting this solution into the left side of Eq. (4–21), we have

$$\int_0^{x_1} w\, \frac{W}{k} \exp\left(\frac{w}{k} x\right) dx + W = W \exp\left(\frac{w}{k} x_1\right) = kA(x_1)$$

Thus, the solution is also the solution of Eq. (4–21). (The student can now solve Problems 4–16 and 4–17.)

Example 4–9. A car starts with initial speed v_0. Find the speed $v(t)$ in linear motion such that the distance traveled up to any time t_1 is proportional to the sum of the instantaneous speeds $v(t_1)$ and v_0.

As specified, $v(t)$ must be such that

$$\int_0^{t_1} v(t)\, dt = k\,[v(t_1)+v_0] \tag{4–23}$$

where k is the constant of proportionality. Upon differentiation with respect to t_1,

$$v(t_1) = k\,\frac{d}{dt_1}\,v(t_1) \tag{4–24}$$

(The subscript can now be omitted.) The general solution of this differential equation is

$$k \log_e v = t + C$$

The constant C is determined from the condition: at $t=0$, $v=v_0$. It is found to be $C=k \log_e v_0$. Thus a particular solution of Eq. (4–24) is

$$v(t) = v_0 \exp\left(\frac{t}{k}\right)$$

Since Eq. (4–24) has been obtained by differentiating Eq. (4–23), it is necessary to verify whether this solution is also a solution of the latter equation. Substituting this solution into the left side of Eq. (4–23), we have

$$\int_0^{t_1} v_0 \exp\left(\frac{t}{k}\right) dt = kv_0 \exp\left(\frac{t_1}{k}\right) - kv_0 = k[v(t_1)-v_0]$$

which does not satisfy Eq. (4–23). Since any solution of Eq. (4–23) must always satisfy Eq. (4–24), and there is no other solution of Eq. (4–24), there is no solution to the problem.

Problems

4–10. Electricity is flowing in a thin plate. Lines of equal voltage near a right-angled corner of the plate have been located experimentally (see Fig. 4–9), and are also found analytically to be representable by a general equation: $x^2-y^2=k$, where k is a constant for each line. Find the general equation of the lines of flow near this corner. The edge of the plate is a line of flow. Find the equation of this line of flow from your general solution.   *Ans.* $xy=C$

4–11. Find the orthogonal trajectories of each of the following families of curves: (a) $y=k \exp(3x)$, where k is a constant for each curve, and (b) $y^2=2kx$, where k is a constant for each curve.

$$\textit{Ans. (a) } x+\tfrac{3}{2}\,y^2-C=0; \text{ (b) } x^2+\frac{y^2}{2}+C=0$$

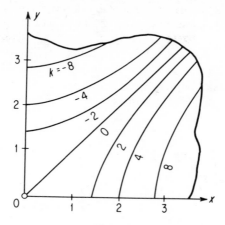

Fig. 4–9

4–12. Heat is flowing in a thin plate. Lines of equal temperature near a corner of the plate with angle α between the two sides have been located experimentally (see Fig. 4–10), and are also found analytically to be representable by a general equation:

$$\rho^{\pi/\alpha} \cos\left(\frac{\pi}{\alpha}\theta\right) = k$$

where k is a constant for each line. Find the general equation of the lines of heat flow near this corner.   *Ans.* $\rho^{\pi/\alpha} \sin\left(\frac{\pi}{\alpha}\theta\right) = C$

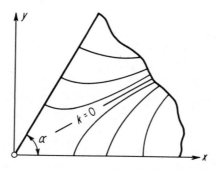

Fig. 4–10

4–13. Find the orthogonal trajectories of the cardioids: $\rho = k(1 + \sin\theta)$.

$$\textit{Ans.} \quad \rho = C(1 - \sin\theta)$$

4–14. Particle B initially located on the y axis is attached by a cable of length L to car A, which starts from the origin and moves along the x axis. Assuming that the motion is slow, so that the path of B is always tangential to the cable AB (see Fig. 4–11), show that the equation of the path of B is

$$x = L \log_e \frac{L + \sqrt{L^2 - y^2}}{y} - \sqrt{L^2 - y^2}$$

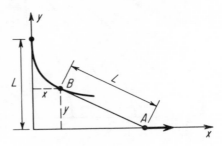

Fig. 4–11

4–15. The flow of water towards a sink may be approximated by assuming that the magnitude of the velocity in the ρ direction is a/ρ, and the velocity in the θ direction is b/ρ, where a and b are constants in a particular case (see Fig. 4–12).

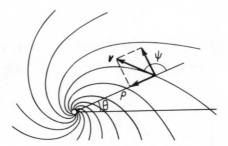

Fig. 4–12

Show that the general equation of the lines of flow is the spiral:

$$\rho \exp\left(\frac{a}{b}\theta\right) = C$$

(Hint: $\tan \psi = -b/a$.)

4–16. A tapered masonry column is used to support a weight of 1800 tons. The column is 100 ft tall and the masonry weighs 200 lb per cu ft. How should the cross-sectional area of the column vary so that the average stress over every cross section is 80,000 lb per sq ft? Compute the cross-sectional area of the base.   *Ans.* 57.8 ft² at base

4–17. Find the equation of the curve $y(x)$ passing through the point $(1, 1)$ with the area under the curve from $x=0$ to any abscissa x_1 equal to one nth of the rectangular area $x_1 y_1$ shown in Fig. 4–13. In particular, find the equation when $n=2$.   *Ans.* $y=x$

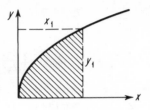

Fig. 4–13

4–18. A particle in linear motion starts with an initial velocity of 2 ft per sec. How should the velocity $v(t)$ vary so that the mean velocity up to any time t_1 is equal to the mean of the initial velocity and the velocity at t_1? You will find that, with one known condition ($v=2$ at $t=0$), you cannot find a unique particular solution. Is this a violation of the theorem given in Art. 4–2? Why?

Ans. $v=2+Ct$

4–4. Derivation by using differentials

In deriving equations for some problems, the law governing the phenomenon must be applied to every infinitesimal element of the system. A differential equation involving an unknown function $y(x)$ is derived by relating $y(x_0)$ at an arbitrary value of x_0 and $y(x_0+\Delta x)$ at a differential Δx or dx apart, according to the law governing the problem. For this purpose, we need the difference between these two values of y. Let this difference be called Δy (see Fig. 1–31).

$$\Delta y = y(x_0+\Delta x)-y(x_0)$$

As Δx or dx approaches zero, we have from Eqs. (1–5) and (1–9),

$$\lim_{\Delta x \to 0} \Delta y = dy = \left(\frac{dy}{dx}\right)_0 dx$$

Here, the subscript 0 denotes values at $x=x_0$. Thus,

$$\lim_{\Delta x \to 0} [y(x_0+\Delta x)-y(x_0)] = \left(\frac{dy}{dx}\right)_0 dx$$

Since x_0 is arbitrary, we have, in general, at any x

$$\lim_{\Delta x \to 0} [y(x+\Delta x)-y(x)] = \left(\frac{dy}{dx}\right) dx \qquad (4\text{–}25)$$

It is instructive to arrive at this equation by using Taylor's series. Expanding $y(x)$ about x_0, we have

$$y(x) = y(x_0) + \left(\frac{dy}{dx}\right)_0 (x - x_0) + \frac{1}{2}\left(\frac{d^2y}{dx^2}\right)_0 (x - x_0)^2 + \dots$$

or

$$y(x_0 + \Delta x) - y(x_0) = \left(\frac{dy}{dx}\right)_0 \Delta x + \frac{1}{2}\left(\frac{d^2y}{dx^2}\right)_0 (\Delta x)^2 + \dots \tag{4-26}$$

When Δx approaches zero, terms with $(\Delta x)^2$ and higher power vanish faster in comparison with Δx. Of course, the term with Δx will also approach zero, but we are interested in the difference between the two values of y, and this difference is of the same order as Δx. Thus, the term with Δx, though infinitesimal, is the largest term left and must be retained. Thus, Eq. (4–26) is reduced to Eq. (4–25) as Δx approaches zero.

The mean value y within the interval Δx is often used in derivation. By definition, we have

$$\text{mean } y \text{ in } \Delta x = \frac{1}{\Delta x} \int_{x_0}^{x_0 + \Delta x} y(x)\, dx$$

$$= \frac{1}{\Delta x} \int_{x_0}^{x_0 + \Delta x} \left[y(x_0) + \left(\frac{dy}{dx}\right)_0 (x - x_0) + \dots \right] dx$$

$$= y(x_0) + \frac{1}{2}\left(\frac{dy}{dx}\right)_0 \Delta x + \dots$$

When Δx approaches zero, terms with Δx vanish compared with $y(x_0)$. Since x_0 is arbitrary, we have in general

$$\lim_{\Delta x \to 0} (\text{mean } y \text{ in } \Delta x) = y \tag{4-27}$$

It should be pointed out that Eqs. (4–25) and (4–27) are exact. Although seemingly they have been obtained with truncated series, the higher order terms which do not appear in these equations vanish faster as Δx approaches zero. This method of letting the higher order terms vanish is also used to obtain exact results for more complicated cases (see Example 4–11). In all cases, when a term of a certain power of Δx is to be retained in an equation, all terms of the same power of Δx must also be retained. In this manner, factors of equal importance will be included in the equation.

Example 4–10. Derive an equation for the distribution of pressure in a fluid at rest.

The pressure p and density ρ of the fluid vary with elevation z. The pressure must vary in such a way that every elementary fluid particle obeys Newton's law: $\sum F = 0$ for equilibrium. Consider an infinitesimal fluid particle at an arbitrary elevation x_0, dz in height ($dz \to 0$), and A in cross section, as shown in Fig. 4–14. The forces acting on this particle are the forces from fluid pressure and gravitational force. Since $dz \to 0$, we have, according to Eq. (4–25),

$$p(z_0 + dz) = p_0 + \left(\frac{dp}{dz}\right)_0 dz$$

For the gravitational force, we have, according to Eq.(4–27),

$$\text{mean } \rho g \text{ in } dz = \rho_0 g_0$$

Since $\sum F = 0$ for this (and every other) particle,

$$\sum F_z = p_0 A - \left[p_0 + \left(\frac{dp}{dz}\right)_0 dz\right] A - \rho_0 g_0 A \, dz = 0$$

Thus

$$\left(\frac{dp}{dz}\right)_0 = -\rho_0 g_0$$

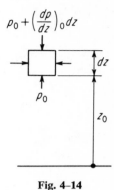

Fig. 4–14

Since this position z_0 is arbitrary, we have the following equation for every particle in the fluid:

$$\frac{dp}{dz} = -\rho g \qquad (4\text{–}28)$$

There are two dependent variables in this equation, namely, p and ρg. To solve this equation, the variable ρg as a function of z or of p must be given. For example, for an ideal gas with uniform temperature, we have from the equation of state

$$\frac{p}{\rho} = \text{constant} = \frac{p_1}{\rho_1}$$

where the subscript indicates known values at a certain point, e.g., at sea level. Considering g as a constant, we have

$$\frac{dp}{dz} = -\frac{\rho_1 g}{p_1} p$$

With the known condition that $p = p_1$ at $z = z_1$, the particular solution is

$$\log_e \frac{p}{p_1} = \frac{\rho_1 g}{p_1}(z_1 - z)$$

This equation is called the *barometric-height relation*. For an isothermal atmosphere, measurements of p_1 and ρ_1 at a base point and a measurement of pressure p (with a barometer) at any point will enable one to compute the elevation z at this point.

Example 4–11. A thin flexible rope is wound around a circular post. Due to friction between the rope and the post, the tension in the rope varies along its length in contact with the post. Find an expression for the rope tension when slipping is impending (e.g., T_1 in Fig. 4–15(a) is just enough to prevent the weight from falling down). The weight of the rope is very small compared with other forces involved.

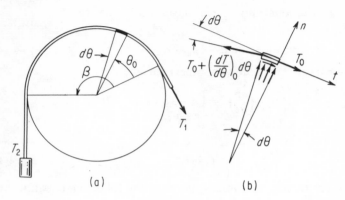

Fig. 4–15

The variation of tension must be such that each element of the rope is in equilibrium obeying Newton's law: $\sum F = 0$. Take an infinitesimal element $R\,d\theta$ in length, as shown in Fig. 4–15(b). It is in equilibrium under the following forces: T_0, $T_0 + \left(\dfrac{dT}{d\theta}\right)_0 d\theta$, normal reactions from the post, and friction. Let $N(\theta)$ be the normal reaction per unit length of rope. According to Eq. (4–27), with $d\theta$ approaching zero,

$$\text{mean } n \text{ component of } N = N_0$$

and the mean t component of N is zero. Since slipping is impending, the friction force per unit length of rope is $fN(\theta)$, where f is the coefficient of friction. This force is directed against the impending motion. According to Eq. (4–27) with $d\theta$ approaching zero,

$$\text{mean } t \text{ component of } fN = fN_0$$

and the mean n component of fN is zero. Thus, for equilibrium of the rope element,

$$\sum F_n = N_0 R\,d\theta - \left[T_0 + \left(\frac{dT}{d\theta}\right)_0 d\theta\right] \sin (d\theta) = 0$$

and

$$\sum F_t = fN_0 R\,d\theta + T_0 - \left[T_0 + \left(\frac{dT}{d\theta}\right)_0 d\theta\right] \cos (d\theta) = 0$$

Here, we have two equations with two unknown functions: $T(\theta)$ and $N(\theta)$. Since $d\theta \to 0$, we proceed with the expectation that only terms of the first order of $d\theta$ need to be retained, and higher order terms will vanish. We can then replace sin $(d\theta)$ and cos $(d\theta)$ by series with terms not higher than the first power of $d\theta$, i.e., sin $(d\theta) \rightarrow d\theta$, and cos $(d\theta) \rightarrow 1$. These expressions are exact, because the higher-power terms vanish faster as $d\theta \rightarrow 0$. Thus, the two equations above become

$$N_0 R \, d\theta - \left[T_0 + \left(\frac{dT}{d\theta} \right)_0 d\theta \right] d\theta = 0$$

and

$$f N_0 R \, d\theta + T_0 - \left[T_0 + \left(\frac{dT}{d\theta} \right)_0 d\theta \right] = 0$$

In the first of these two equations, the term with $(d\theta)^2$ vanishes in comparison with other terms. Thus

$$N_0 R \, d\theta - T_0 \, d\theta = 0$$

Note that these terms with $d\theta$, though infinitesimally small, are the largest terms in the equation, and therefore must be retained. Substituting into the second equation, we have

$$\left(\frac{dT}{d\theta} \right)_0 = f N_0 R = f T_0$$

Since this elementary length of rope has been arbitrarily chosen, we have for any section of rope in contact with the post,

$$\frac{dT}{d\theta} = fT$$

The solution of this equation, for the condition $T = T_1$ at $\theta = 0$, is

$$T = T_1 e^{f\theta} \tag{4-29}$$

For a rope in contact with the post over an angle β (see Fig. 4-15(a)), the tension T_2 is

$$T_2 = T_1 e^{f\beta}$$

Note that T_1 for preventing the weight from slipping is smaller than the weight T_2.

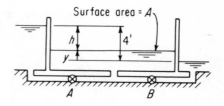

Fig. 4-16

Example 4-12. Figure 4-16 is a schematic drawing of a canal lock. The water level in the lock is raised by closing the valve B and opening the valve A. The lock is 50 ft by 20 ft, and the discharge $Q(t)$ (volume per unit time) through the one-foot-square culvert is given by

$$Q = 0.4 a \sqrt{2gh}$$

where a is the cross-sectional area of the culvert, g is the gravitational acceleration, and $h(t)$ is the instantaneous difference of water-surface elevation across the culvert. If the upstream gate can be opened when h is 1 in. and the initial value of h is 4 ft, what is the time required for the operation? The water surfaces outside the lock may be considered stationary.

The principle governing this problem is expressed as what is generally known as the *equation of continuity*:

$$\text{Income} - \text{outgo} = \text{increase of storage} \qquad (4\text{–}30)$$

This equation is valid for any differential time element dt. Let $y(t)$ in ft be the instantaneous elevation of the surface in the lock above the downstream surface. Then $h(t)$ in ft $=4-y$. During dt, the income volume $= Q\,dt$ $= 0.4a\sqrt{2gh}\,dt$, the outgo volume $=0$, and the increase of storage $= A\,dy$. Thus, with all quantities in ft-sec units ($a=1$, $g=32.2$, $A=50 \times 20$), Eq. (4–30) becomes

$$0.4\sqrt{2g(4-y)}\,dt - 0 = 50 \times 20\,dy$$

With the initial condition that, at $t=0$, $h=4$ ft (i.e., $y=0$), the solution of this equation is

$$t = \frac{1000}{0.4\sqrt{2g}}\,[4 - 2\sqrt{4-y}]$$

For $h=(4-y)=\frac{1}{12}$ ft, the time required is $t=1190$ sec. (The differential equation is one of the second degree. Other solutions of this equation will be discussed in Article 4–7.)

Example 4–13. Two spherical containers are connected by a pipe of cross-sectional area a. The top of each container is open so that the discharge through the pipe is

$$Q = \frac{a}{3}\sqrt{2gh}$$

where $h(t)$ is the instantaneous difference of water-surface elevation between the two containers. Initially, one container is full while the other is empty. Find the time taken to have the two surfaces level. The radius of the containers is R.

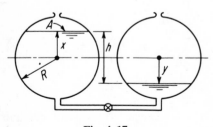

Fig. 4–17

The problem is governed by the equation of continuity, Eq. (4–30). Let the water surfaces be located by $x(t)$ and $y(t)$, measured from the final common elevation, as shown in Fig. 4–17. Due to symmetry, we have at any t, $x=y$. Thus, $h(t)=x+y=2x$.

Writing the equation of continuity for the container on the left, we have, for any dt

$$0 - \frac{a}{3} \sqrt{2g(2x)} \, dt = A(x) \, dx$$

where $A \, dx$ stands for the "increase of storage" in Eq. (4-30). The surface area $A(x)$ can easily be shown to be $A = \pi(R^2 - x^2)$. Thus

$$\frac{-2a\sqrt{g}}{3\pi} \, dt = \frac{R^2 - x^2}{\sqrt{x}} \, dx$$

With the initial condition $x = R$ at $t = 0$, the solution can be shown to be

$$\frac{5a\sqrt{g}}{3\pi} \, t = 4R^{5/2} - 5R^2 x^{1/2} + x^{5/2}.$$

To have $x = 0$, the time required is $t = 12\pi R^{5/2}/(5a\sqrt{g})$.

Example 4-14. There is in a tank 100 gal of brine solution with 50 lb of dissolved salt. If pure water is added to the tank at a rate of 4 gal per min, and at the same time, the mixture in the tank is withdrawn at a rate of 3 gal per min, find the amount of dissolved salt left in the tank after one hour.

Let $t = $ time in min, $V(t) = $ volume in gal of mixture in the tank, $x(t) = $ lb of salt, and $c(t) = $ concentration in lb of salt per gal, in tank. The equation of continuity of flow of salt is, according to Eq. (4-30)

$$0 - 3c \, dt = dx$$

where $3c \, dt$ is the outflow of salt in lb during dt. The variable c can be expressed as

$$c = \frac{x}{V}$$

and the variable $V(t)$ is governed by the equation of continuity of flow of mixture:

$$4 \, dt - 3 \, dt = dV$$

Here, we have three equations for the three variables x, c, and V. These equations can easily be solved as follows:

$$\frac{dV}{dt} = 1$$

With the initial condition $V = 100$ at $t = 0$, this yields

$$V = 100 + t$$

Thus, $c = x/(100 + t)$, and

$$\frac{dx}{dt} = -\frac{3x}{100 + t}$$

With the initial condition $x = 50$ at $t = 0$, this gives

$$x = 50\left(\frac{100}{100 + t}\right)^3$$

At $t = 60$ min ($= 1$ hr),

$$x = 50\left(\frac{100}{160}\right)^3 = 12.2 \text{ lb}$$

Problems

4–19. In the study of stability of the atmosphere, a reference condition of neutral stability is that $p \propto \rho^k$, where $k = 1.4$ (approximately) for air. Find the pressure distribution in this reference atmosphere, given p_1 and ρ_1 at sea level, and g considered as constant. (Hint: make use of Eq. (4–28).)

$$\textit{Ans.} \quad z - z_1 = \frac{k}{k-1} \frac{p_1}{\rho_1 g} \left[1 - \left(\frac{p}{p_1}\right)^{(k-1)/k}\right]$$

4–20. The density of water in deep seas varies with depth. It has been found that the bulk modulus of elasticity K of water is practically constant (300,000 lb/sq in.). Find the pressure-depth relationship in terms of K, and p_0 and ρ_0, the pressure and the density, respectively, at the surface of the sea. Compute the pressure 5 miles below the surface when $p_0 = 14.7$ lb/sq in. and sea water at the surface weighs 64.0 lb/ft³. g may be considered as a constant.

(Hint: $K = \lim\limits_{\Delta V \to 0} \dfrac{\Delta p}{\left(\dfrac{-\Delta V}{V}\right)} = \lim\limits_{\Delta \rho \to 0} \dfrac{\Delta p}{\left(\dfrac{\Delta \rho}{\rho}\right)} = \rho \dfrac{dp}{d\rho}.$ First find $\rho(p)$.)

$$\textit{Ans.} \quad p = p_0 - K \log_e\left(1 + \frac{\rho_0 g}{K} z\right)$$

4–21. Find $p(z)$ in an isothermal atmosphere, taking into account the variation of gravitational acceleration g with height. (Hint: let $g_0 =$ gravitational acceleration at sea level at radius R from center of earth. Find $g(z)$ according to the inverse-square law of gravitation.)

4–22. A slender uniform rod of deformable material is resting in a vertical position and is deformed under its own weight, as shown in Fig. 4–18. The material is

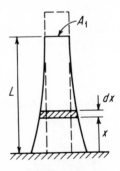

Fig. 4–18

such that its unit weight w remains constant upon being deformed, and the cross-sectional area A varies with the compressive force F at the section: $A = A_1 / [1 - (F/EA_1)]$, where E is the Young's modulus of the material. By considering the equilibrium of each infinitesimal layer, find an expression for the deformed shape $A(x)$, or $F(x)$.

$$Ans. \quad F - \frac{F^2}{2EA_1} = wA_1 (L - x)$$

4–23. An elastic rod of uniform cross-sectional area A_1 is put on an inclined plane, as shown by the dotted lines in Fig. 4–19.

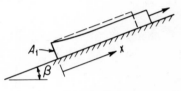

When a force is applied to the top, the rod is stretched as shown. The material of the rod is such that its weight per unit volume w remains constant upon being stretched, and the cross-sectional area A at a section with tensile force F is $A = A_1/[1 + (F/EA_1)]$, where E is the Young's modulus of the material. Show

Fig. 4–19

that, when motion of the whole rod is impending, the tensile force $F(x)$ in the rod is given by

$$\left(1 + \frac{F}{EA_1}\right)^2 = 1 + \frac{2w(\sin\beta + f\cos\beta)}{E} x$$

where f is the coefficient of static friction between the rod and the plane.

4–24. A pulley of radius R is being driven by a thin flexible belt, as shown in Fig. 4–20. The gravitational force on the belt is negligible. Find the difference between the forces T_1 and T_2, taking into account friction and centrifugal force. The weight per unit length of belt is w and its speed is v. (Hint: elements of the belt have an acceleration toward the center equal to v^2/R.)

$$Ans. \quad T_1 - T_2 = (e^{f\pi} - 1)\left(T_2 - \frac{wv^2}{g}\right)$$

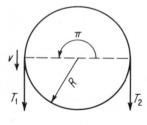

Fig. 4–20

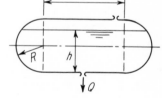

Fig. 4–21

4–25. A tank in the form of a circular cylinder with semispherical ends is placed with its axis horizontal, as shown in Fig. 4–21. Find the time required to empty a full tank of liquid through an orifice at the bottom. The discharge through the orifice is $Q = 0.6a\sqrt{2gh}$, where $h(t)$ is the distance from the orifice to the liquid surface. The length L and the radius R of the cylinder are 30 ft and 10 ft, respectively. The diameter of the orifice is 6 inches.   *Ans.* 5360 sec

4-26. In an emergency repair of a bridge pier, a coffer dam is built around the pier and the water inside is removed by pumping, as shown in Fig. 4–22. The discharge of the pump is $\frac{1}{2}\left(1-\frac{H}{20}\right)$, all quantities being in ft-sec units. Due to leakage and seepage, there is an inflow in cu ft per sec equal to $0.02h$. Find the time required for the removal of the first 10 ft of water. The area enclosed by the coffer dam, minus the area occupied by the pier, is 400 sq ft. *Ans.* 26,200 sec

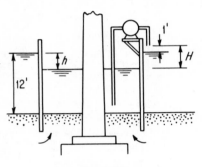

Fig. 4–22

4-27. Two vertical prismatic tanks as shown in Fig. 4–23 are connected by a pipe, the discharge through which is $Q=0.5a\sqrt{2gh}$ when the valve is open, where $h(t)$ is the instantaneous difference in surface elevation between the two tanks. The larger tank is 200 sq ft in cross-sectional area, and is initially filled to a depth of 10 ft. The smaller tank is 100 sq ft in area, and is initially filled to a depth of 1 ft. The area a of the pipe is one sq ft. Find the time taken to have the two water surfaces at the same level. *Ans.* 99.5 sec

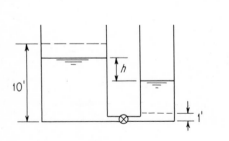

Fig. 4–23

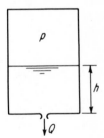

Fig. 4–24

4-28. A prismatic tank with air trapped in the upper portion is shown in Fig. 4–24 discharging water through an orifice at the bottom. Initially, the pressure of the air is p_1 and its density is ρ_1 when the water is h_1 deep. The discharge through the orifice is given by

$$Q = 0.6a\sqrt{2g\left(h+\frac{p-p_a}{w}\right)}$$

where $p(t)$ is the absolute pressure of the trapped air, w is the unit weight of water, and p_a is the atmospheric pressure. Derive a differential equation for $h(t)$, assuming isothermal process. The cross-sectional area of the tank is A.

4-29. After a performance, the air in a theatre is found to contain 0.2% of carbon dioxide (by volume). It is necessary to have the CO_2 content reduced to 0.05% in the 15 minutes between performances. What is the required capacity of the blower (in cu ft per min)? The air outside contains 0.02% of CO_2, and the theatre is 100 ft by 200 ft by 30 ft. Assume that the air is well mixed before being exhausted.   *Ans.* 71,670 cu ft/min

4-30. A tank contains 100 gal of brine with 50 lb of dissolved salt. While 2 gal per minute is being taken out from the tank, the brine is being diluted by adding brine with $\frac{1}{4}$ lb of salt per gal at a rate of 3 gal per min. How much dissolved salt is in the tank after 1 hour?   *Ans.* 49.7 lb

4-31. The supply to a water tank in a water system is constant, at a rate of 10^5 gal per day. The outflow rate from the tank to the consumers in gpd is $10^5 [1 - \sin (2\pi t)]$, where $t =$ time in days. At $t = 0$, the volume of water V in the tank is $5 \times 10^5/\pi$ gals. Bacteria grow in the tank at a rate (in number per day) numerically equal to $1/20$ the number N of bacteria in the tank. Show that there is no danger of increase of bacteria in the tank. (Hint: first find $V(t)$. Derive and solve the equation for $N(t)$, and compare N at $t = 0$, say, and N at $t = 1$.)

$$\text{Ans. } \log N = \frac{t}{20} - \frac{2}{\sqrt{120}} \tan^{-1}\left(\frac{\sqrt{120}\,\tan\frac{z\pi t - \pi}{2}}{12}\right) + \log(11 - \cos 2\pi t) + C$$

4-5. One-dimensional steady flow of heat and electricity

Heat may be transferred from one place to another by conduction, convection, and radiation. In this article, some problems of heat flow by conduction and an analogous phenomenon are studied. When there is spatial variation in temperature, there is a flow of heat from points of higher temperature to points of lower temperature by conduction. Take a body in which heat is being conducted. Imagine all the points with the same temperature. These points form an isothermal surface, as shown by a dashed line in Fig. 4-25. There is one surface for one temperature. It has been found that the flow of heat is in the direction n normal to these surfaces, and the intensity of flow is

$$q = -k\frac{\partial T}{\partial n} \qquad (4\text{-}31)$$

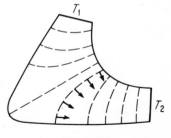

Fig. 4-25

where q is the flow of heat per unit time per unit area of the isothermal surface, k is the conductivity of the material, and T is the temperature. The negative sign is used to indicate that the flow is in the direction in which the temperature decreases. In general, the temperature changes from place to place and also varies with time; i.e., T is a function of space and time. The partial derivative in Eq. (4–31) is used to indicate the instantaneous (time being held constant) temperature gradient at the point under consideration.

When outside thermal conditions remain constant, the temperature distribution in a body will, if given enough time, become fixed. Under this time-independent condition, the imaginary isothermal surfaces will be stationary, and the flow is referred to as a *steady flow*. In this article, only one-dimensional steady flows are discussed. By *one-dimensional*, we mean that the temperature is a function of one coordinate only. This condition may be realized because of symmetry of the system; e.g., the temperature distribution in a circular steam pipe is a function of the coordinate ρ only, as shown in Fig. 4–26(a). This condition may also be realized approximately when the temperature varies at a much greater rate in one direction than in other directions; e.g., the flow of heat in a thin long metal bar with little loss of heat through the side, as shown in Fig. 4–26(b). In these cases, the direction n in Eq. (4–31) is then the directions ρ and x, respectively.

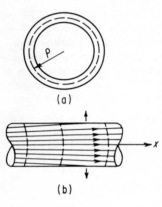

(a)

(b)

Fig. 4–26

Equation (4–31) can also be written in another form. With Q indicating the steady flow of heat per unit time across the area A of an isothermal surface, we have

$$Q = -kA\frac{dT}{dn} \qquad (4\text{–}32)$$

In Eq. (4–31) or (4–32), there are two unknowns, namely, the temperature $T(n)$ and the rate of flow $Q(n)$. Another equation for these unknowns is obtained by the consideration of continuity. In general, the resultant equation is a second-order differential equation (see Example 4–24). However, in the case of steady flow in one direction only (thus excluding cases like the metal bar shown in Fig. 4–26), the equation of continuity Eq. (4–30) states that the inflow to must be equal to the outflow from any volume bounded by two isothermal surfaces. In other words, across all the isothermal surfaces, we have the same Q:

$$Q = \text{constant} \qquad (4\text{–}33)$$

There are many phenomena analogous to the conduction of heat. For example, the conduction of electricity. The flow of electric charges is in the direction normal to surfaces of constant voltage or electrical potential, and the intensity of flow is

$$J = -k\frac{\partial V}{\partial n} \tag{4–34}$$

where J is the current intensity in charges per unit time per unit area of the constant-potential surface, k is the electrical conductivity of the material, and V is the voltage. In the case of steady one-dimensional flow, V is independent of time, and is a function of one coordinate only. In this case, it is convenient to use the current $i(=AJ)$ in charges per unit time passing a constant-voltage surface with area A. Equation (4–34) becomes

$$i = -kA\frac{dV}{dn} \tag{4–35}$$

Again, another equation is furnished by the equation of continuity. For cases with steady flow in one direction only, the equation of continuity indicates that the number of charges passing every surface of constant voltage is the same. Thus

$$i = \text{constant} \tag{4–36}$$

Note that Eqs. (4–34), (4–35), and (4–36) are completely analogous to Eqs. (4–31), (4–32), and (4–33), respectively.

Example 4–15. A steam pipe 20 cm in outside diameter is covered with a 10-cm layer of magnesia, as shown in Fig. 4–27. The temperature of the

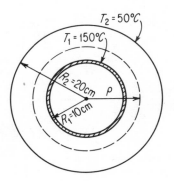

Fig. 4–27

steam and the pipe is 150°C and that of the outside surface of the covering is 50°C. The conductivity of magnesia is 0.0002 cal-cm/sec-cm²-°C. Find the rate of heat loss per cm of pipe.

Here we have one-dimensional steady flow in the ρ direction. Take a unit length of pipe. Equations (4–32) and (4–33) give

$$-kA\frac{dT}{d\rho} = \text{constant } Q$$

where A per unit length of pipe of any isothermal surface is $2\pi\rho$, and Q is the rate of heat loss per unit length. Thus

$$-k2\pi\rho\frac{dT}{d\rho} = Q$$

The solution of this equation with the known condition of $T=T_1$ at $\rho=R_1$ is

$$\frac{2\pi k}{Q}(T_1-T) = \log_e\frac{\rho}{R_1}$$

The unknown constant Q in the differential equation is determined with another known condition: $T=T_2$ at $\rho=R_2$. Thus

$$Q = \frac{2\pi k\,(T_1-T_2)}{\log_e\dfrac{R_2}{R_1}}$$

With $k=0.0002$, $T_1=150$, $T_2=50$, $R_1=10$, and $R_2=20$, all quantities being in cal-cm-sec units, we have $Q=0.18$ cal per sec (per cm of pipe).

Example 4–16. The inner radius of a pipe is R_1, and the outer radius R_2. The thermal conductivity of the material is k_1. The pipe is covered with

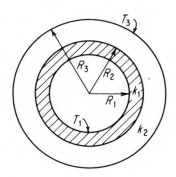

Fig. 4–28

another material of conductivity k_2. The outer radius of the covering is R_3. Given the inner surface temperature T_1 and the outer surface temperature T_3, as shown in Fig. 4–28, find the rate of heat loss in a length L.

Here, we have two differential equations, each for a different region:

$$-k_1(2\pi L\rho)\frac{dT}{d\rho} = \text{constant } Q \qquad (\text{for } R_1 \leqq \rho \leqq R_2)$$

and

$$-k_2(2\pi L\rho)\frac{dT}{d\rho} = \text{constant } Q \qquad (\text{for } R_2 \leqq \rho \leqq R_3)$$

Since the amount of heat passing both materials is the same, we have the same Q in both equations. For the first equation, we know that, at $\rho = R_1$, $T = T_1$. For the second, we know that $T = T_3$ at $\rho = R_3$. The solutions of these two equations can be shown to be

$$\frac{2\pi L k_1}{Q}(T_1 - T) = \log_e \frac{\rho}{R_1} \qquad (\text{for } R_1 \leqq \rho \leqq R_2)$$

and

$$\frac{2\pi L k_2}{Q}(T - T_3) = \log_e \frac{R_3}{\rho} \qquad (\text{for } R_2 \leqq \rho \leqq R_3)$$

The unknown constant Q must be such that both equations yield the same value of T_2 at R_2. Thus

$$\frac{2\pi L k_1}{Q}(T_1 - T_2) = \log_e \frac{R_2}{R_1}$$

$$\frac{2\pi L k_2}{Q}(T_2 - T_3) = \log_e \frac{R_3}{R_2}$$

To solve for Q, eliminate the unknown T_2 by multiplying the first equation by k_2 and the second by k_1, and adding the two equations. Thus we have

$$Q = \frac{2\pi L k_1 k_2 (T_1 - T_3)}{\log_e\left[\left(\dfrac{R_3}{R_2}\right)^{k_1}\left(\dfrac{R_2}{R_1}\right)^{k_2}\right]}$$

When $k_1 = k_2 = k$, this solution is reduced to the solution of the previous example.

Example 4–17. An electrical resistance in the form of a wire has a slight variation in cross section, such that the cross-sectional area $A(x)$ is

$$A = a + b \sin\left(\frac{2\pi x}{L}\right)$$

where a is the mean value of A over the length L, and b is the amplitude of the small variation (see Fig. 4–29). Given the conductivity k of the material, find the resistance of this wire. Since the variation of A is small, the flow of

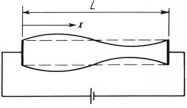

Fig. 4–29

electricity in the wire may be considered to be one-dimensional; i.e., the voltage V can be considered to be a function of x only.

For steady flow in one direction only, we have from Eqs. (4–35) and (4–36),

$$-kA(x)\frac{dV}{dx} = \text{constant } i$$

Substituting in $A(x)$, we have

$$\frac{L}{2\pi}\cdot\frac{d\left(\dfrac{2\pi x}{L}\right)}{a+b\sin\left(\dfrac{2\pi x}{L}\right)} = -\frac{k}{i}\,dV$$

$$\frac{L}{2\pi}\cdot\frac{2}{\sqrt{a^2-b^2}}\tan^{-1}\left[\frac{a\tan\left(\dfrac{\pi x}{L}\right)+b}{\sqrt{a^2-b^2}}\right] = C-\frac{kV}{i}$$

To determine C and i, let $V=V_1$ at $x=0$, and $V=V_2$ at $x=L$. We want the resistance of the wire which is defined as $(V_1-V_2)/i$. With $x=0$,

$$\frac{L}{\pi\sqrt{a^2-b^2}}\tan^{-1}\left(\frac{b}{\sqrt{a^2-b^2}}\right) = C-\frac{k}{i}V_1$$

With $x=L$,

$$\frac{L}{\pi\sqrt{a^2-b^2}}\tan^{-1}\left(\frac{b}{\sqrt{a^2-b^2}}\right) = C-\frac{k}{i}V_2$$

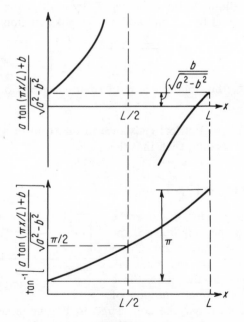

Fig. 4–30

The inverse trigonometric function is multivalued. We have to trace its variation as x varies from zero to L. As shown in Fig. 4–30, its value at $x=L$ is greater by π than that at $x=0$. Thus, subtracting the first equation from the second, we have

$$\frac{L}{\pi\sqrt{a^2-b^2}}\,\pi = \frac{k}{i}\,(V_1-V_2)$$

$$\text{resistance} \equiv \frac{V_1-V_2}{i} = \frac{L}{k\sqrt{a^2-b^2}}$$

This result is valid only when b is small compared with a, so that the one-dimensional approximation is allowable. When $b=0$, this result is reduced to the well-known result for a uniform wire: resistance$=L/ka$.

Problems

4–32. A hollow spherical shell of inner radius a and outer radius b is made of a material of thermal conductivity k. The temperature inside is T_1 and that of the outer surface is T_2. Find the rate of heat loss Q, and the temperature distribution $T(\rho)$ in the shell. Sketch the T-ρ curve.

$$\textit{Ans. } Q=\frac{4\pi kab(T_1-T_2)}{b-a}, \; T=T_1-\frac{\rho-a}{\rho}\cdot\frac{b}{b-a}(T_1-T_2)$$

4–33. The flat wall of a furnace consists of a layer of bricks 30 cm thick, and an outer covering of magnesia 40 cm thick. The thermal conductivity of brick is 0.0010 and that of magnesia is 0.0002 cal-cm/sec-cm^2-°C. The inside temperature is 400°C and the temperature of the outside surface is 50°C. Find the heat loss per sec per sq meter of the wall, and the temperature distribution $T(x)$ through the wall. Sketch the T-x curve.

$$\textit{Ans. } 152 \text{ cal/sec}; \; T=400-1.52x(0\leqq x\leqq 30), \text{ etc.}$$

4–34. A steam pipe of inner radius a and outer radius b is made of a material of thermal conductivity k. The temperature of the inner surface is T_1, and the room temperature is T_r. According to Newton's law of cooling in moving air, the rate of heat loss per unit area of the outer surface is numerically equal to n times the difference between the surface temperature (unknown) and the room temperature. Find the rate of heat loss per unit length of pipe in terms of the given constant values.

$$\textit{Ans. } \frac{2\pi kbn(T_1-T_r)}{k+bn\log_e(b/a)}$$

4–35. The cross-sectional area of a thin wire is A_1 at one end, and varies linearly along its length to nA_1 at the other end. The length of the wire is L. The variation of cross section is small, so that the flow of electrical current in this wire may be considered to be one-dimensional. The electrical conductivity of the material is k. Find the resistance of this wire. Show that, when $n=1$, your answer can be reduced to L/kA_1.

$$\textit{Ans. } \frac{L}{kA_1}\cdot\frac{\log_e n}{(n-1)}$$

4-6. Hyperbolic functions

In this article, the hyperbolic functions are presented. In analysis, functions in the form of $(e^x - e^{-x})/2$, $(e^x + e^{-x})/2$, etc., are often encountered. For convenience of manipulation, these functions are given special names and their characteristics are studied. The *hyperbolic functions* are defined as follows:

$$\left.\begin{array}{ll} \sinh x = \dfrac{e^x - e^{-x}}{2} & \cosh x = \dfrac{e^x + e^{-x}}{2} \\[2mm] \tanh x = \dfrac{\sinh x}{\cosh x} & \coth x = \dfrac{\cosh x}{\sinh x} \\[2mm] \operatorname{sech} x = \dfrac{1}{\cosh x} & \operatorname{csch} x = \dfrac{1}{\sinh x} \end{array}\right\} \quad (4\text{--}37)$$

The function $\sinh x$, for example, is read as hyperbolic sine of x. These functions are given these names because they bear relations to the rectangular hyperbolic that are very similar to those borne by the trigonometric functions to the circle. However, this fact is not of great importance in analysis. To become more familiar with these functions, the student is advised to construct the curves in Problem 4-36 and memorize them.

With Eqs. (4-37), the following relations among the hyperbolic functions can be easily verified:

$$\left.\begin{array}{l} \cosh^2 x - \sinh^2 x = 1 \\[1mm] 1 - \tanh^2 x = \operatorname{sech}^2 x \\[1mm] \sinh (x \pm y) = \sinh x \cosh y \pm \cosh x \sinh y \\[1mm] \cosh (x \pm y) = \cosh x \cosh y \pm \sinh x \sinh y \end{array}\right\} \quad (4\text{--}38)$$

The following derivatives of the hyperbolic functions can also be verified:

$$\left.\begin{array}{ll} \dfrac{d}{dx} (\sinh x) = \cosh x; & \dfrac{d}{dx} (\coth x) = -\operatorname{csch}^2 x \\[2mm] \dfrac{d}{dx} (\cosh x) = \sinh x; & \dfrac{d}{dx} (\operatorname{sech} x) = -\operatorname{sech} x \tanh x \\[2mm] \dfrac{d}{dx} (\tanh x) = \operatorname{sech}^2 x; & \dfrac{d}{dx} (\operatorname{csch} x) = -\operatorname{csch} x \coth x \end{array}\right\} \quad (4\text{--}39)$$

Equivalent to the inverse trigonometric functions in the case of circular functions, there are the *inverse hyperbolic functions*: when $\sinh y = x$, then y is called $\sinh^{-1} x$. As the hyperbolic functions are related to the exponential functions, it can be shown that the inverse hyperbolic functions are related to the inverse of the exponential functions, that is, the logarithmic functions. For example, take the case of $\sinh^{-1} x$: let $y = \sinh^{-1} x$ and find y in terms of x. By definition, we have

$$x = \sinh y = \frac{e^y - e^{-y}}{2} = \frac{1}{2e^y} (e^{2y} - 1)$$

This is a quadratic equation of e^y in terms of x. Solving, we have

$$e^y = x \pm \sqrt{x^2 + 1}$$

where only the positive sign is valid, since e^y is always positive. Thus

$$\sinh^{-1} x = y = \log_e [x + \sqrt{x^2 + 1}]$$

This result and others relating the inverse hyperbolic functions and the logarithmic functions are listed below:

$$\left.\begin{array}{ll}
\sinh^{-1} x = \log_e (x + \sqrt{x^2 + 1}); & \log_e x = \sinh^{-1}\left(\dfrac{x^2 - 1}{2x}\right) \\[2ex]
\cosh^{-1} x = \pm\log_e (x + \sqrt{x^2 - 1}); & \log_e x = \cosh^{-1}\left(\dfrac{x^2 + 1}{2x}\right) \\[2ex]
\tanh^{-1} x = \dfrac{1}{2}\log_e\left(\dfrac{1 + x}{1 - x}\right) & \text{where } x^2 < 1 \\[2ex]
\coth^{-1} x = \dfrac{1}{2}\log_e\left(\dfrac{x + 1}{x - 1}\right) & \text{where } x^2 > 1 \\[2ex]
\text{sech}^{-1} x = \pm\log_e \dfrac{1 + \sqrt{1 - x^2}}{x} & \text{where } 0 < x \leq 1 \\[2ex]
\text{csch}^{-1} x = \log_e \dfrac{1 \pm \sqrt{x^2 + 1}}{x} & \text{when } x \gtrless 0
\end{array}\right\} \quad (4\text{-}40)$$

These relations become useful when it is necessary to convert an inverse hyperbolic function into a logarithmic function, and vice versa. From Eqs. (4-40), the following differentials can be obtained:

$$\left.\begin{array}{ll}
d(\sinh^{-1} x) = \dfrac{dx}{\sqrt{x^2 + 1}} & d(\cosh^{-1} x) = \dfrac{dx}{\sqrt{x^2 - 1}} \\[2ex]
d(\tanh^{-1} x) = \dfrac{dx}{1 - x^2} \ (x^2 < 1) & d(\coth^{-1} x) = \dfrac{dx}{1 - x^2} \ (x^2 > 1) \\[2ex]
d(\text{sech}^{-1} x) = \dfrac{-dx}{x\sqrt{1 - x^2}} & d(\text{csch}^{-1} x) = \dfrac{-dx}{x\sqrt{1 + x^2}}
\end{array}\right\} (4\text{-}41)$$

Example 4–18. In uniform flows in straight prismatic channels, the mean velocity of flow, V, is experimentally found to be proportional to a certain power (about $\frac{1}{2}$ to $\frac{2}{3}$) of the ratio of the cross-sectional area A of flow and the wetted perimeter p; i.e., $V \propto (A/p)^n$, n being constant. Given the channel section for the minimum flow, with A_0 and p_0, design a channel such that V is the same for all larger discharges (at greater depths). (This type of channel is found useful for conveying liquids with suspended materials in treatment plants.)

The problem is to find a channel section with the value of A/p at any depth $= A_0/p_0$. Let the coordinate axes be located as shown in Fig. 4–31. Then, for any depth of flow y_1,

$$A = A_0 + 2 \int_0^{y_1} x(y)\, dy$$

$$p = p_0 + 2 \int_0^{y_1} \sqrt{1 + \left(\frac{dx}{dy}\right)^2}\, dy$$

It is required that $A/p = A_0/p_0$. Thus

$$A_0 + 2 \int_0^{y_1} x(y)\, dy = \frac{A_0}{p_0} \left[p_0 + 2 \int_0^{y_1} \sqrt{1 + \left(\frac{dx}{dy}\right)^2}\, dy \right]$$

Both sides are functions of y_1. Differentiating with respect to y_1 (see Eq. (4–16)),

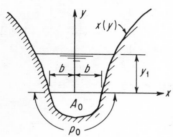

Fig. 4–31

$$x = \frac{A_0}{p_0} \sqrt{1 + \left(\frac{dx}{dy}\right)^2}$$

or

$$\frac{dx}{dy} = \pm \sqrt{\frac{p_0 x^2}{A_0} - 1}$$

With the aid of Eq. (4–41), the solution of this equation, with the known condition that $x = b$ at $y = 0$, is

$$\pm \frac{p_0 y}{A_0} = \cosh^{-1}\left(\frac{p_0 x}{A_0}\right) - \cosh^{-1}\left(\frac{p_0 b}{A_0}\right)$$

(The differential equation is one of the second degree. For further discussion, see the next article.) Here, only the positive values of y need to be considered; i.e., only the positive sign is to be used. With the aid of Eq. (4–40), this result can also be converted to a logarithmic function:

$$\frac{p_0 y}{A_0} = \log_e \frac{x + \sqrt{x^2 - (A_0/p_0)^2}}{b + \sqrt{b^2 - (A_0/p_0)^2}}$$

It can be verified that this solution of the differential equation satisfies the requirement $A/p = A_0/p_0$ (see Problem 4–39).

Problems

4–36. Compute $\sinh x$, $\cosh x$ and $\tanh x$ for $x = -\infty$, 0, $+\infty$, and a few other values, so as to sketch the curves of these functions against x.

4–37. A slender wire of length L has nonuniform cross-sectional area $A = A_0$ sech (x/L), where A_0 is A at $x = 0$ at one end. The conductivity of the material is k. Find the electrical resistance of this wire.

$$Ans. \quad \frac{L}{2A_0 k}\left(e - \frac{1}{e}\right)$$

4–38. Prove the following indentities:

$$\sinh \cosh^{-1} x = \sqrt{x^2 - 1}$$

$$\cosh \sinh^{-1} x = \sqrt{x^2 + 1}$$

$$\tanh \cosh^{-1} x = \frac{\sqrt{x^2 - 1}}{x}$$

(Hint: make use of Eq. (4–38).)

4–39. In Example 4–18, a solution $y(x)$ is obtained.

(a) Show that this solution can be transformed into

$$x = b \cosh \left(\frac{y}{m}\right) + \sqrt{b^2 - m^2} \sinh \left(\frac{y}{m}\right) \qquad \text{where } m = A_0/p_0$$

(b) Verify if the required condition $A/p = m$ is satisfied by this solution for all values of y.

4–40. A solid body is falling from rest under the influence of gravity and air resistance. The air resistance is proportional to the square of the velocity v.

(a) Using Newton's law of motion, $F = \dfrac{d}{dt} (mv)$, show that at time $t, v = U \tanh (gt/U)$, where U is the terminal velocity at $t = \infty$ when the air resistance is large enough to balance the weight.

(b) Show that the distance traveled up to t is

$$s = \frac{U^2}{g} \log_e \cosh \left(\frac{gt}{U}\right)$$

(c) Show that at any t, v is related to s by the following relationship:

$$v = U \sqrt{1 - \exp \left(-\frac{2gs}{U^2}\right)}$$

(d) Show that, when there is no air resistance ($U \to \infty$ or $k \to 0$, where $k = $ resistance$/v^2$), the three results above can be reduced to $v = gt$, $s = \frac{1}{2}gt^2$ and $v = \sqrt{2gs}$.

4–7. First order ordinary differential equations of the second degree

In Article 4–2, a theorem is stated which gives the conditions for first-order ordinary differential equations to have one unique solution for each point. One of the conditions stated in this theorem is that, in the equation $dy/dx = f(x, y)$, the function $f(x, y)$ should be single-valued. This condition is not satisfied when the equation is of the second degree. In such an equation, the function $f(x, y)$ is double-valued. For example, take the equation

$$\left(\frac{dx}{dy}\right)^2 + 2y \frac{dy}{dx} + x - 1 = 0$$

This can be rewritten as

$$\frac{dy}{dx} = y \pm \sqrt{y^2 - x + 1}$$

Thus, the theorem gives no information in connection with equations of the second degree. It is to be demonstrated in this article that there are more than one integral curves through a point. There may be more than one general solution, and there may be solutions not belonging to the general solutions.

Geometrically, a double-valued function $f(x, y)$ means that there are, in general, two integral curves passing a point at different slopes. One possibility is that the two curves belong to different families of curves. For example, take the equation

$$xy \left(\frac{dy}{dx}\right)^2 + (y^2 - 4x^2) \frac{dy}{dx} - 4xy = 0$$

Solving for dy/dx, we have

$$\frac{dy}{dx} = \frac{-(y^2 - 4x^2) \pm (y^2 + 4x^2)}{2xy} = \frac{4x}{y} \quad \text{or} \quad \frac{-y}{x}$$

There is one general solution for each of the two cases:

$$4x^2 - y^2 = C \quad \text{and} \quad xy = k$$

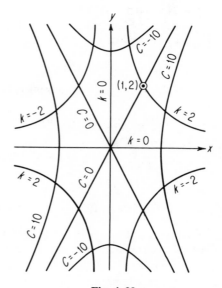

Fig. 4–32

Thus, for the point $(1, 2)$, the two particular solutions are obtained from two different general solutions: $4x^2 - y^2 = 0$ and $xy = 2$, as shown in Fig. 4–32. Another possibility is that the two curves passing the same point may be curves belonging to the same general solution. Take for example

$$\left(\frac{dy}{dx}\right)^2 - \frac{1}{y^2} + 1 = 0$$

Solving for dy/dx, we have

$$\frac{dy}{dx} = \frac{\pm\sqrt{1-y^2}}{y} \tag{4–42}$$

The general solution, for both cases with the positive and negative signs, is

$$(x-C)^2 + y^2 = 1$$

This is a family of circles, as shown in Fig. 4–33. For the point $(\frac{1}{2}, \sqrt{\frac{3}{2}})$, the two particular solutions are obtained from the same general solution with $C=0$ and $C=1$.

At some points in the x–y plane, the two values of dy/dx of a second-degree equation may coincide. These points sometimes form an envelope to the curves of the general solution. Since the envelope has the same slope as the curves to which it is tangent, the envelope also satisfies the slope requirement of the differential equation. Thus, the envelope is also a solution of the equation, although it does not belong to the general solution. Such a solution which cannot be obtained from the general solution by specifying the value of the arbitrary constant is called a *singular solution*. For example, in Eq. (4–42) dy/dx is single-valued at $y=\pm 1$, which represents the two en-

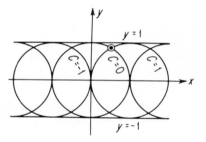

Fig. 4–33

velopes of the circles. It can be easily verified that $y=\pm 1$ are solutions of the differential equation, but they do not belong to the family of circles of the general solution. Singular solutions can sometimes be found by determining the locus of points where dy/dx is single-valued. However, this method does not always work. For example, take the equation

$$\left(\frac{dy}{dx}\right)^2 - 4\frac{dy}{dx} + y + 3 = 0$$

from which

$$\frac{dy}{dx} = 2\pm\sqrt{1-y}$$

Here, dy/dx becomes single-valued at $y=1$. However, $y=1$ is only a cusp locus, as shown in Fig. 4–34. It is not an envelope of the general solution, and is not a solution of the differential equation.

When there are more than one integral curves through a point, it is necessary to determine whether one or all of the curves are valid according to the conditions of the problem. Take, for example, the problem of filling a ship lock in Example 4–12. The equation for this problem is

$$50 \times 20 \frac{dy}{dt} = 0.4a\sqrt{2g(4-y)}$$

with the condition $y=0$ at $t=0$. Upon removal of the radical sign, this equation is one of second degree.

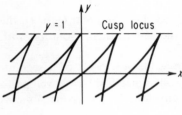

Fig. 4–34

$$(50 \times 20)^2 \left(\frac{dy}{dt}\right)^2 = (0.4a)^2 \, 2g(4-y)$$

from which

$$50 \times 20 \frac{dy}{dt} = \pm 0.4a\sqrt{2g(4-y)}$$

The solutions of this equation are shown in Fig. 4–35. However, the term on the right-hand side of this equation is the discharge into the lock, implying that only the non-negative value of dy/dt is valid. The solution presented in Example 4–12 is therefore the only solution to the problem until $y=4$. For larger values of t, there is the singular

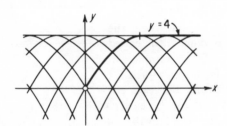

Fig. 4–35

solution $y=4$. For an example where all integral curves, including the singular solution, may be valid solutions to the problem, see Example 4–19.

Example 4–19. If in Example 4–18 the channel for minimum flow is rectangular in section, 4 ft wide, and 2 ft deep, as shown in Fig. 4–36, find all possible channel sections giving the same A/p at all greater depths.

In this case, for the minimum-flow section $A_0=2 \times 4=8$ ft², $p_0=4+(2 \times 2)$ $=8$ ft, $A_0/p_0=1$ ft and $b=2$ ft. The differential equation has been shown in Example 4.18 to be

$$\frac{dx}{dy} = \pm \sqrt{\left(\frac{p_0 x}{A_0}\right)^2 - 1} = \pm \sqrt{x^2-1}$$

Upon removal of the radical sign, this equation becomes one of the second degree. From physical considerations, there is no reason why any one of the two values of dy/dx is not valid. Integrating, we have

$$x = \cosh(C \pm y)$$

The curves of this general solution for positive values of x are shown in Fig. 4-37. Since $x=2$ at $y=0$, the value of C is given by $C=\cosh^{-1} 2 = \pm \log_e (2+\sqrt{2^2-1}) = \pm 1.32$. Since $\cosh u = \cosh(-u)$, there are altogether only two particular solutions from the general equation:

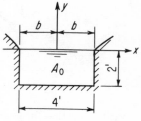

$$x = \cosh(y \pm 1.32)$$

Fig. 4-36

There is also a singular solution to the equation

$$x = \pm 1$$

Note that there are an infinite number of possible solutions to the problem, consisting of the curves of the general solutions, and, in some of them, with a portion of the singular solution, as shown in Fig. 4-37.

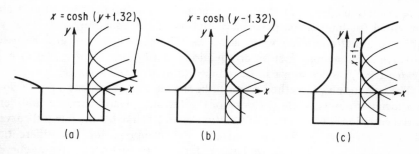

Fig. 4-37

Problems

4-41. Find all the solutions of the following equation, and sketch them in the x-y plane:

$$x^2 \left(\frac{dy}{dx}\right)^2 - y^2 + 4 = 0$$

4-42. A reflector is formed by revolving a curve $y(x)$ about the x axis. This curve is such that light coming from a point source at the origin is reflected to a direction parallel to the x axis, in one or the other direction, as shown in Fig. 4-38(a) and (b).

(a) Show that, in both cases, the differential equation for the curve is $yp^2 + 2xp - y = 0$, where $p = dy/dx$.

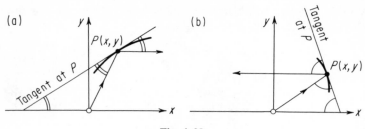

Fig. 4-38

(b) Show that the general solution of this equation is $y^2 = 2Cx + C^2$. Determine the equations of the curves passing the point $(1, 1)$, and sketch these curves. (Hint: first find $p(y)$ by differentiating the differential equation in (a) with respect to y.)

4-8. Graphical and numerical methods of solving first-order equations

Several types of first-order ordinary differential equations have been dealt with in Art. 4-2. Very often, however, equations encountered in practice cannot be integrated in finite form. One must therefore have recourse to approximate methods. In this article, graphical and numerical methods are presented for finding the particular solution of the equation $dy/dx = f(x, y)$ with the initial condition $y = y_0$ at $x = x_0$. These methods can also be used to solve simultaneous first-order equations of the form $dx/dt = F(x, y)$ and $dy/dt = G(x, y)$, since they can be reduced to $dy/dx = G/F = f(x, y)$.

The best graphical method seems to be the method of isoclines. An *isocline* is a locus of points where the slope of the various integral curves of a differential equation is constant. The equation of an isocline for the integral curves of $dy/dx = f(x, y)$ is $f(x, y) = $ constant. For example, for the differential equation $dy/dx = x^2/(x - y)$, we have a slope $dy/dx = 1$ for all integral curves on the isocline $x^2/(x - y) = 1$ or $y = x - x^2$. Similarly, the equation of the isocline for slope $dy/dx = 2$ is $2y = 2x - x^2$. In Fig. 4-39, these and other isoclines are constructed. The pattern of the integral curves of the differential equation can be shown by drawing short lines on each isocline at the corresponding slope. To construct a particular integral curve from an initial condition, say point a at $(0, \frac{3}{2})$, draw from a a line at the (zero) slope corresponding to its isocline, to intersect the next isocline at point b. Also draw from a a line at the slope $-\frac{1}{15}$ corresponding to this second isocline, to intersect this isocline at point c. The midpoint between points b and c is taken to be the next point on the required integral curve. In a similar manner, other points of the integral curve can be obtained. Obviously, the accuracy of the result increases with the number of isoclines used. This method is useful when the pattern of the integral curves is wanted.

There is a somewhat similar step-by-step numerical method which is usually referred to as the *modified Euler's method*. Given an equation dy/dx

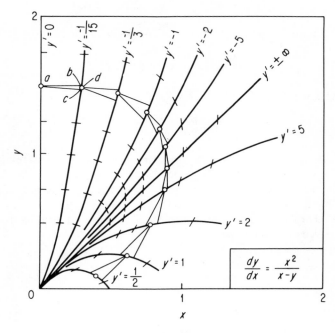

Fig. 4–39

$=f(x, y)$ and a known point (x_0, y_0) on the integral curve, we want to compute y_1 of the next point at $x_1 = x_0 + b$ where b is an arbitrarily chosen distance. The differential equation $dy/dx = f(x, y)$ gives

$$y_1 = y_0 + \int_{x_0}^{x_0+b} f(x, y)\, dx \tag{4-43}$$

However, the integral cannot be evaluated, because the unknown $y(x)$ is involved in the integrand. To find an approximate value for y_1, note that the integral is equal to the product of b and the mean value of $f(x, y)$ in this interval. As an approximation, consider this mean value to be the mean of $f(x_0, y_0)$ and $f(x_1, y_1)$. Thus

$$y_1 \doteq y_0 + \frac{b}{2} [f(x_0, y_0) + f(x_1, y_1)] \tag{4-44}$$

The value of y_1 on the left-hand side is to be obtained by iteration with approximate values of y_1 on the right-hand side. The first approximate value of y_1, denoted by $y_1{}^{(1)}$, is obtained with y_0 as an approximation of y_1 in computing $f(x_1, y_1)$:

$$y_1{}^{(1)} = y_0 + \frac{b}{2} [f(x_0, y_0) + f(x_1, y_0)]$$

The second approximation $y_1{}^{(2)}$ is then computed from

$$y_1{}^{(2)} = y_0 + \frac{b}{2} [f(x_0, y_0) + f(x_1, y_1{}^{(1)})]$$

This process is repeated with

$$y_1{}^{(n+1)} = y_0 + \frac{b}{2} [f(x_0, y_0) + f(x_1, y_1{}^{(n)})] \tag{4-45}$$

until no change of y_1 is necessary to the number of digits retained (see Example 4–20). With y_1 thus determined, the next value y_2 can be obtained from y_1 in a similar manner. It should be mentioned that the values of y thus obtained are not accurate to the number of digits retained, since Eq. (4–44) is not exact. Although this method is slow and of limited accuracy, it is useful because of its simplicity.

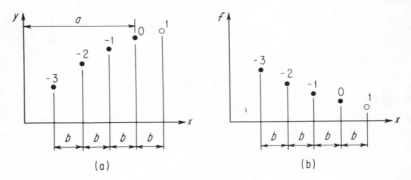

Fig. 4–40

Another method which yields more accurate results is by approximating $f(x, y)$ in Eq. (4–43) with a Taylor's expansion. Suppose we have already obtained several values of y at equal intervals up to $x=a$, as shown by the dots in Fig. 4–40(a). (We will discuss later how these values are obtained from the given initial condition.) The problem is to find the next value of y at an interval b away. For this value of y at $x=a+b$, Eq. (4–43) may be rewritten as

$$y(a+b) = y(a) + \int_a^{a+b} f(x, y)\, dx$$

This method consists of approximating $f(x, y)$ in this interval with a finite Taylor's expansion about $x=a$, where the last known value has been obtained. This expansion is a series in x because, for a particular integral curve, y is a function of x and, therefore, $f(x, y)$ or $f[x, y(x)]$ is a function of x only. In Fig. 4–40(b), the computed values of f corresponding to the known values of y are shown. Let the subscripts 0, -1, -2, etc., indicate these values as shown in the figure. Replacing $f(x, y)$ with a Taylor's series, we have

$$y_1 = y_0 + \int_a^{a+b} \left[f_0 + f_0' \cdot (x-a) + \frac{f_0''}{2!} (x-a)^2 + \frac{f_0'''}{3!} (x-a)^3 + \ldots \right] dx$$

$$= y_0 + f_0 b + \frac{f_0'}{2!} b^2 + \frac{f_0''}{3!} b^3 + \frac{f_0'''}{4!} b^4 + \ldots \tag{4-46}$$

With known values f_0, f_{-1}, f_{-2}, etc., we can compute f_0', f_0'', etc., to a certain degree of accuracy. We are now going to obtain, as an example, the formula for using three known values ($f_0, f_{-1},$ and f_{-2}). With these three known values, we can compute f_0' and f_0'' with backward differences as follows (also see Eq. (1–29)). With f_{-1} and f_{-2} expressed in the following two equations with two unknowns f_0' and f_0'':

$$f_{-1} = f_0 - f_0'b + \frac{1}{2}f_0''b^2 - \left(\frac{1}{6}f_0'''b^3 - \ldots\right)$$

$$f_{-2} = f_0 - 2f_0'b + 2f_0''b^2 - \left(\frac{4}{3}f_0'''b^3 - \ldots\right)$$

we obtain

$$f_0' = \frac{3f_0 - 4f_{-1} + f_{-2}}{2b} + \left(\frac{f_0'''}{3} b^2 + \ldots\right)$$

$$f_0'' = \frac{f_0 - 2f_{-1} + f_{-2}}{b^2} + \left(f_0'''b + \ldots\right)$$

Substituting these values into Eq. (4–46) and simplifying, we have

$$y_1 = y_0 + \frac{b}{12} (23f_0 - 16f_{-1} + 5f_{-2}) + \left(\frac{3}{8}f_0'''b^4 + \ldots\right) \tag{4-47}$$

Thus, we can compute the value y_1 from the three known values (by neglecting terms in the last parentheses) with an error of the order of $3f_0'''b^4/8$. With y_1 thus determined, f_1 can be computed. In practice, a further refinement is usually made. Here, the value of y_1 in Eq. (4–47) has been obtained by extrapolating from the known values $f_{-2}, f_{-1},$ and f_0. Now that we have a good estimate of f_1, we can have a still better approximation of function

f within the interval between points 0 and 1 by interpolation. Let the approximate value of f_1 we have just determined from y_1 in Eq. (4–47) be denoted by f_1^*. Using the three values of f_{-1}, f_0, and f_1^*, we can obtain a better estimate of f_0' and f_0'' for Eq. (4–46) as follows: from

$$f_{-1} = f_0 - f_0'b + \frac{1}{2}f_0''b^2 - \left(\frac{1}{6}f_0'''b^3 - \cdots\right)$$

$$f_1^* = f_0 + f_0'b + \frac{1}{2}f_0''b^2 + \left(\frac{1}{6}f_0'''b^3 + \cdots\right)$$

we obtain f_0' and f_0''. Substituting these values into Eq. (4–46), we have

$$y_1 = y_0 + \frac{b}{12}(5f_1^* + 8f_0 - f_{-1}) - \left(\frac{1}{24}f_0'''b^4 - \cdots\right) \qquad (4\text{–}48)$$

The value of y_1 computed from this equation (by neglecting the terms in the last parentheses) is very close to that of Eq. (4–47), and therefore also serves as a partial check against mistakes in computation. With y_1 thus determined, f_1 can be computed, and the process is repeated to find the next point. However, to start the computation, we must first obtain a set of three known values from the given initial condition. Values of y near the initial condition can be computed directly from the differential equation $dy/dx = f(x, y)$ as follows. For example, for $x = x_0 + b$ and $x = x_0 - b$, we have, by Taylor's series,

$$\left.\begin{aligned}
y(x_0 + b) &= y_0 + y_0'b + \frac{1}{2}y_0''b^2 + \frac{1}{3!}y_0'''b^3 + \frac{1}{4!}y_0^{iv}b^4 + \cdots \\
y(x_0 - b) &= y_0 - y_0'b + \frac{1}{2}y_0''b^2 - \frac{1}{3!}y_0'''b^3 + \frac{1}{4!}y_0^{iv}b^4 - \cdots
\end{aligned}\right\} \qquad (4\text{–}49)$$

where $y_0' = f(x_0, y_0)$, $y_0'' = f'(x_0, y_0)$, $y_0''' = f''(x_0, y_0)$, etc., can be computed if these derivatives of the known function $f(x, y)$ exist at (x_0, y_0). These computed values of y must be accurate to the number of significant figures desired in the solution. (One may use the Taylor's expansion from (x_0, y_0), similar to Eqs. (4–49), to determine the whole integral curve, but for the same accuracy, the work involved is much greater than that of using Eqs. (4–47) and (4–48).) For an example of solution by this method, see Example 4–21.

The last method presented above represents one of the simplest methods using series. Other similar methods have been devised for increasing the accuracy, for checking the results, and for machine computation. For discussion of these topics, consult books on numerical analysis. However, it can be mentioned here that the accuracy can be improved either by decreasing the interval b, or by increasing the number of known values used in each step. Formulas for using larger number of known values can be derived in a similar manner.

Numerical solution of first-order equations is of great interest in engineering analysis, because equations of higher order can be rewritten as simultaneous first-order equations. For example, the second-order equation

$$\frac{d^2y}{dx^2} = F\left(\frac{dy}{dx}, y, x\right)$$

can be rewritten as $dy/dx=p$ and $dp/dx=F(p, y, x)$. These are two simultaneous first-order equations for the unknown functions $y(x)$ and $p(x)$. The methods represented above can be extended to solve these equations.

Example 4–20. Using the modified Euler's method, find the particular solution of $dy/dx=x^2/(x-y)$ for the initial condition $y=\frac{3}{2}$ at $x=0$. (This problem has been solved graphically in Fig. 4–39.)

Use intervals of $\Delta x=0.1$. Then, for y_1 at $x_1=0.1$, Eq. (4–45) gives

$$y_1^{(1)} = y_0+\frac{b}{2}\left[f(x_0, y_0)+f(x_1, y_0)\right]$$

$$= \frac{3}{2}+\frac{0.1}{2}\left[\frac{0^2}{0-\frac{3}{2}}+\frac{0.1^2}{0.1-\frac{3}{2}}\right] = 1.49964$$

$$y_1^{(2)} = \frac{3}{2}+\frac{0.1}{2}\left[0+\frac{0.1^2}{0.1-1.49964}\right] = 1.49964$$

Similarly, for y_2 at $x_2=0.2$

$$y_2^{(1)} = y_1+\frac{b}{2}\left[f(x_1, y_1)+f(x_2, y_1)\right]$$

$$= 1.49964+\frac{0.1}{2}\left[-0.00715+\frac{0.2^2}{0.2-1.49964}\right] = 1.49774$$

$$y_2^{(2)} = 1.49964+\frac{0.1}{2}\left[-0.00715+\frac{0.2^2}{0.2-1.49774}\right] = 1.49774$$

Other points on the integral curve can be obtained in a similar manner. When the slope $f(x, y)$ becomes large (near $x=0.9$, as shown in Fig. 4–39), it is better to treat the equation as $dx/dy=(x-y)/x^2$. Note that the values obtained by this method are not accurate to the number of digits retained, because Eq. (4–44) is not exact. Compare with results obtained by a more accurate method in the following example.

Example 4–21. Solve the problem of Example 4–20 by using Eqs. (4–49), (4–47), and (4–48).

To start the numerical solution by this method, we need three known values near the given initial condition $(0, \frac{3}{2})$. These can be obtained by using Eqs. (4–49). First evaluate the values of y_0, y_0', etc., at the initial point. In general,

$$\frac{dy}{dx} = \frac{x^2}{x-y}$$

$$\frac{d^2y}{dx^2} = \frac{2x}{x-y} - \frac{x^2}{(x-y)^2} + \frac{x^4}{(x-y)^3}$$

$$\frac{d^3y}{dx^3} = \frac{2}{x-y} - \frac{4x}{(x-y)^2} + \frac{6x^3}{(x-y)^3} + \frac{2x^2}{(x-y)^3} - \frac{5x^4}{(x-y)^4} + \frac{3x^6}{(x-y)^5}$$

$$\frac{d^4y}{dx^4} = -\frac{6}{(x-y)^2} + \frac{x}{(x-y)^3}(8+\ldots)$$

Thus at $(0, \frac{3}{2})$, $y'=0$, $y''=0$, $y'''=-\frac{4}{3}$, and $y^{iv}=-\frac{8}{3}$. From Eqs. (4–49), with interval $b=0.1$, we have at $x=0.1$:

$$y = \frac{3}{2} + 0 + 0 - \frac{\frac{4}{3}}{3!}(0.1)^3 - \frac{\frac{8}{3}}{4!}(0.1)^4 + \ldots$$

$$= \frac{3}{2} - 0.00022 - 0.00001 + \ldots = 1.49977$$

Similarly, at $x=-0.1$, we have $y=1.50021$. These values of y can be shown to be accurate to five decimal places by using the remainder of the series.

For these three known points $(-0.1, 1.50021)$, $(0, \frac{3}{2})$, and $(0.1, 1.49977)$, we can compute $f=x^2/(x-y)=-0.00625$, 0, and -0.00715, respectively. Extrapolating with Eq. (4–47), we have, at $x=0.2$

$$y = 1.49977 + \frac{0.1}{12}[23(-0.00715)-0+5(-0.00625)] = 1.4981$$

$$f = \frac{0.2^2}{0.2-1.4981} = -0.0308$$

Improving the result by intrapolation with Eq. (4–48),

$$y = 1.49977 + \frac{0.1}{12}[5(-0.0308)+8(-0.00715)-0] = 1.4980$$

$$f = \frac{0.2^2}{0.2-1.4980} = -0.0308$$

Similarly, for $x=0.3$, we have from Eq. (4–47)

$$y = 1.4980 + \frac{0.1}{12}[23(-0.0308)-16(-0.00715)+0] = 1.4930$$

$$f = \frac{0.3^2}{0.3-1.4930} = -0.0754$$

and from Eq. (4-48),

$$y = 1.4980 + \frac{0.1}{12}[5(-0.0754) + 8(-0.0308) - (-0.00715)] = 1.4929$$

$$f = \frac{0.3^2}{0.3 - 1.4929} = -0.0754$$

The computation can be continued in a similar manner. A table of the computed values is useful during the computation.

x	y	$f(x, y)$
-0.1	1.50021	-0.00625
0	1.50000	0
0.1	1.49977	-0.00715
0.2	1.4980	-0.0308
0.3	1.4929	-0.0754

Problems

4-43. By the method of isoclines, find the integral curve of the equation $dy/dx = x + y$, passing through the point (0, 0). (Suggested isoclines: $dy/dx = 0, \frac{1}{2}, 1, \frac{3}{2},$ ...) *Ans.* $y = 2$ at $x = 1.53$

4-44. By the modified Euler's method, find the values of y at $x = 0.4$ in the previous problem, to three decimal places. Use $\Delta x = 0.2$ in each step. *Ans.* 0.094

4-45. Solve the previous problem by using Eqs. (4-47) and (4-48). First find the values of y at $x = -0.2$ and 0.2, by using Eqs. (4-49). *Ans.* 0.0918

4-9. Higher-order ordinary differential equations

As in the case of first-order differential equations, known conditions are needed for the determination of a particular solution. These conditions may be known at one value of the independent variable (e.g., $y, dy/dx, ..., d^{n-1}y/dx^{n-1}$ at x_0), or at more than one value of the independent variable (e.g., y at x_0, and dy/dx and d^2y/dx^2 at x_1, etc.). In the former case, the known conditions are called *initial conditions*, and in the latter case, they are called *boundary conditions*. It will be seen that the nature of the particular solution depends greatly upon the nature of the known conditions.

Corresponding to the theorem in Article 4-2 for first-order equations, there is a theorem for nth-order equations which is stated here without proof.

Theorem: if in the equation

$$\frac{d^n y}{dx^n} = f\left(x, y, \frac{dy}{dx}, ..., \frac{d^{n-1}y}{dx^{n-1}}\right)$$

the function f is defined and has continuous first partial derivatives in a domain, there is a unique particular solution $y(x)$ for each set of n initial conditions at x_0 in the domain.

A solution with n arbitrary constants, giving a unique particular solution for each set of n initial conditions in the domain, is called a *general solution*.

In the case of second-order equations, there is a simple geometrical interpretation of the solutions. The general form of a second-order equation may be written as

$$\frac{d^2y}{dx^2} = f\left(\frac{dy}{dx}, y, x\right)$$

If f is single-valued, this equation specifies the value of d^2y/dx^2, or the radius of curvature of the integral curve (which is $[1+(dy/dx)^2]^{3/2}/(d^2y/dx^2)$) at each point (x, y) for each slope dy/dx. Thus, through each point (x, y), there are an infinite number of possible integral curves, each at a different slope with a different curvature determined by the differential equation. In the case with known initial conditions y_0 and $(dy/dx)_0$ at x_0, one can compute the radius of curvature at (x_0, y_0). With the given slope and the computed radius, a short (to be exact, infinitesimal) arc can be drawn for the particular solution, as shown in Fig. 4–41. Since a point with a new slope has now been obtained, the process can be repeated until the whole integral curve is obtained. In the case of known boundary conditions, e.g., y_0 at x_0 and y_1 at x_1, one may try to construct integral curves through x_0 with various slopes $(dy/dx)_0$. There may be one or more of these curves passing the point (x_1, y_1), as shown in Fig. 4–41. Thus, even when a unique particular solution can be obtained with known initial conditions, there may be more than one integral curve for known boundary conditions. This behavior will be discussed further in Article 4–15.

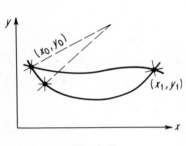

Fig. 4–41

As in the case of nonlinear first-order equations, there may be more than one general solution, and there may be singular solutions in the case of nonlinear equations. Nonlinear equations of second and higher orders are beyond the scope of this book (except for the simple cases of Eqs. (4–55) and (4–56)). In fact, very few nonlinear equations are solvable by exact methods. Subsequent discussions in this and the following chapter will be confined to linear equations. Fortunately, many engineering problems are described by linear equations and many more can be approximated with linearized equations.

The general form of a linear equation of the nth order is

$$a_0(x)\frac{d^ny}{dx^n} + a_1(x)\frac{d^{n-1}y}{dx^{n-1}} + \ldots + a_{n-1}(x)\frac{dy}{dx} + a_n(x)y = f(x) \qquad (4\text{–}50)$$

The functions a_0, a_1, ..., a_n, and f are known functions of the independent variable x. This equation is linear because it does not involve the products of the unknown function y and its derivatives. Due to linearity, this equation has several interesting properties. First consider the case where $f(x)$ is zero.

$$a_0(x) \frac{d^n y}{dx^n} + a_1(x) \frac{d^{n-1}}{dx^{n-1}} + \ldots + a_{n-1}(x) \frac{dy}{dx} + a_n(x) y = 0 \qquad (4\text{-}51)$$

This equation is called *homogeneous* because each term is of the same (first) power of y or its derivatives. It is to be shown that, if $y_1(x)$ is a solution of Eq. (4–51), $c_1 y_1(x)$ is also a solution, where c_1 is an arbitrary constant. If $y_2(x)$ is another solution, then $c_1 y_1(x) + c_2 y_2(x)$ is also a solution, where c_2 is another arbitrary constant. That this is true can be easily verified as follows. Substitute $(c_1 y_1 + c_2 y_2)$ for y in Eq. (4–51) and collect terms:

$$c_1 \left(a_0 \frac{d^n y_1}{dx^n} + \ldots + a_n y_1 \right) + c_2 \left(a_0 \frac{d^n y_2}{dx^n} + \ldots + a_n y_2 \right) = 0$$

Since y_1 and y_2 are given solutions of Eq. (4–51), the value in each parenthesis must be zero. Thus, Eq. (4–51) is satisfied by $(c_1 y_1 + c_2 y_2)$. This property can be extended to include the sum of more than two solutions. Thus, if n independent solutions can be found, a general solution with n arbitrary constants may be expressed as

$$y(x) = c_1 y_1(x) + c_2 y_2(x) + \ldots + c_n y_n(x) \qquad (4\text{-}52)$$

The n solutions $y_1(x)$, $y_2(x)$, ... $y_n(x)$ must be linearly independent (i.e., none of them can be expressed as a linear combination of the others, such as $y_1 = 2y_2 + 3y_6$), so that Eq. (4–52) cannot be reduced to contain less than n arbitrary constants.

Now consider the *nonhomogeneous* linear equation, Eq. (4–50). Let $Y(x)$ be any solution of Eq. (4–50), and $y_1(x)$, ..., $y_n(x)$ be solutions of the *associated homogeneous equation*, Eq. (4–51), with the same coefficients $a_0(x)$, etc. It can be verified that $(c_1 y_1 + \ldots c_n y_n + Y)$ is a solution of Eq. (4–50), and, since this solution contains n arbitrary constants, it is a general solution. To verify, substitute this solution into the left-hand side of Eq. (4–50) to get

$$c_1 \left(a_0 \frac{d^n y_1}{dx^n} + \ldots + a_n y_1 \right) + \ldots + c_n \left(a_0 \frac{d^n y_n}{dx^n} + \ldots + a_n y_n \right) + \left(a_0 \frac{d^n Y}{dx^n} + \ldots a_n Y \right)$$

Since each of y_1, ..., y_n is a solution of the homogeneous equation, the value in every parenthesis, except the last, is zero. Since $Y(x)$ is a solution of Eq. (4–50), the value in the last parenthesis is $f(x)$. Thus, Eq. (4–50) is satisfied by the general solution $(c_1 y_1 + \ldots c_n y_n + Y)$.

In the discussion above, we have assumed that there are n linearly independent solutions of the homogeneous Eq. (4–51). For the existence and uniqueness of the solutions suggested above for linear equations, we have a theorem which is stated here without proof.

Theorem: if in Eq. (4–50) $a_0(x)$, $a_1(x)$, ..., $a_n(x)$, and $f(x)$ are continuous and single-valued functions in an interval of x and $a_0(x) \neq 0$ in this interval, there is a general solution which is the complete solution in the form of

$$y(x) = c_1 y_1(x) + c_2 y_2(x) + ... + c_n y_n(x) + Y(x) \qquad (4\text{–}53)$$

where the constants are arbitrary, the n functions $y_1(x)$, $y_2(x)$, ..., $y_n(x)$ are linearly independent solutions of the associated homogeneous equation, Eq. (4–51), and $Y(x)$ is any function that satisfies Eq. (4–50).

This theorem is a uniqueness theorem as well as an existence theorem, in that it gives the conditions under which a general solution in the form of Eq. (4–53) exists which includes all possible solutions. The function $Y(x)$ is called the *particular integral*, and the rest of the solution in Eq. (4–53) is called the *complementary function*.

In later articles, methods of obtaining the n independent solutions of the homogeneous equation and the particular integral $Y(x)$ of the nonhomogeneous equation will be discussed. Obviously, in the case of an equation in the form

$$\frac{d^n y}{dx^n} = f(x)$$

the general solution can be obtained by successive integration (see Example 4–22).

Example 4–22. A flexible cable hangs between two points under a given distributed load $f(x)$ per unit horizontal distance, as shown in Fig. 4–42. Find the general equation for the curve $y(x)$ of the cable.

The stress in a flexible cable acts along the cable. Each element of the cable is in equilibrium under the cable tension and the applied load, as shown in Fig. 4–42. Applying the equation of statics, $\sum \boldsymbol{F} = 0$, we find that, since $\sum F_x = 0$, the horizontal component H of the cable tension must be constant. Noting that the vertical component of a tensile force is $\pm H \cdot dy/dx$, and that dy/dx at $(x_0 + dx)$, according to Eq. (4–25), is

$$\left(\frac{dy}{dx}\right)_0 + \left[\frac{d}{dx}\left(\frac{dy}{dx}\right)\right]_0 dx = \left(\frac{dy}{dx}\right)_0 + \left(\frac{d^2 y}{dx^2}\right)_0 dx$$

we have from $\sum F_y = 0$,

$$-H\frac{dy}{dx} + H\left(\frac{dy}{dx} + \frac{d^2 y}{dx^2}\,dx\right) - f(x)\,dx = 0$$

and

$$\frac{d^2 y}{dx^2} = \frac{f(x)}{H} \qquad (4\text{–}54)$$

where H is an unknown constant. Since the general solution of this second-order equation contains two arbitrary constants, and H is unknown, we need altogether three known conditions to determine the curve $y(x)$ completely.

For example, let a symmetrical cable be loaded with a uniform load per unit horizontal distance (approximately similar to the cable of a uniformly

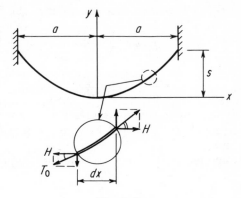

Fig. 4–42

loaded suspension bridge). Then f=constant, and the three known conditions are: $y=0$ at $x=0$, and $y=s$ at $x=a$ and at $x=-a$, as shown in Fig. 4–42. Eq. (4–54) becomes

$$\frac{d^2y}{dx^2} = \frac{f}{H}$$

Integrating, we have

$$\frac{dy}{dx} = \frac{fx}{H} + C_1$$

$$y = \frac{fx^2}{2H} + C_1 x + C_2$$

This solution, with two arbitrary constants C_1 and C_2, is the general solution. Using the three known conditions, we have $H=fa^2/2s$, and $C_1=C_2=0$. Thus the particular solution is

$$y = \frac{s}{a^2} x^2$$

Example 4–23. A uniform flexible cable hangs under its own weight w per unit length. Find the shape of the cable.

The derivation of the differential equation for this problem is similar to that in the previous problem except that, instead of $f(x) \cdot dx$, the load on a cable element in this case is

$$w \, dL = w\sqrt{(dx)^2 + (dy)^2} = w\sqrt{1 + \left(\frac{dy}{dx}\right)^2} \, dx$$

Thus, instead of Eq. (4–54), the differential equation is

$$\frac{d^2y}{dx^2} = \frac{w}{H}\sqrt{1+\left(\frac{dy}{dx}\right)^2}$$

This equation is nonlinear, but can be solved by first reducing it to a first-order equation. In fact, all second-order equations of the forms

$$\frac{d^2y}{dx^2} = f\left(x, \frac{dy}{dx}\right) \tag{4–55}$$

and

$$\frac{d^2y}{dx^2} = f\left(y, \frac{dy}{dx}\right) \tag{4–56}$$

can be reduced to first-order equations involving x and p, and y and p, respectively, where $p=dy/dx$. We shall have many occasions to put these two equations to use.

Using $p=dy/dx$ and $dp/dx=d^2y/dx^2$, we have for this problem

$$\frac{dp}{dx} = \frac{w}{H}\sqrt{1+p^2}$$

Separating variables and integrating, we have

$$\frac{dy}{dx} = p = \sinh\left(\frac{w}{H}x+C_1\right)$$

Since $\sinh 0=0$, let us for convenience put the lowest point of the cable at $x=0$ (see Fig. 4–43), so as to make $C_1=0$. This is equivalent to saying that the first known condition is $dy/dx=0$ at $x=0$. Integrating again, we have

$$y = \frac{H}{w}\cosh\left(\frac{wx}{H}\right)+C_2$$

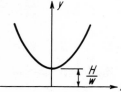

Since $\cosh 0=1$, let the origin be so chosen that the second known condition is $y=H/w$ at $x=0$, so that $C_2=0$. Then

Fig. 4–43

$$y = \frac{H}{w}\cosh\left(\frac{wx}{H}\right) \tag{4–57}$$

which is the question of a catenary. Here, H is an unknown constant from the differential equation. To determine H, one more known condition is necessary; e.g., $y=(H/w)+s$ at $x=a$.

Example 4–24. Heat is being conducted steadily by a uniform slender rod with temperatures T_1 and T_2 at the two ends. Assuming that heat loss f per unit length per unit time is constant, find the temperature distribution $T(x)$. Because the rod is slender, the flow may be considered to be one-dimensional.

According to the law of heat conduction, we have from Eq. (4–32) for one-dimensional flow,

$$Q = -kA\frac{dT}{dx}$$

where k and A are the conductivity and cross-sectional area of the rod, respectively. Here $Q(x)$, the heat passing a section per unit time, varies with x because of heat loss. Take an element dx in length, as shown in Fig. 4–44.

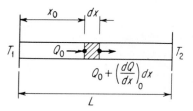

Fig. 4–44

The equation of continuity of flow of heat is, according to Eq. (4–30),

$$Q_0 - \left[Q_0 + \left(\frac{dQ}{dx}\right)_0 dx\right] - f\,dx = 0$$

(Here, the change of heat storage in the element is zero because in steady flow, the temperature of, and therefore the amount of heat in, the element is constant.) Thus

$$\frac{dQ}{dx} = -f$$

We now have two differential equations for the two unknowns $T(x)$ and $Q(x)$.

Eliminating Q from the two differential equations, we have for $T(x)$

$$kA\frac{d^2T}{dx^2} = f$$

The general solution is

$$T = \frac{fx^2}{2kA} + C_1 x + C_2$$

Using the two known conditions, $T = T_1$ at $x = 0$, and $T = T_2$ at $x = L$, we have the particular solution

$$T(x) = T_1 - \frac{T_1 - T_2}{L}x - \frac{f}{2kA}(L - x)x$$

From this, we have

$$Q(x) = -kA\frac{dT}{dx} = \frac{kA}{L}(T_1 - T_2) + \frac{f}{2}(L - 2x)$$

Problems

4-46. A flexible cable of negligible weight hangs between the two points $(0, 0)$ and $(L, 0)$. The cable is loaded with a distributed load per unit horizontal distance $f(x) = k \sin (\pi x/L)$, where k is a known constant. The sag of the cable is s. Find the cable tensions at the midpoint and at the two ends of the cable.

$$Ans. \quad \frac{kL^2}{\pi^2 s}, \frac{kL}{\pi} \sqrt{1 + \left(\frac{L}{\pi s}\right)^2}$$

4-47. A viaduct supported by a thin arch spans a valley, as shown in Fig. 4-45. Find the shape of the arch such that, when it is loaded uniformly with f per unit horizontal distance, the stress acts along the arch.

$$Ans. \quad y = r (1 - x^2/a^2)$$

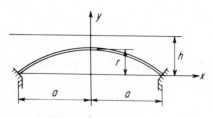

Fig. 4-45

4-48. The equation of a catenary with an unknown H is given by Eq. (4-57) and sketched in Fig. 4-43. To determine H, it is given that the cable spans between $x = \pm 100$ ft and its sag is 100 ft. Find H for $w = 5$ lb per ft. Also find the length L of the cable. (Hint: solve equations like $\cosh u = u$ by trials. Make use of identities given in Article 4-6.)

4-49. The following equations belong to the families of Eqs. (4-55) and (4-56). Find their general solutions.

(a) $\dfrac{d^2y}{dx^2} + \dfrac{1}{1+x} \cdot \dfrac{dy}{dx} = 0$

$$Ans. \quad y = c_1 \log_e (1+x) + c_2$$

(b) $y \dfrac{d^2y}{dx^2} - \left(\dfrac{dy}{dx}\right)^2 - 1 = 0$

$$Ans. \quad y = \frac{1}{c_1} \cosh (c_1 x + c_2)$$

4-50. If the loss of electricity (charges) per unit length per unit time from a d-c line is assumed to be $f(x) = ax^2 + bx + c$, where a, b, and c are known constants, and x is the distance from one end, find the voltage $V(x)$. It is observed that $V = V_0$ and the current is i_0 at $x = 0$.

$$Ans. \quad kAV = kAV_0 - i_0 x + \frac{ax^4}{12} + \frac{bx^3}{6} + \frac{cx^2}{2}$$

4-51. A vessel is at the origin at $t = 0$ and is sailing along the x axis with a speed v. A homing torpedo is sent out at $t = 0$ from a submarine located at $x = 0$, $y = S$. The constant speed of the torpedo is nv and it is always directed toward the vessel, as shown in Fig. 4–46. Show that the equation for the path of the torpedo is

$$\frac{d^2x}{dy^2} = \frac{1}{ny}\sqrt{1+\left(\frac{dx}{dy}\right)^2}$$

and find the time taken to hit the vessel.   *Ans.* $\dfrac{n}{n^2-1}\cdot\dfrac{L}{v}$

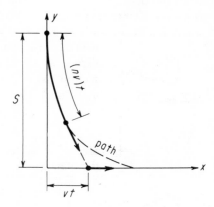

Fig. 4–46

4–10. Deflection of slender beams under bending

In the design of machines and structures, their parts must not only be strong enough to withstand the applied loads, but must also be stiff enough so that the deformations do not exceed certain allowable limits. In Chapter 3, the deformations of bars under axial tension and of shafts under twisting have been discussed. In this article, the deflections of beams under transverse loads are studied. Only cases with the loads in the plane of a principal axis of the sections are considered. In these cases, the beam is bent in the plane of the loads.

In engineering analysis of beams, it is assumed that a plane section remains a plane after deformation. This approximate method has been found satisfactory by comparing with results obtained with the more rigorous method of Elasticity. Using this approximation, a beam element can be seen to deform due to actions of bending and shearing, as shown in Fig, 4–47(b) and (c), respectively. However, unless the beam is very short and deep, the deflection due to shearing can be shown to be negligible compared with that due to bending. Thus, in ordinary cases, only deflection due to bending is considered. We are going to derive the equation for the curve of the deformed axis (passing centroids of the cross sections) of the beam, usually called the *elastic curve* (see Fig. 4–47).

Take a short length dL of beam, as shown in Fig. 4–47(b). Let s be the stress of the top fiber. Then, according to Hooke's law, $\epsilon = (s/E)dL$ is its deformation, where E is the Young's modulus of the material. By similar triangles, it can be seen that

$$\frac{dL}{R} = \frac{\epsilon}{c} = \frac{s\,dL}{Ec}$$

To relate the curvature of the beam to the external forces, we note that the stress in the fiber depends on the bending moment M at this section. From Eq. (3–29), $s = Mc/I$, where I is the moment of inertia of the section about its

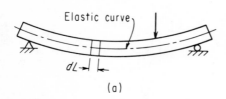

Elastic curve

(a)

neutral axis. Thus, the radius of curvature R of the elastic curve at a section is related to the bending moment M at this section:

$$\frac{1}{R} = \frac{M}{EI}$$

Since the radius R of a curve in the x-y plane is

$$R = \frac{\left[1 + \left(\dfrac{dy}{dx}\right)^2\right]^{3/2}}{\left|\dfrac{d^2y}{dx^2}\right|}$$

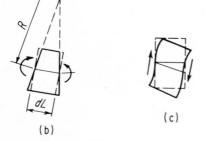

(b)

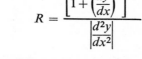

(c)

Fig. 4–47

the differential equation for the elastic curve is

$$\frac{d^2y}{dx^2} = \pm\frac{M}{EI}\left[1 + \left(\frac{dy}{dx}\right)^2\right]^{3/2}$$

The sign depends on the direction of the y axis. For example, since a positive M is defined to be one giving a curve concave upward, the negative sign should be used if the y axis is pointing downward.

When M is a function of x or y only (e.g., a deflected slender column under axial loads at the ends), this equation belongs to the family of Eq. (4−55) or Eq. (4–56), respectively. However, while the equation can be solved, the result is usually complicated due to nonlinearity. In practice, the deflections of machines and structures under working conditions are usually small. With the x axis parallel to the (undeformed) beam, dy/dx will be small. For such cases with

$$\left[1 + \left(\frac{dy}{dx}\right)^2\right]^{3/2} = 1 + \frac{3}{2}\left(\frac{dy}{dx}\right)^2 + \ldots \doteq 1$$

we have the equation linearized as

$$\frac{d^2y}{dx^2} = \pm\frac{M}{EI} \tag{4–58}$$

Here again, the positive (or negative) sign should be used when the y axis is pointing upward (or downward). In solving this equation, the function M/EI must first be found. The boundary conditions are given by the arrangement at the supports. For example, a hinge allows no deflection (i.e., $y=0$), and a built-in or clamped support allows no turning and no deflection (i.e., $dy/dx=0$ and $y=0$).

Example 4–25. A uniform cantilever beam is loaded uniformly with w per unit length, as shown in Fig. 4–48. Find the deflection of the free end.

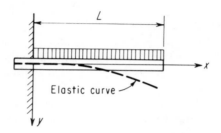

Fig. 4–48

First find the equation of the bending moment $M(x)$. (The student is advised to review Article 3–3 if necessary.) It can be shown that

$$M = -\frac{w}{2}(L-x)^2$$

Thus, with y axis pointing downward, we have

$$EI\frac{d^2y}{dx^2} = -M = \frac{w}{2}(L-x)^2$$

Integrating, we have

$$EI\frac{dy}{dx} = \frac{wL^2x}{2} - \frac{wLx^2}{2} + \frac{wx^3}{6} + c_1$$

The first known condition, $dy/dx=0$ at $x=0$ at the built-in support, gives $c_1=0$. Integrating again, we have

$$EIy = \frac{wL^2x^2}{4} - \frac{wLx^3}{6} + \frac{wx^4}{24} + c_2$$

The second known condition, $y=0$ at $x=0$, gives $c_2=0$. Thus, the equation for the elastic curve is

$$EIy = \frac{wL^2x^2}{4} - \frac{wLx^3}{6} + \frac{wx^4}{24}$$

At the free end where $x=L$,

$$y = \left(\frac{1}{4}-\frac{1}{6}+\frac{1}{24}\right)\frac{wL^4}{EI} = \frac{wL^4}{8EI}$$

Example 4–26. A uniform beam is clamped at one end and is supported with a roller at the other, as shown in Fig. 4–49. The beam is loaded with a nonuniformly distributed load as shown, with w_0 per unit length at the clamped end. Find the elastic curve of the beam.

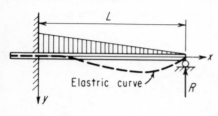

Elastric curve

Fig. 4–49

This beam is statically indeterminate to the first degree, because the number of unknown reactions is greater by one than the number of available equations of Statics. One of the unknown reactions, say R at the roller, must be retained as an unknown constant. The other reactions can then be expressed in terms of this unknown constant, if necessary.

The load $w(x)$ on the beam is $w=w_0\left(1-\frac{x}{L}\right)$ and the bending moment at a section at x_1 is

$$M = R(L-x_1)-\int_{x_1}^{L}(x-x_1)\,w_0\left(1-\frac{x}{L}\right)dx$$

$$= R(L-x_1)-\frac{w_0L^2}{6}+\frac{w_0L}{2}x_1-\frac{w_0}{2}x_1^2+\frac{w_0}{6L}x_1^3$$

(The subscript 1 can now be dropped.) Thus, with the y axis pointing downward,

$$EI\frac{d^2y}{dx^2} = -M = -R(L-x)+\frac{w_0L^2}{6}-\frac{w_0L}{2}x+\frac{w_0}{2}x^2-\frac{w_0}{6L}x^3$$

Here, R is an unknown constant. As the general solution has two arbitrary constants, we need altogether three boundary conditions for determining the particular solution. We have three known conditions: $dy/dx=0$ and $y=0$ at $x=0$, and $y=0$ at $x=L$. Integrating, we have

$$EI\frac{dy}{dx} = -RLx+\frac{R}{2}x^2+\frac{w_0L^2}{6}x-\frac{w_0L}{4}x^2+\frac{w_0}{6}x^3-\frac{w_0}{24L}x^4+c_1$$

With the condition $dy/dx=0$ at $x=0$, we have $c_1=0$. Integrating again, we obtain

$$EIy = -\frac{RL}{2}x^2+\frac{R}{6}x^3+\frac{w_0L^2}{12}x^2-\frac{w_0L}{12}x^3+\frac{w_0}{24}x^4-\frac{w_0}{120L}x^5+c_2$$

where $c_2=0$, because of the condition $y=0$ at $x=0$. The unknown R is determined from the third condition $y=0$ at $x=L$:

$$0 = -RL^3\left(\frac{1}{2}-\frac{1}{6}\right)+w_0L^4\left(\frac{1}{12}-\frac{1}{12}+\frac{1}{24}-\frac{1}{120}\right)$$

Thus, $R=w_0L/10$. The other reactions can now be determined by the equations of Statics. This is an example of solving statically indeterminate problems by considering the elastic properties of the structure. With R determined, the elastic curve is

$$EIy = \frac{w_0L^2}{30}x^2-\frac{w_0L}{15}x^3+\frac{w_0}{24}x^4-\frac{w_0}{120L}x^5$$

Example 4–27. A simply supported beam is loaded unsymmetrically with a concentrated load P, as shown in Fig. 4–50. Find the equation of the elastic curve.

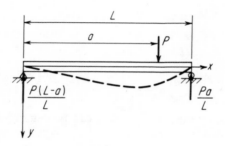

Fig. 4–50

The reactions at the supports can easily be found to be $P(L-a)/L$ and Pa/L. In this case, different functions of $M(x)$ are used for different intervals of x:

$$M = \frac{P(L-a)}{L}x \qquad \text{(for } 0 \leqq x \leqq a)$$

$$M = \frac{Pa}{L}(L-x) \qquad \text{(for } a \leqq x \leqq L)$$

Thus, we have two differential equations, each for a different interval of x:

$$EI\frac{d^2y}{dx^2} = -M = -\frac{P(L-a)}{L}x \qquad \text{(for } 0 \leqq x \leqq a)$$

$$EI\frac{d^2y}{dx^2} = -M = -\frac{Pa}{L}(L-x) \qquad \text{(for } a \leqq x \leqq L)$$

The general solution of each of these two equations will involve two arbitrary constants. Altogether we need four boundary conditions which are: $y=0$

at $x=0$, $y=0$ at $x=L$, and both solutions yielding the same dy/dx and y at the common point $x=a$. Integrating, we have

$$\left.\begin{aligned} EI\frac{dy}{dx} &= -\frac{P(L-a)}{2L}x^2+c_1 \\ EIy &= -\frac{P(L-a)}{6L}x^3+c_1x+c_2 \end{aligned}\right\} \quad \text{for } 0 \leqq x \leqq a$$

$$\left.\begin{aligned} EI\frac{dy}{dx} &= -Pa\,x+\frac{Pa}{2L}x^2+c_3 \\ EIy &= -\frac{Pa}{2}x^2+\frac{Pa}{6L}x^3+c_3x+c_4 \end{aligned}\right\} \quad \text{for } a \leqq x \leqq L$$

Since $y=0$ at $x=0$, we have $c_2=0$. Since $y=0$ at $x=L$, we have

$$0 = PaL^2\left(-\frac{1}{2}+\frac{1}{6}\right)+c_3L+c_4$$

With the other two known conditions, we have

$$-\frac{P(L-a)}{2L}a^2+c_1 = -Pa^2+\frac{Pa^3}{2L}+c_3$$

and

$$-\frac{P(L-a)}{6L}a^3+c_1a = -\frac{Pa^3}{2}+\frac{Pa^4}{6L}+c_3a+c_4$$

From these three equations, c_1, c_3 and c_4 can be determined. Eliminating c_1 and c_3 in the last two equations, we have $c_4=-Pa^3/6$. We can then easily obtain $c_3=(PaL/3)+(Pa^3/6L)$ and $c_1=(PLa/3)-(Pa^2/2)+(Pa^3/6L)$.

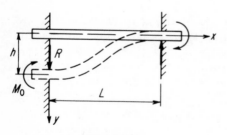

Fig. 4-51

Example 4-28. A straight uniform beam with two ends built into walls is shown in Fig. 4-51. If one of the walls settles vertically through a short distance h, find the bending moment $M(x)$ thus created in the beam. (Assume that the walls can yield slightly to relieve any longitudinal stress that may be created.)

This beam is statically indeterminate, with the number of unknown reactions exceeding by two that of useful equations of Statics. Two reactions, say M_0 and R at the left wall, must be retained as unknown constants. Then

$$M(x) = M_0-Rx$$

$$EI\frac{d^2y}{dx^2} = -M = -M_0+Rx$$

$$EI\frac{dy}{dx} = -M_0\,x + \frac{R}{2}\,x^2 + c_1$$

$$EIy = -\frac{M_0}{2}\,x^2 + \frac{R}{6}\,x^3 + c_1 x + c_2$$

For the determination of the two arbitrary constants and M_0 and R, we need altogether four known conditions. They are: $dy/dx=0$ and $y=h$ at $x=0$, and $dy/dx=0$ and $y=0$ at $x=L$. With these known conditions, we find $c_1=0$, $c_2=EIh$, $R=12EIh/L^3$ and $M_0=6EIh/L^2$. Thus, the bending moment on the beam is

$$M(x) = M_0 - Rx = \frac{6EIh}{L^2}\left(1 - \frac{2x}{L}\right)$$

Problems

4–52. A simply supported uniform beam is loaded as shown in Fig. 4–52, with w_0 per unit length at one end. Find the equation of the elastic curve.

$$Ans.\ \ y = \frac{w_0 L^4}{EI}\left[\frac{1}{120}\left(\frac{x}{L}\right)^5 - \frac{1}{36}\left(\frac{x}{L}\right)^3 + \frac{7}{360}\left(\frac{x}{L}\right)\right]$$

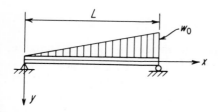

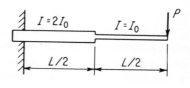

Fig. 4–52 Fig. 4–53

4–53. A cantilever beam is supporting a concentrated load P at the free end. There is a change in the cross section of the beam, as shown in Fig. 4–53. Neglecting its weight, find the deflection of the beam at the free end. *Ans.* $3PL^3/16EI_0$

4–54. A continuous uniform beam with two equal spans is loaded uniformly with w per unit length, as shown in Fig. 4–54. Find the end reactions and a to locate the maximum deflection of the beam. (Hint: make use of symmetry about the middle support, and put the origin there.) *Ans.* $3wL/8$, $L(15-\sqrt{33})/16$

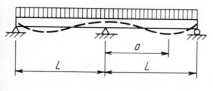

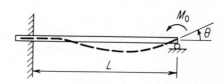

Fig. 4–54 Fig. 4–55

4-55. A uniform beam is built-in at one end and simply supported at the other. Find the externally applied torque M_0 required to rotate the end at the simple support through a small angle θ, as shown in Fig. 4-55. *Ans.* $4EI\theta/L$

4-56. A uniform beam with both ends built into walls supports a concentrated load P at mid span. Find the bending moment created at each end. *Ans.* $PL/8$

4-11. Dynamics of a particle

The motion of a particle is governed by Newton's law of motion:

$$\sum \boldsymbol{F} = k \frac{d}{dt} (m\boldsymbol{v})$$

where $\sum \boldsymbol{F}$ is the sum of the forces acting on the particle, m is its mass, $\boldsymbol{v}$ is its velocity, t is the time, and k is the constant of proportionality. In this equation, four fundamental quantities are involved, namely, force, mass, length and time. Dimensionally, the constant k is $[FT^2/ML]$. However, it is convenient to define units in such a manner that $k=1$. For example, $k=1$ when F is in lb, m in slugs, v in fps and t in sec; or F in dynes, m in grams, v in cm per sec, and t in sec. Then

$$\sum \boldsymbol{F} = \frac{d}{dt} (m\boldsymbol{v})$$

Furthermore, we consider that $k(=1)$ is dimensionless. This is equivalent to accepting $[F]$ as being the same as $[ML/T^2]$.

In this article, only particles with constant mass are considered. With the position of a particle described by $x(t)$, $y(t)$ and $z(t)$ in a fixed rectangular coordinate system, the equation of motion can be rewritten in its three component parts, as shown in Eq. (2-47):

$$\left.\begin{aligned} \sum F_x &= m \frac{d^2x}{dt^2} = m\ddot{x} \\[2mm] \sum F_y &= m \frac{d^2y}{dt^2} = m\ddot{y} \\[2mm] \sum F_z &= m \frac{d^2z}{dt^2} = m\ddot{z} \end{aligned}\right\} \qquad (4\text{-}59)$$

where the dots have been used to indicate derivatives with respect to time; e.g., $\ddot{x}$ represents d^2x/dt^2. When the forces are known functions of t, x, y, z, $\dot{x}$, $\dot{y}$, and $\dot{z}$, Eqs. (4-59) are in general simultaneous second-order differential equations for $x(t)$, $y(t)$, and $z(t)$. The two constants of integration of each equation are usually determined by the initial position and velocity. In this article, attention is limited to problems where these equations can be integrated one at a time. Other problems of dynamics of particles can be found in subsequent articles.

Very often, it is more convenient to use polar-cylindrical coordinates $\theta(t)$, $\rho(t)$, and $z(t)$ to locate the particle. To find the components of v and a along the (variable) directions of increasing ρ and increasing θ (see Fig. 4–56), we

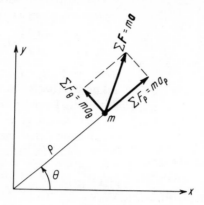

Fig. 4–56

make use of the fact that the projection of a vector on an axis is equal to the sum of the projections of its components (see Example 2–8):

$$v_\rho = v_x \cos\theta + v_y \sin\theta = \frac{dx}{dt}\cos\theta + \frac{dy}{dt}\sin\theta$$

$$= \cos\theta\frac{d}{dt}(\rho\cos\theta) + \sin\theta\frac{d}{dt}(\rho\sin\theta)$$

$$= \cos\theta(-\rho\sin\theta\,\dot\theta + \cos\theta\,\dot\rho) + \sin\theta(\rho\cos\theta\,\dot\theta + \sin\theta\,\dot\rho) = \dot\rho$$

$$v_\theta = v_x\sin\theta + v_y\cos\theta = \rho\dot\theta$$

$$a_\rho = a_x\cos\theta + a_y\sin\theta = \cos\theta\frac{d^2}{dt^2}(\rho\cos\theta) + \sin\theta\frac{d^2}{dt^2}(\rho\sin\theta) = \ddot\rho - \rho\dot\theta^2$$

$$a_\theta = -a_x\sin\theta + a_y\cos\theta = \rho\ddot\theta + 2\dot\rho\dot\theta = \frac{1}{\rho}\frac{d}{dt}(\rho^2\dot\theta)$$

Thus

$$\left.\begin{array}{l} \sum F_\rho = m\,(\ddot\rho - \rho\dot\theta^2) \\[2mm] \sum F_\theta = m\,(\rho\ddot\theta + 2\dot\rho\dot\theta) = \dfrac{m}{\rho}\dfrac{d}{dt}(\rho^2\dot\theta) \\[2mm] \sum F_z = m\ddot z \end{array}\right\} \qquad (4\text{–}60)$$

For the equations of motion in polar-spherical coordinates, see Eq. (4–100).

Example 4–29. A simple pendulum consisting of a point mass and a string of negligible mass swings in a vertical plane. Find the period of a pendulum of length L and amplitude β, as shown in Fig. 4–57.

Use polar-cylindrical coordinates in this problem. The forces acting on the mass are its weight mg and the string tension $T(t)$. For any position, we have $\sum F_\rho = mg \cos \theta - T$, $\sum F_\theta = -mg \sin \theta$, and $\sum F_z = 0$. Substituting into Eqs. (4–60) with $\rho = L$, we have

$$-mL\dot{\theta}^2 = mg \cos \theta - T$$
$$mL\ddot{\theta} = -mg \sin \theta$$
$$m\ddot{z} = 0$$

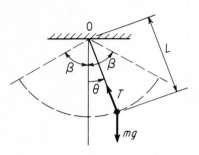

Fig. 4–57

Here, we have three equations and three unknown functions, $\theta(t)$, $T(t)$ and $z(t)$. With initial condition $z = 0$ and $\dot{z} = 0$, the third equation gives $z = 0$ for all values of t, meaning that the motion takes place in a plane. The second equation will give $\theta(t)$. With $\theta(t)$, $T(t)$ can be found from the first equation.

The second equation is similar to Eq. (4–56). To form an equation between θ and $\dot{\theta}$, use the relation

$$\frac{d\dot{\theta}}{d\theta} = \frac{d\dot{\theta}}{dt}\frac{dt}{d\theta} = \frac{\ddot{\theta}}{\dot{\theta}}$$

The second equation becomes

$$\dot{\theta}\frac{d\dot{\theta}}{d\theta} = -\frac{g}{L} \sin \theta$$

$$\frac{\dot{\theta}^2}{2} = \frac{g}{L} \cos \theta + c_1$$

With known condition: $\dot{\theta} = 0$ when $\theta = \beta$, we determine c_1 to get

$$\left(\frac{d\theta}{dt}\right)^2 = \frac{2g}{L}(\cos \theta - \cos \beta)$$

Integrating again

$$t = \sqrt{\frac{L}{2g}} \int_0^\theta \frac{d\theta}{\sqrt{\cos \theta - \cos \beta}}$$

with $t = 0$ when $\theta = 0$. This integral has been shown to be an elliptic integral of the first kind in Example 3–34.

Example 4–30. A particle of mass m is projected with initial speed U at an angle α with the horizon. The air resistance to motion is found to be cmv, where c is a constant and $v(t)$ is the speed of the particle. Study the motion of the particle.

Let the starting point be the origin, with the initial velocity vector in the

x-z plane as shown in Fig. 4–58. The forces acting on the particle in flight are its weight $-mg\mathbf{k}$ and the air resistance $-cm\mathbf{v}$. Thus

$$\sum \mathbf{F} = -mg\mathbf{k} - cm\mathbf{v}$$
$$= -cm\dot{x}\mathbf{i} - cm\dot{y}\mathbf{j} - (cm\dot{z} + mg)\,\mathbf{k}$$

According to Eqs. (4–59)

$$m\ddot{x} = -cm\dot{x}$$
$$m\ddot{y} = -cm\dot{y}$$
$$m\ddot{z} = -(cm\dot{z} + mg)$$

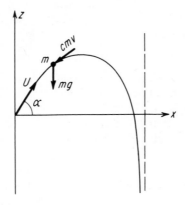

Fig. 4–58

Here, we have three equations with three unknown functions. These equations are similar to Eq. (4–55), which can be solved by first finding the first derivative. The first equation gives

$$\frac{d\dot{x}}{dt} = -c\dot{x}$$

$$\log_e \dot{x} = -ct + C_1$$

Since $\dot{x} = U \cos \alpha$ at $t = 0$, we have $C_1 = \log_e U \cos \alpha$ and

$$\frac{dx}{dt} = U \cos \alpha \, e^{-ct}$$

With the initial condition $x = 0$ at $t = 0$, this equation gives

$$x = \frac{U \cos \alpha}{c} (1 - e^{-ct})$$

The second equation yields $y = \dot{y} = 0$ for all values of t. The third equation gives

$$\frac{d\dot{z}}{dt} = -c \left(\dot{z} + \frac{g}{c} \right)$$

$$\log_e \left(\dot{z} + \frac{g}{c} \right) = -ct + C_2$$

With $\dot{z} = U \sin \alpha$ at $t = 0$, we determine C_2 to get

$$\frac{dz}{dt} = U \sin \alpha \, e^{-ct} - \frac{g}{c} (1 - e^{-ct})$$

Integrating and using the condition $z = 0$ at $t = 0$, we have

$$z = \frac{U \sin \alpha}{c} (1 - e^{-ct}) - \frac{gt}{c} \left[1 - \frac{1}{ct} (1 - e^{-ct}) \right]$$

The problem is now solved. From these results, one can obtain other desired information. For example, the path $z(x)$ of the projectile can be obtained by eliminating t in $x(t)$ and $z(t)$. The maximum horizontal displacement is given as $x = (U \cos \alpha)/c$ as $t \to \infty$. The terminal velocity of fall is $\dot{z} = -g/c$ as $t \to \infty$.

Example 4–31. After the fuel has burned out, a rocket is found to have a speed U directed in a direction perpendicular to the line joining it and the earth, as shown in Fig. 4–59. The rocket is then at a distance a from the center of the earth. Assuming that the earth remains at the same location during the interval of interest, find the path of the rocket. Neglect air resistance, if any.

It is more convenient to use polar-cylindrical coordinates in this case. The only force to be considered is the gravitational pull of the earth, $F_\rho = -m\lambda/\rho^2$,

Fig. 4–59

where m is the mass of the rocket and λ is a constant. Substituting into Eqs. (4–60), we have

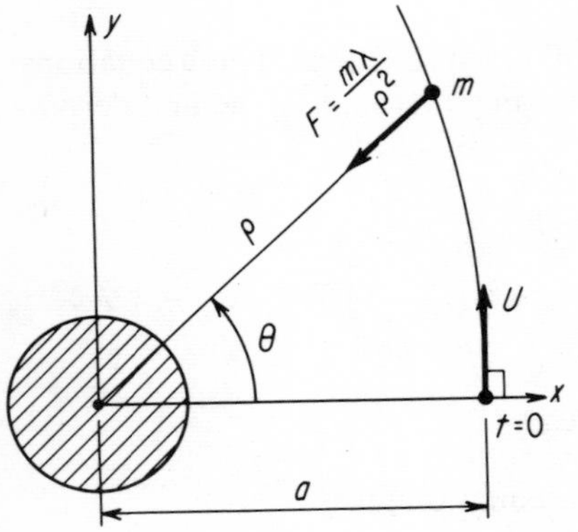

$$m(\ddot{\rho} - \rho\dot{\theta}^2) = -\frac{m\lambda}{\rho^2}$$

$$\frac{m}{\rho} \frac{d}{dt} (\rho^2 \dot{\theta}) = 0$$

$$m\ddot{z} = 0$$

We have here three equations with three unknown functions, namely $\rho(t)$, $\theta(t)$ and $z(t)$.

With the initial condition $z = 0$ and $\dot{z} = 0$ at $t = 0$, the third equation gives $z = 0$ for all values of t. This means that the motion remains in the plane containing the vector U and the line joining the earth and the rocket.

The second equation indicates that $\rho^2\dot{\theta}$ is constant. With the initial condition $\rho = a$ and $\dot{\theta} = U/a$ at $t = 0$, we have $\rho^2\dot{\theta} = aU$. (Since the area swept out by the radius vector per unit time is $\rho(\rho\dot{\theta})/2$, we have the well known Kepler's second law of planetary motion: the radius vector sweeps out equal areas in equal times.)

With $\theta = aU/\rho^2$, the first equation becomes

$$\ddot{\rho} = \frac{a^2 U^2}{\rho^3} - \frac{\lambda}{\rho^2}$$

This equation is similar to Eq. (4–56), which may be solved by first obtaining an equation of ρ and $\dot{\rho}$. Using

$$\frac{d\dot{\rho}}{d\rho} = \frac{d\dot{\rho}}{dt} \cdot \frac{dt}{d\rho} = \frac{\ddot{\rho}}{\dot{\rho}}$$

we have

$$\dot{\rho}\frac{d\dot{\rho}}{d\rho} = \frac{a^2 U^2}{\rho^3} - \frac{\lambda}{\rho^2}$$

and

$$\frac{1}{2}\dot{\rho}^2 = -\frac{a^2 U^2}{2\rho^2} + \frac{\lambda}{\rho} + C_1$$

With the initial condition $\rho = a$ and $\dot{\rho} = 0$ at $t = 0$, we determine C_1 to get

$$\left(\frac{d\rho}{dt}\right)^2 = -a^2 U^2 \left(\frac{1}{\rho^2} - \frac{1}{a^2}\right) + 2\lambda\left(\frac{1}{\rho} - \frac{1}{a}\right)$$

Integrating this, one can find the relationship between ρ and t, and from

$$\frac{d\theta}{dt} = \frac{aU}{\rho^2}$$

one can then find θ as a function of t.

To find the path $\rho(\theta)$ directly, we eliminate t in the last two equations:

$$\frac{d\rho}{d\theta} = \frac{\rho^2}{aU}\sqrt{2\lambda\left(\frac{1}{\rho} - \frac{1}{a}\right) - a^2 U^2\left(\frac{1}{\rho^2} - \frac{1}{a^2}\right)}$$

$$d\theta = \frac{d\rho}{\rho^2\sqrt{\dfrac{2\lambda}{a^2 U^2}\cdot\dfrac{1}{\rho} - \dfrac{1}{\rho^2} + \dfrac{1}{a^2} - \dfrac{2\lambda}{a^3 U^2}}}$$

To integrate the right-hand side, we try $u = A\left(\dfrac{1}{\rho} - B\right)$, where A and B are constants to be determined, because

$$d\cos^{-1} u = \frac{-du}{\sqrt{1 - u^2}} = \frac{d\rho}{\rho^2\sqrt{\dfrac{2B}{\rho} - \dfrac{1}{\rho^2} + \dfrac{1}{A^2} - B^2}}$$

By comparing the coefficients, we determine A and B to obtain

$$u = \left(\frac{1}{\rho} - \frac{\lambda}{a^2 U^2}\right)\Big/\left(\frac{1}{a} - \frac{\lambda}{a^2 U^2}\right)$$

Integrating and using the initial condition $\theta = 0$ and $\rho = a$ at $t = 0$,

$$\theta = \cos^{-1}\left[\left(\frac{1}{\rho} - \frac{\lambda}{a^2 U^2}\right)\Big/\left(\frac{1}{a} - \frac{\lambda}{a^2 U^2}\right)\right]$$

or

$$\frac{a}{\rho} = \frac{\lambda}{aU^2}\left[1+\left(\frac{aU^2}{\lambda}-1\right)\cos\theta\right]$$

The shape of the path depends on the value of the parameter aU^2/λ. If $aU^2/\lambda > 2$ (with relatively high speed), the path is a hyperbola. If $aU^2/\lambda = 2$, the path is a parabola. In both cases, the rocket will neither return to nor orbit around the earth. With $aU^2/\lambda < 2$, the path is an ellipse and takes the shape of a circle when $aU^2/\lambda = 1$. In cases with relatively low speeds, the path may pass through the earth's atmosphere, which offers considerable resistance (neglected in this analysis), or may actually meet the earth. Paths for various values of U, other things being constant, are shown in Fig. 4–60.

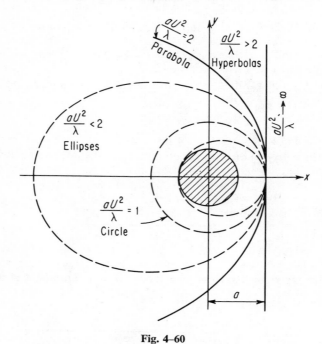

Fig. 4–60

Problems

4–57. A particle of mass m has an initial speed U in a linear motion on a smooth horizontal floor. At this speed, it is found that the air resistance to motion is R. Find the distance traveled before it comes to a stop, (a) by assuming that air resistance is proportional to the first power of the instantaneous speed, and (b) by assuming that it is proportional to the second power of the speed.

Ans. mU^2/R; ∞

4–58. A plane is flying horizontally at an elevation h above ground at a speed U. It is flying toward a target on the ground. How far from the target should a bomb be dropped? Neglect air resistance.   *Ans.* $U\sqrt{2h/g}$

4–59. A particle is projected from a horizontal ground with velocity U at an angle α with the horizontal. Find the maximum height it will reach and the time taken to reach it. Also find the equation of the path and its range.

Ans. Range $= U^2 \sin 2\alpha/g$

4–60. A particle is projected from an inclined plane which makes an angle β with the horizontal. Given the initial speed U, show that the longest range up the plane is obtained by shooting at an angle $[(\pi/2)-\beta]/2$ with the vertical.

4–61. A particle is projected vertically upward from the earth and travels with negligible resistance. Assuming that the earth remains at the same location, show that the initial speed required to send the particle away from the earth is $\sqrt{2gR}$, where g is the gravitational acceleration on the surface of the earth, and R is the radius of the earth. (Hint: it is required that the speed be zero only at infinite time and infinite distance away.)

4–62. A particle is projected upward with an initial speed U. Its weight is mg and the air resistance is cv^2. Find the maximum height it will reach. Also find its speed when it falls back to its starting point.

$$\text{Ans.} \quad \frac{1}{2}\frac{m}{c}\log_e\left(1+\frac{cU^2}{mg}\right), \quad U\Big/\sqrt{1+\frac{cU^2}{mg}}$$

4–63. A conical pendulum consists of a particle m and a string of negligible mass which swings (with one end fixed) at a constant angular speed at an angle α with the vertical. Verify that this motion satisfies the equations of motion, and find the tension in the string and its angular speed.

Ans. $mg/\cos\alpha$, $\sqrt{g/L}$

4–64. A particle resting on the top of a fixed frictionless circular cylinder (or sphere) is falling off under gravity. Using the equations of motion, find the angle that the radius vector has swept out when it falls off the cylinder. (Hint: the reaction between the particle and the sphere vanishes when the two separate.)

Ans. $\cos^{-1}(2/3)$

4–12. Homogeneous linear equations with constant coefficients

The general form of a linear differential equation with constant coefficients is

$$a_0\frac{d^ny}{dx^n}+a_1\frac{d^{n-1}y}{dx^{n-1}}+ \ldots +a_{n-1}\frac{dy}{dx}+a_ny = f(x) \tag{4–61}$$

where $a_0, a_1 \ldots a_n$ are constants. According to the theorem stated in Article 4–9, its general solution is

$$y(x) = c_1y_1(x)+c_2y_2(x)+ \ldots +c_ny_n(x)+ Y(x)$$

where $Y(x)$ is the particular integral, and $y_1(x), \ldots, y_n(x)$ are linearly independent solutions of the associated homogeneous equation

$$a_0 \frac{d^n y}{dx^n} + a_1 \frac{d^{n-1} y}{dx^{n-1}} + \ldots + a_{n-1} \frac{dy}{dx} + a_n y = 0 \qquad (4\text{--}62)$$

In this article, we shall proceed to find the n linearly independent solutions of
this homogeneous equation. The result is interesting, not only because it is a
part of the general solution of the nonhomogeneous Eq. (4–61), but also
because many engineering problems are described by homogeneous equations.

By virtue of the uniqueness theorem, we can obtain our solutions by trials.
It has been found that $y = e^{mx}$ (m being a constant to be determined) is a
solution of Eq. (4–62). Substituting $dy/dx = me^{mx}, \ldots d^n y/dx^n = m^n e^{mx}$ into
Eq. (4–62), we have the following equation, from which we can determine the
value of m:

$$e^{mx} (a_0 m^n + a_1 m^{n-1} + \ldots + a_{n-1} m + a_n) = 0$$

If $e^{mx} = 0$, we have the correct but trivial particular solution $y = 0$. Thus, for a
nontrivial and general solution, the value of m must be such that

$$a_0 m^n + a_1 m^{n-1} + \ldots + a_{n-1} m + a_n = 0 \qquad (4\text{--}63)$$

This is called the *characteristic* or *auxiliary equation* of Eq. (4–62). There are
n solutions for m from this equation. Let them be denoted by $m_1, m_2, \ldots, m_n$.
There are two possibilities:

(a) If these solutions for m are all distinct, we have obtained n linearly
independent solutions. The general solution of the homogeneous equation is
then

$$y(x) = c_1 e^{m_1 x} + c_2 e^{m_2 x} + \ldots + c_n e^{m_n x} \qquad (4\text{--}64)$$

For example, consider the equation

$$\frac{d^2 y}{dx^2} - 3 \frac{dy}{dx} + 2y = 0$$

The characteristic equation is $m^2 - 3m + 2 = 0$, giving $m = 1$ and 2. Thus, the
general solution is

$$y = c_1 e^x + c_2 e^{2x}$$

(b) If some of the solutions for m are equal, we have not obtained n linearly
independent solutions. For example, consider the equation

$$\frac{d^2 y}{dx^2} - 4 \frac{dy}{dx} + 4y = 0$$

The characteristic equation is $m^2 - 4m + 4 = 0$, giving $m = 2$ and 2. The solution

$$y = c_1 e^{2x} + c_2 e^{2x} = (c_1 + c_2) e^{2x} = c e^{2x}$$

is not a general solution, since it does not include n (two) arbitrary constants.
It has been found that, if some solutions of the characteristic equation are
equal, say $m_1 = m_2 = \ldots = m_k$, we have k linearly independent solutions in

terms of m_1, in the form of $e^{m_1 x}$, $xe^{m_1 x}$, $x^2 e^{m_1 x}$, ... $x^{k-1} e^{m_1 x}$. The general solution is

$$y(x) = e^{m_1 x} (c_1 + c_2 x + c_3 x^2 + \ldots + c_k x^{k-1}) + c_{k+1} e^{m_{k+1} x} + \ldots + c_n e^{m_n x}$$

(4–65)

For example, in the previous case of

$$\frac{d^2 y}{dx^2} - 4 \frac{dy}{dx} + 4y = 0$$

we have $m_1 = m_2 = 2$. The general solution, according to Eq. (4–65) is

$$y = e^{2x} (c_0 + c_2 x)$$

That this is the general solution can be verified by substitution, and can also be derived as follows. The differential equation can be written as

$$\frac{d}{dx} \left(\frac{dy}{dx} - 2y \right) - 2 \left(\frac{dy}{dx} - 2y \right) = 0$$

One solution is obtained for the case with the value in the parentheses equal to zero, i.e.,

$$\frac{dy}{dx} - 2y = 0$$

The solution is $y = c_1 e^{2x}$. A second solution is obtained for the case

$$\left(\frac{dy}{dx} - 2y \right) = u \neq 0$$

but

$$\frac{du}{dx} - 2u = 0$$

This gives $u = c_2 e^{2x}$. With

$$\frac{dy}{dx} - 2y = u = c_2 e^{2x}$$

we obtain the second solution

$$y = c_2 x e^{2x} + c_1 e^{2x}$$

which includes the first solution. Thus, this is the general solution. By an entirely similar argument, Eq. (4–65) for the general case can be established. (The student can now study Examples 4–32 and 4–33, and solve Problems 4–65 and 4–66.)

In solving the characteristic equation for m, complex values are sometimes obtained. For example, for the differential equation

$$\frac{d^3 y}{dx^3} - 7 \frac{d^2 y}{dx^2} + 19 \frac{dy}{dx} - 13 = 0$$

the characteristic equation can be factorized as

$$(m-1)(m^2 - 6m + 13) = 0$$

The three solutions of m are 1 and $3 \pm 2i$, where $i \equiv \sqrt{-1}$. The solutions of the form $e^{(a\pm ib)x}$ can be reduced to a more familiar form as follows. Consider that the series in Eq. (1–15) for e^x is valid for imaginary values, as well as real ones. We have

$$e^{ix} = 1 + ix + \frac{(ix)^2}{2!} + \frac{(ix)^3}{3!} + \cdots$$

By definition, $i^2 = -1$, $i^3 = i^2 i = -i$, etc.

$$e^{ix} = \left(1 - \frac{x^2}{2!} + \frac{x^4}{4!} - \cdots\right) + i\left(x - \frac{x^3}{3!} + \frac{x^5}{5!} - \cdots\right)$$

The series in the parentheses are those of cos x and sin x in Eqs. (1–16) and (1–14). Hence, we have the useful relations known as the *Euler formulas*:

$$\left.\begin{array}{l} e^{ix} = \cos x + i \sin x \\ e^{-ix} = \cos x - i \sin x \end{array}\right\} \qquad (4\text{–}66)$$

Thus, when $m = a \pm ib$, we have a solution

$$\begin{aligned} c_1 e^{(a+ib)x} + c_2 e^{(a-ib)x} &= e^{ax}(c_1 e^{ibx} + c_2 e^{-ibx}) \\ &= e^{ax}[(c_1+c_2)\cos bx + i(c_1-c_2)\sin bx] \\ &= e^{ax}(A \cos bx + B \sin bx) \end{aligned}$$

where A and B are two new arbitrary constants. The quantity in the parentheses can be further reduced to another familiar form:

$$A \cos bx + B \sin bx = C \cos(bx - \psi) \quad \text{or} \quad C \sin(bx + \phi) \qquad (4\text{–}67)$$

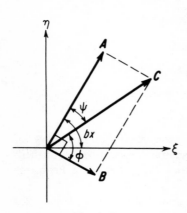

Fig. 4–61

where $C = \sqrt{A^2 + B^2}$, $\psi = \tan^{-1}(B/A)$ and $\phi = \tan^{-1}(A/B)$.

(The student can verify this equation by expanding the right-hand side.) In each of these forms, the solution still contains two arbitrary constants, C and ψ or ϕ. This result is sometimes presented with the aid of vectors. With the vectors A and B at 90 degrees apart, as shown in Fig. 4–61, the sum $(A \cos bx + B \sin bx)$ is the sum of the ξ components of these vectors. According to Eq. (2–13), this sum is equal to the ξ component of the sum of A and B, i.e., the vector C. The angle ψ is the phase difference between A and C.

It is interesting to note the similarity between the trigonometric functions and the hyperbolic functions. From the definition of sinh x and cosh x in Eq. (4–37), we have

$$\left.\begin{array}{l} e^x = \cosh x + \sinh x \\ e^{-x} = \cosh x - \sinh x \end{array}\right\} \qquad (4\text{–}68)$$

Whereas

$$c_1 e^{ibx} + c_2 e^{-ibx} = A \cos bx + B \sin bx \tag{4-69}$$

we can also write

$$c_1 e^{bx} + c_2 e^{-bx} = A \cosh bx + B \sinh bx \tag{4-70}$$

Whereas $\sinh x = (e^x - e^{-x})/2$ and $\cosh x = (e^x + e^{-x})/2$, we have from Eqs. (4–66)

$$\left. \begin{aligned} \sin x &= \frac{e^{ix} - e^{-ix}}{2i} \\ \cos x &= \frac{e^{ix} + e^{-ix}}{2} \end{aligned} \right\} \tag{4-71}$$

Example 4–32. An infinitely long string under initial tension is resting against an elastic foundation. When the string is depressed, the reaction from the foundation is assumed to be proportional to the local deformation y, as shown in Fig. 4–62, i.e., ky per unit distance. (This idealized foundation

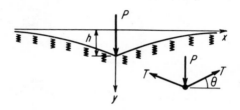

Fig. 4–62

behaves like a set of individual springs.) Find the force P required for the small depression h. (For a small depression, dy/dx of the curve of the string may be considered to be small compared with unity.)

For a small depression, $dy/dx \ll 1$ and the reaction ky may be considered to be acting vertically upward. For the equilibrium of each element of the string, we have from Eq. (4–54) with y axis point downward

$$\frac{d^2y}{dx^2} = \frac{f}{H} = \frac{ky}{T}$$

where $f = ky$ (for $x \neq 0$) and $H \doteq T$ (for small dy/dx). Thus

$$T \frac{d^2y}{dx^2} - ky = 0$$

The characteristic equation of this homogeneous linear equation, according to Eq. (4–63) is

$$Tm^2 - k = 0$$

giving two distinct values of m: $\pm \sqrt{k/T}$. Thus, the general solution is (see Eq. (4–64))

$$y = c_1 e^{\sqrt{k/T}\,x} + c_2 e^{-\sqrt{k/T}\,x}$$

This solution is to be used separately for $x>0$ and $x<0$, because it is not applicable at $x=0$. For $x>0$, we have the known conditions $y\to0$ as $x\to\infty$, and $y\to h$ as $x\to0$. The first condition requires $c_1=0$. The second condition gives $c_2=h$. Thus, for $x>0$,

$$y = he^{-\sqrt{k/T}\,x} \quad \text{and} \quad \frac{dy}{dx} = -\sqrt{\frac{k}{T}}he^{-\sqrt{k/T}\,x}$$

The force P is found by considering the equilibrium of the particle under it. For a small depression,

$$P = 2T \sin \theta = 2T \tan \theta = -2T \left(\frac{dy}{dx}\right)_0$$

We have, as $x\to0$, $(dy/dx)_0 = -h\sqrt{k/T}$. Thus, $P=2h\sqrt{kT}$.

Example 4–33. A bead is sliding on a smooth straight wire which revolves at a constant angular speed ω, as shown in Fig. 4–63. Given $\dot{z}=0$ and $z=h$ at $t=0$, find the motion of the bead.

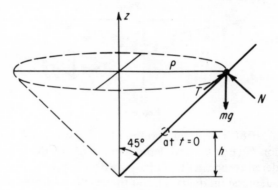

Fig. 4–63

It is more convenient to use polar-cylindrical coordinates in this problem. The forces acting on the bead include its weight mg and the (varying) reaction from the wire. Since the wire is assumed to be smooth, the reaction must be normal to the wire. Let T and N be the components of the reaction, with T in the θ direction, as shown in Fig. 4–63. Thus $\sum F_\rho = -N/\sqrt{2}$, $\sum F_\theta = T$, and $\sum F_z = -mg+(N/\sqrt{2})$. Substituting into Eqs. (4–60),

$$m(\ddot{\rho} - \rho\dot{\theta}^2) = \frac{-N}{\sqrt{2}}$$

$$\frac{m}{\rho} \frac{d}{dt}(\rho^2\dot{\theta}) = T$$

$$m\ddot{z} = -mg + \frac{N}{\sqrt{2}}$$

Since it is given that $\dot{\theta} = \omega$, we have here three equations with four unknown functions, namely, ρ, z, T and N. An additional equation is furnished by the fact that, in this case, $\rho = z$ at all values of t.

Changing ρ to z in the first equation, we have

$$m(\ddot{z} - z\omega^2) = -\frac{N}{\sqrt{2}}$$

Eliminating N from this equation and the third equation, we have

$$\ddot{z} - \frac{\omega^2}{2} z = -\frac{g}{2}$$

The constant on the right-hand side can be removed by changing the dependent variable to

$$s = z - \frac{g}{\omega^2}$$

The resultant equation is

$$\ddot{s} - \frac{\omega^2}{2} s = 0$$

The characteristic equation $m^2 - (\omega^2/2) = 0$ gives $m = \pm \omega/\sqrt{2}$. Thus

$$z - \frac{g}{\omega^2} = s = A e^{\omega t/\sqrt{2}} + B e^{-\omega t/\sqrt{2}}$$

and

$$\dot{z} = \frac{\omega}{\sqrt{2}} A e^{\omega t/\sqrt{2}} - \frac{\omega}{\sqrt{2}} B e^{-\omega t/\sqrt{2}}$$

With the initial conditions $z = h$ and $\dot{z} = 0$ at $t = 0$, we have

$$z - \frac{g}{\omega^2} = \frac{1}{2}\left(h - \frac{g}{\omega^2}\right)(e^{\omega t/\sqrt{2}} + e^{-\omega t/\sqrt{2}}) = \left(h - \frac{g}{\omega^2}\right) \cosh \frac{\omega t}{\sqrt{2}}$$

As $\cosh (\omega t/\sqrt{2})$ increases indefinitely with t (>0), the bead will rise if $h > g/\omega^2$, and will drop if $h < g/\omega^2$. For the particular case with the bead placed at $h = g/\omega^2$, we have mathematically $z = h$ as a solution. This is a position of equilibrium satisfying the three equations of motion. However, this equilibrium is unstable; i.e., the bead will move away from this position when it is disturbed, even very slightly.

Example 4–34. Undamped free linear vibrations: a mass M is hanging on a spring of negligible mass, as shown in Fig. 4–64. The spring constant is k. The mass M is pulled down through distance x_0 from its position of equilibrium and then sent off with speed $\dot{x}_0$. Find the motion of M.

Let x be the displacement of M from its position of equilibrium. At the position of equilibrium, the spring is stretched by the weight through a distance Mg/k, as shown in Fig. 4–64. At any other position x, the spring is elongated by the amount $x+(Mg/k)$, and the spring force on M is $-i k$ $[x+(Mg/k)]$ or $-i(kx+Mg)$. The weight of M is iMg. Thus, the net force on M from the spring and gravity is $-ikx$. The negative sign indicates a restoring force which acts toward the position of equilibrium. Substituting into the equation of motion, Eq. (4–59),

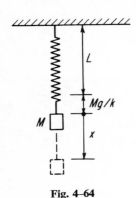

Fig. 4–64

$$M\ddot{x} = -kx$$

or

$$\ddot{x}+p^2x = 0 \tag{4–72}$$

where $p=\sqrt{k/M}$. The characteristic equation of this linear equation is

$$m^2+p^2 = 0$$

giving $m = \pm\, ip$. The general solution is therefore

$$x = c_1 e^{ipt}+c_2 e^{-ipt}$$

According to Eq. (4–69),

$$x = A\cos pt + B\sin pt \tag{4–73}$$

The constants A and B are to be determined from the initial conditions: $x=x_0$ and $\dot{x}=\dot{x}_0$ at $t=0$. These conditions give $A=x_0$ and $B=\dot{x}_0/p$. According to Eq. (4–67), this result can also be written as

$$x = \sqrt{x_0^2+\left(\frac{\dot{x}_0}{p}\right)^2}\,\cos(pt-\psi) = \sqrt{x_0^2+\left(\frac{\dot{x}_0}{p}\right)^2}\,\sin(pt+\phi)$$

where

$$\psi = \tan^{-1}(\dot{x}_0/x_0 p) \quad\text{and}\quad \phi = \tan^{-1}(x_0 p/\dot{x}_0)$$

This is a simple harmonic motion with an amplitude $\sqrt{x_0^2+(\dot{x}_0/p)^2}$ and a

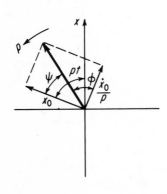

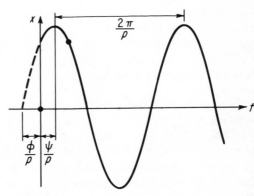

Fig. 4–65

period $2\pi/p$. The value x can be represented as the x component of the fictitious vector with a magnitude $\sqrt{x_0^2+(\dot{x}_0/p)^2}$, as shown in Fig. 4–65. (Compare with Fig. 4–61.) This vector rotates at an angular speed of p radians per unit time. For this reason, the quantity p is called the *circular frequency*, while the *frequency* of the oscillation in cycles per unit time is $p/2\pi$, which is the reciprocal of the *period*. The *phase angles* ψ and ϕ are indicated in Fig. 4–65.

This result indicates a perpetual motion which is not realistic. The reason is that we have neglected damping forces, such as air friction and internal friction in the spring. However, when damping effect is small, this solution describes the motion adequately for some time. To study the decay of the motion, damping effect must be included (see the following example).

Example 4–35. Damped free linear vibrations: in Fig. 4–66 is shown a mass M, a spring of negligible mass, and a dashpot which offers a resistance to motion proportional to the speed. Find the motion of mass M with initial speed $\dot{x}_0$ and initial displacement x_0 from the position of equilibrium.

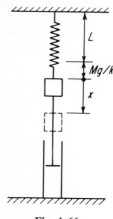

Let $x(t)$ be the displacement of M from the position of equilibrium. At any instant, the forces acting on M are: $-kx$ from gravity and the spring (see the previous example), and a damping force equal to $-c\dot{x}$, where c is the coefficient of damping and the negative sign indicates that this force is directed against the velocity. Thus, the equation of motion is

$$M\ddot{x} = -kx - c\dot{x}$$

or

$$\ddot{x} + 2n\dot{x} + p^2 x = 0 \qquad (4\text{–}74)$$

where $n = c/2M$ and $p = \sqrt{k/M}$. The characteristic equation is

$$m^2 + 2nm + p^2 = 0$$

Fig. 4–66   which gives $m = -n \pm \sqrt{n^2 - p^2}$. There are three possibilities according to the relative values of n and p.

(a) Light damping with $n^2 < p^2$. Let $q = +\sqrt{p^2 - n^2}$, which is a positive real value. Then the solutions of the characteristic equation are $m = -n \pm iq$. According to Eqs. (4–69) and (4–67), the general solution is

$$x = C_1 e^{(-n+iq)t} + C_2 e^{(-n-iq)t} = e^{-nt}(A \cos qt + B \sin qt)$$
$$= e^{-nt} C \cos(qt - \psi) \qquad (4\text{–}75)$$

The arbitrary constants are found from the initial conditions to be $A = x_0$ and $B = (\dot{x}_0 + nx_0)/q$. C and ψ can be obtained from A and B according to Eq. (4–67). This motion is oscillatory with decreasing amplitude $e^{-nt}C$, as shown in Fig. 4–67. The maximum and minimum values of x (shown as dots in Fig. 4–67) occur when $\dot{x}=0$. Since

$$\dot{x} = -Ce^{-nt}\,[q\sin(qt-\psi)+n\cos(qt-\psi)]$$

the mass M is at its extreme positions when

$$qt-\psi = \tan^{-1}\left(\frac{-n}{q}\right) = r\pi - \tan^{-1}\left(\frac{n}{q}\right) \qquad (r = 1, 2, \ldots)$$

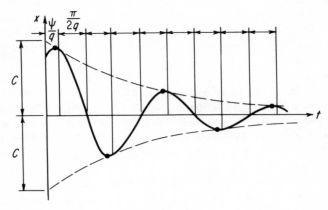

Fig. 4–67

(b) Heavy damping with $n^2 > p^2$. The solutions of the characteristic equation are then $m = -(n+\sqrt{n^2-p^2})$ and $-(n-\sqrt{n^2-p^2})$. Both of these values are negative. The general solution is

$$x = C_1 \exp[-(n+\sqrt{n^2-p^2})t] + C_2 \exp[-(n-\sqrt{n^2-p^2})t] \quad (4\text{–}76)$$

The constants C_1 and C_2 can be determined from the initial conditions. The solution consists of two exponential decay functions. Depending on the initial values of x_0 and $\dot{x}_0$, the graph of the solution may have different forms. Several possible solutions are shown in Fig. 4–68.

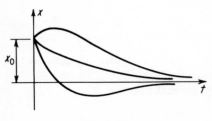

Fig. 4–68

(c) Critical damping with $n^2 = p^2$. In this case, both values of m are equal to $-n$. According to Eq. (4–65), the general solution is

$$x = e^{-nt}(c_1 + c_2 t) \quad (4\text{–}77)$$

The constants are found from the initial conditions to be $c_1 = x_0$ and $c_2 = \dot{x}_0 + nx_0$. This case lies between the two previous cases. Since this motion has $x = 0$ at $t = \infty$ and, at most, at one other value of t (if c_1 and c_2 are opposite in sign), the graph of this motion is similar to one of those shown in Fig. 4-68. This motion is usually called a *dead beat*.

Problems

4-64. Find the general solution of each of the following equations:

(a) $\dfrac{d^3y}{dx^3} - \dfrac{d^2y}{dx^2} - 6\dfrac{dy}{dx} = 0$

(d) $\dfrac{d^4y}{dx^4} - 4\dfrac{d^3y}{dx^3} + 14\dfrac{d^2y}{dx^2} - 20\dfrac{dy}{dx} + 25 = 0$

(b) $\dddot{x} - 3\ddot{x} + 3\dot{x} - x = 0$

(Hint: two of the solutions of the characteristic equation are $1 \pm 2i$.)

(c) $\dfrac{d^2x}{dy^2} - 4\dfrac{dx}{dy} + 5x = 0$

4-65. An arch with a rise r and a span $2a$ is filled with earth to give a level top at a distance h above the springing line, as shown in Fig. 4-45. Assuming that the load on each element of the arch is directly proportional to the depth of earth $(h - y)$ above it, find the shape of the arch such that the stresses under this dead load act along the arch. (Hint: change the variable to $u = h - y$ when necessary.)

Ans. $y = h - (h - r)\cosh\left(\dfrac{x}{a}\cosh^{-1}\dfrac{h}{h-r}\right)$

4-66. A slender uniform rod of thermal conductivity k and cross-sectional area A is connected at one end to a furnace where the temperature T_1 is constant (see Fig. 4-69). The room temperature surrounding the rod is T_0 ($< T_1$). Assuming that the rate of heat loss from the rod to the air is equal to $\lambda(T - T_0)$ per unit length, λ being a constant, find the temperature distribution $T(x)$ in the rod. The rod is so slender that the flow of heat can be considered to be one-dimensional, and the loss of heat from the end surface is negligible.

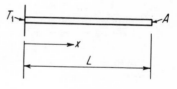

Fig. 4-69

Ans. $\dfrac{T - T_0}{T_1 - T_0} = \cosh nx - \tanh nL \cdot \sinh nx, \quad n = \sqrt{\dfrac{\lambda}{kA}}$

4-67. For a body immersed in a liquid, the resultant hydrostatic pressure acts upward and is equal to the weight of liquid displaced (Archimedes' principle). A homogeneous right cylinder of length L and specific gravity σ is floating in water with its axis vertical. This cylinder is pressed down until its top is level with the water surface, and then released. Assuming that the fluid pressure can be approximated by the hydrostatic pressure, and neglecting fluid resistance, find the period and the amplitude of the resultant oscillations.

Ans. Period $= 2\pi\sqrt{\sigma L/g}$

4-68. A particle on a smooth floor weighs 15 lb, and is attached to two weightless springs, as shown in Fig. 4-70. Both springs are 2 ft long, unstretched. The spring constant of spring A is 10 lb per ft and spring B 20 lb per ft. Find the position of equilibrium. If the particle is kicked off along the springs with an initial speed of 4 ft per sec, find the frequency and the amplitude of the resultant oscillations.   *Ans.* 1.28 cps, 0.50 ft

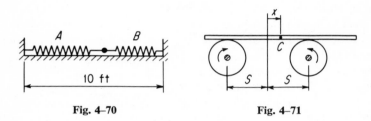

Fig. 4-70   Fig. 4-71

4-69. A uniform bar is put on top of two cylinders rotating in opposite directions about two fixed axes, as shown in Fig. 4-71. The coefficient of kinetic friction between the bar and cylinders is μ. Find the circular frequency of the oscillations when the bar is disturbed from its position of equilibrium. Also show that, if the directions of rotation of the cylinders are reversed, the bar will not stay on the cylinders if disturbed. (Hint: $F = ma$ describes the motion of the center of gravity of a body.)   *Ans.* $\sqrt{\mu g/s}$

4-70. One end of a spring of constant k is fixed at the origin. A moving particle of mass M is attached on the other end. At a certain instant, the particle passes the point $(a, 0, 0)$ with a speed U in the y direction. Find the path of the particle. The mass of the spring is negligible compared with that of the particle. The weight of the particle is negligible compared with the tension in the spring. The natural length of the spring is negligible compared with its stretched length, so that the spring tension can be assumed to be proportional to its stretched length.   *Ans.* $\dfrac{x^2}{a^2} + \dfrac{ky^2}{U^2 M} = 1$

4-71. A weighing platform weighs 100 lb and is supported by springs with (combined) spring constant $k = 10,000$ lb/ft. There is damping in the system with damping coefficient $C = 1000$ lb-sec/ft. A package of 1000 lb is dropped on the platform so that the two move together upon contact at a speed of 2 ft/sec. Show that the resultant motion is oscillatory. Find the maximum displacement of the platform. What is the maximum weight that can be dropped on this platform without creating oscillatory motion?   *Ans.* 0.1077 ft, 705 lb

4-13. Nonhomogeneous linear equations with constant coefficients

As stated in previous articles, the general solution of a nonhomogeneous linear equation

$$a_0 \frac{d^n y}{dx^n} + a_1 \frac{d^{n-1} y}{dx^{n-1}} + \ \ldots \ + a_{n-1} \frac{dy}{dx} + a_n y = f(x)$$

consists of two parts, namely, the complementary function which is the general solution of the associated homogeneous equation, and a particular integral $Y(x)$:

$$y = c_1 y_1(x) + c_2 y_2(x) + \ldots + c_n y_n(x) + Y(x)$$

In the case of linear equations with constant coefficients, the solution of the associated homogeneous equation has been discussed in the previous article. In this article, methods of finding a particular integral for these equations are presented.

There are an infinite number of possible particular integrals for a differential equation. Since there are n arbitrary constants in the complementary function, any $Y(x)$ that satisfies the differential equation can be used to form the general equation. Thus, we can sometimes obtain a particular integral by inspection; e.g., if $f(x) = $ constant K, we have $Y = K/a_n$. Also, when we obtain alternative solutions for $Y(x)$, we can choose the simplest one.

The following are the standard methods of obtaining particular integrals for linear equations with constant coefficients. Other methods applicable also to equations with variable coefficients are presented in Art. 4–18.

(1) Method of undetermined coefficients:

This method is applicable when each term in $f(x)$ has a finite number of linearly independent derivatives, e.g., a constant, x^α (α being a positive integer), $\sin \beta x$, $\cos \beta x$, $\sinh \beta x$, $\cosh \beta x$, and $e^{\beta x}$ (β being a constant). This is the simplest method, and should be used when applicable.

Take the equation

$$\frac{d^2 y}{dx^2} - 5 \frac{dy}{dx} + 6y = 52 \sin 2x$$

For a term in $Y(x)$, we may try $\alpha \sin 2x$, where α is a constant to be determined. Substituting into the left side of the equation, we have from the derivatives terms of $\cos 2x$ which are not present on the right side of the equation. This suggests that we should try

$$Y(x) = \alpha \sin 2x + \beta \cos 2x$$

Substituting this trial solution into the equation with

$$6Y = 6 \,(\alpha \sin 2x + \beta \cos 2x)$$

$$-5 \frac{dY}{dx} = -5 \,(2\alpha \cos 2x - 2\beta \sin 2x)$$

$$\frac{d^2 Y}{dx^2} = -4\alpha \sin 2x - 4\beta \cos 2x$$

we have

$$(2\alpha + 10\beta) \sin 2x + (2\beta - 10\alpha) \cos 2x = 52 \sin 2x$$

i.e., $2\alpha + 10\beta = 52$ and $2\beta - 10\alpha = 0$. Therefore, $\alpha = 1$ and $\beta = 5$. Thus, a particular solution is $Y(x) = \sin 2x + 5 \cos 2x$. Since the complementary function is $c_1 e^{2x} + c_2 e^{3x}$, the general solution of the nonhomogeneous equation is

$$y = c_1 e^{2x} + c_2 e^{3x} + \sin 2x + 5 \cos 2x$$

Note that the coefficients α and β in $Y(x)$ have specific values, and must not be confused with the arbitrary constants in the general solution.

Take another equation

$$\frac{d^2y}{dx^2} + 4y = 8 \sin 2x$$

The complementary function is $c_1 \sin 2x + c_2 \cos 2x$. In this case, it is useless to try $(\alpha \sin 2x + \beta \cos 2x)$ for $Y(x)$, because it is nothing but a particular case of the complementary function, and will not satisfy the nonhomogeneous equation. However, we can try

$$Y(x) = \alpha x \sin 2x + \beta x \cos 2x$$

which derivatives contain terms of $\sin 2x$. Substituting into the equation with

$$4Y = 4 (\alpha x \sin 2x + \beta x \cos 2x)$$
$$\frac{d^2 Y}{dx^2} = -4 (\alpha x \sin 2x + \beta x \cos 2x) - 4\beta \sin 2x + 4\alpha \cos 2x$$

we find that $\alpha = 0$ and $\beta = -2$. Thus, the general solution is

$$y = c_1 \sin 2x + c_2 \cos 2x - 2x \cos 2x$$

Note that the terms $x \sin 2x$ and $x \cos 2x$ in $4Y$ and $d^2 Y/dx^2$ cancel out. This is not just a happy coincidence. Take any linear equation, say

$$a_0 \frac{d^2y}{dx^2} + a_1 \frac{dy}{dx} + a_2 y = f(x)$$

Let u be a term in $f(x)$ and also a term in the complementary function (for example, $\sin 2x$ in the example above). If we use xu as a term in $Y(x)$, we have $x(du/dx) + u$ in dy/dx, and $x(d^2u/dx^2) + 2(du/dx)$ in d^2y/dx^2. Upon substituting into the differential equation, we have on the left side

$$x \left(a_0 \frac{d^2u}{dx^2} + a_1 \frac{du}{dx} + a_2 u \right) + 2a_0 \frac{du}{dx} + a_1 u$$

Thus, we have the desired term u and its derivative only since, with u being a solution of the associated homogeneous equation, the value in the parentheses is zero.

The method of undetermined coefficients may be summarized as follows. Use for a trial solution a linear combination of all the terms in $f(x)$ and their derivatives. (This method is not applicable when these terms have an infinite number of linearly independent derivatives, e.g., $1/x$ and $\tan x$.) If any one of the terms in this trial solution, say u, is already included in the complementary function, replace it with xu. If there is already a term xu in the trial solution, replace it with x^2u. Substitute this modified trial solution in the equation to determine the coefficients.

For example, take the equation

$$\frac{d^3y}{dx^3} - 4\frac{d^2y}{dx^2} + 4\frac{dy}{dx} = 12\left(e^{2x} + x^2\right)$$

The complementary function is $C_1 + C_2 e^{2x} + C_3 xe^{2x}$. For the trial solution, we start with the terms in $f(x)$, e^{2x} and x^2, and their derivatives, x and a constant. However, e^{2x} is a term of the complementary function and, therefore, should be replaced by xe^{2x}. This in turn is a term of the complementary function, and should be replaced by x^2e^{2x}. The constant in the trial solution is included in the constant C_1 in the complementary function. Therefore, instead of a constant, x and x^2, we use x, x^2 and x^3. Thus, the trial solution should be

$$Y(x) = \alpha x^3 + \beta x^2 + \gamma x + \delta x^2 e^{2x}$$

where α, β, γ, and δ are constants to be determined. Substituting into the differential equation, we have

$$12\alpha x^2 + (8\beta - 24\alpha)x + (4\gamma - 8\beta + 6\alpha) + 4\delta e^{2x} = 12\left(e^{2x} + x^2\right)$$

With $12\alpha = 12$, $8\beta - 24\alpha = 0$, $4\gamma - 8\beta + 6\alpha = 0$, and $4\delta = 12$, we have $\alpha = 1$, $\beta = 3$, $\gamma = \frac{9}{2}$, and $\delta = 3$. Thus, the general solution is

$$y = C_1 + C_2 e^{2x} + C_3 xe^{2x} + x^3 + 3x^2 + \tfrac{9}{2}x + 3x^2 e^{2x}$$

Many equations in engineering problems can be solved by this method. The student can now study the examples of this article and solve Problems 4–72 to 4–80.

(2) Method of successive integration:

If m_1, m_2, ... m_n are the roots of a characteristic equation

$$a_0 m^n + a_1 m^{n-1} + \ldots + a_n = 0$$

this equation can be written as

$$(m - m_1)(m - m_2) \ldots (m - m_n) = 0$$

Now let an operator be defined as

$$\left(\frac{d}{dx} - \lambda\right)y \equiv \frac{dy}{dx} - \lambda y \tag{4–78}$$

where λ is a constant. It can be verified that, the nth order linear differential equation with constant coefficients can be rewritten symbolically as

$$\left(\frac{d}{dx} - m_1\right)\left\{\left(\frac{d}{dx} - m_2\right)\left[\ldots \left(\frac{d}{dx} - m_n\right)y\right]\right\} = f(x)$$

or simply

$$\left(\frac{d}{dx} - m_1\right)\left(\frac{d}{dx} - m_2\right) \ldots \left(\frac{d}{dx} - m_n\right)y = f(x) \tag{4–79}$$

For example, for the equation

$$\frac{d^2y}{dx^2} + y = e^x$$

the characteristic equation gives $m_1 = i$ and $m_2 = -i$. We have

$$\left(\frac{d}{dx} - i\right)\left(\frac{d}{dx} + i\right) y = \frac{d}{dx}\left(\frac{dy}{dx} + iy\right) - i\left(\frac{dy}{dx} + iy\right) = \frac{d^2y}{dx^2} + y = e^x$$

As Eq. (4–79) indicates a succession of operations, the solution of the equation can be obtained by successive integration. Since the complementary function is already known, we use Eq. (4–79) to obtain a particular integral. Calling

$$u_1 = \left(\frac{d}{dx} - m_2\right) \cdots \left(\frac{d}{dx} - m_n\right) Y$$

we have

$$\left(\frac{d}{dx} - m_1\right) u_1 = f(x)$$

which is a linear equation of the first order. According to Eq. (4–13), its solution is

$$u_1 = e^{m_1 x} \int e^{-m_1 x} f(x)\, dx + C e^{m_1 x}$$

where the constant of integration C can be chosen to be zero for simplicity. Thus

$$\left(\frac{d}{dx} - m_2\right)\left(\frac{d}{dx} - m_3\right) \cdots \left(\frac{d}{dx} - m_n\right) Y = e^{m_1 x} \int e^{-m_1 x} f(x)\, dx$$

In a similar manner, call

$$u_2 = \left(\frac{d}{dx} - m_3\right) \cdots \left(\frac{d}{dx} - m_n\right) Y$$

We obtain

$$u_2 = \left(\frac{d}{dx} - m_3\right) \cdots \left(\frac{d}{dx} - m_n\right) Y = e^{m_2 x} \int e^{-m_2 x} \left[e^{m_1 x} \int e^{-m_1 x} f(x)\, dx \right] dx$$

$$= e^{m_2 x} \int e^{(m_1 - m_2)x} \int e^{-m_1 x} f(x)(dx)^2$$

Repeating the process n times, we finally obtain

$$Y(x) = e^{m_n x} \int e^{(m_{n-1} - m_n)x} \int e^{(m_{n-2} - m_{n-1})x} \int \cdots \int e^{(m_1 - m_2)x} \int e^{-m_1 x} f(x)\,(dx)^n$$

$$(4\text{–}80)$$

For example, for the equation

$$\frac{d^2y}{dx^2} - y = e^{2x}(1 + e^x)^{-2}$$

we have $m_1 = 1$, $m_2 = -1$, and its complementary function $C_1 e^x + C_2 e^{-x}$. A particular integral can be obtained with Eq. (4-80):

$$Y(x) = e^{m_2 x} \int e^{(m_1 - m_2)x} \int e^{-m_1 x} e^{2x} (1 + e^x)^{-2} (dx)^2$$

$$= e^{-x} \int e^{2x} \left[\int e^x (1 + e^x)^{-2} \, dx \right] dx = -e^{-x} \int \frac{e^{2x}}{1 + e^x} \, dx$$

$$= -e^{-x} \int e^x \left(1 - \frac{1}{1 + e^x} \right) dx = -1 + e^{-x} \log_e (1 + e^x)$$

Although this method is supposedly applicable in general, the integration is sometimes impossible. Sometimes simpler integration is facilitated by rearranging the order of the m's.

(3) Method of partial fractions:

For the equation

$$\left(\frac{d}{dx} - m \right) y = f(x)$$

we have a particular solution

$$Y(x) = e^{mx} \int e^{-mx} f(x) \, dx$$

Let an operator be defined as

$$\left(\frac{1}{\dfrac{d}{dx} - m} \right) f(x) \equiv e^{mx} \int e^{-mx} f(x) \, dx \qquad (4\text{-}81)$$

The particular integral of Eq. (4-79) by successive integration can then be rewritten as

$$Y(x) = \frac{1}{\dfrac{d}{dx} - m_1} \left\{ \frac{1}{\dfrac{d}{dx} - m_2} \left[\cdots \frac{1}{\dfrac{d}{dx} - m_n} f(x) \right] \right\}$$

or simply

$$Y(x) = \frac{1}{\dfrac{d}{dx} - m_1} \cdot \frac{1}{\dfrac{d}{dx} - m_2} \cdot \cdots \frac{1}{\dfrac{d}{dx} - m_n} f(x)$$

It is found that we can treat this expression by the rules of algebra and write it in terms of partial fractions. (The student should review the method of finding partial fractions, if necessary.)

$$Y(x) = \frac{A}{\dfrac{d}{dx} - m_1} f(x) + \frac{B}{\dfrac{d}{dx} - m_2} f(x) + \frac{C}{\dfrac{d}{dx} - m_n} f(x) + \cdots$$

where A, B, C, ... are constants that can be determined. Thus

$$Y(x) = Ae^{m_1 x} \int e^{-m_1 x} f(x)\, dx + Be^{m_2 x} \int e^{-m_2 x} f(x)\, dx + \dots \qquad (4\text{-}82)$$

and, if there are repeated roots of m, say $m_1 = m_2 = m_3$,

$$Y(x) = \frac{A}{\left(\dfrac{d}{dx} - m_1\right)^3} f(x) + \frac{B}{\dfrac{d}{dx} - m_4} f(x) + \dots$$

$$= Ae^{m_1 x} \iiint e^{-m_1 x} f(x)\, (dx)^3 + Be^{m_4 x} \int e^{-m_4 x} f(x)\, dx + \dots \qquad (4\text{-}83)$$

The validity of the last two equations can be verified by operating with the operator

$$\left(\frac{d}{dx} - m_1\right) \left(\frac{d}{dx} - m_2\right) \dots \left(\frac{d}{dx} - m_n\right)$$

on both sides of the equality

$$\frac{1}{\dfrac{d}{dx} - m_1} \cdot \frac{1}{\dfrac{d}{dx} - m_2} \dots \frac{1}{\dfrac{d}{dx} - m_n} f(x) = \frac{A}{\dfrac{d}{dx} - m_1} f(x) + \frac{B}{\dfrac{d}{dx} - m_2} f(x) + \dots$$

For example, for the equation

$$\frac{d^2 y}{dx^2} - y = f(x) = e^{2x} (1 + e^x)^{-2}$$

with $m_1 = 1$ and $m_2 = -1$, this method gives for a particular integral

$$\frac{1}{\dfrac{d}{dx} - 1} \cdot \frac{1}{\dfrac{d}{dx} + 1} f(x) = \frac{\frac{1}{2}}{\dfrac{d}{dx} - 1} f(x) + \frac{\frac{1}{2}}{\dfrac{d}{dx} + 1} f(x)$$

To verify this equality, operate on both sides with $\left(\dfrac{d}{dx} - 1\right)\left(\dfrac{d}{dx} + 1\right)$. We obtain the equality

$$f(x) = \frac{1}{2}\left(\frac{d}{dx} + 1\right) f(x) - \frac{1}{2}\left(\frac{d}{dx} - 1\right) f(x)$$

thus justifying the use of the rule of partial fractions here. Therefore

$$Y(x) = \frac{1}{2} e^x \int e^{-x} e^{2x} (1 + e^x)^{-2}\, dx - \frac{1}{2} e^{-x} \int e^x e^{2x} (1 + e^x)^{-2}\, dx$$

$$= -1 + e^{-x} \log_e (1 + e^x)$$

Example 4–36. Undamped forced linear vibrations: a monocycle is represented by a mass M and a spring of constant k, as shown in Fig. 4–72. The road becomes wavy at $x=0$ with $\epsilon=h \sin(2\pi x/L)$ for $x>0$. Assuming that the horizontal speed v is constant and the cycle remains in a vertical position, find the vertical motion of the mass M.

Let $z=$ vertical displacement of M from its position of equilibrium if the road were smooth. The net vertical upward force from gravity and the spring

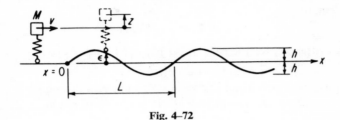

Fig. 4–72

is proportional to the change in the length of the spring: $-k(z-\epsilon)$. The equation of motion is

$$M\ddot{z} = -k(z-\epsilon) = -kz+kh \sin \frac{2\pi x}{L}$$

With $x=vt$, we have

$$M\ddot{z}+kz = F \sin \omega t$$

where $F=kh$ is the magnitude of the forcing function, and $\omega=2\pi v/L$ is its circular frequency. The equation can be rewritten as

$$\ddot{z}+p^2z = \frac{F}{M} \sin \omega t \qquad (4\text{–}84)$$

where $p=\sqrt{k/M}$. The complementary function of this equation is $A \cos pt + B \sin pt$ (see Eq. (4–73)).

To find a particular integral, we must consider two separate cases:

(a) When $\omega \neq p$. For a particular integral, try

$$z(t) = \alpha \sin \omega t + \beta \cos \omega t$$

Substitute into Eq. (4–84),

$$\alpha(p^2-\omega^2) \sin \omega t + \beta(p^2-\omega^2) \cos \omega t = \frac{F}{M} \sin \omega t$$

Thus, $\alpha=F/M(p^2-\omega^2)$ and $\beta=0$. The general solution of Eq. (4–84) is therefore

$$z = A \cos pt + B \sin pt + \frac{F}{M(p^2-\omega^2)} \sin \omega t \qquad (4\text{–}85)$$

where A and B are constants to be determined from the initial conditions. With $z_0=0$ and $\dot{z}_0=0$ at $t=0$, we have

$$z = -\frac{F}{M(p^2-\omega^2)} \cdot \frac{\omega}{p} \sin pt + \frac{F}{M(p^2-\omega^2)} \sin \omega t$$

This motion consists of two simple harmonic motions, one with the circular frequency p of free vibrations, and the other with the circular frequency ω of the forcing function. The combination may not be periodic unless the ratio of ω and p is a rational number.

When ω is very close to p, the interesting phenomenon of beats occurs. In general, a combination of two simple harmonic motions of different frequencies and amplitudes

$$z = a \sin pt + b \sin \omega t$$

can be rewritten as, for the case of $\omega > p$,

$$z = a \sin pt + b \sin [p + (\omega - p)]t$$
$$= a \sin pt + b [\sin pt \cos (\omega - p)t + \cos pt \sin (\omega - p)t]$$
$$= [a + b \cos (\omega - p)t] \sin pt + [b \sin (\omega - p)t] \cos pt$$

Using Eq. (4–67) and simplifying, we have

$$z = \sqrt{a^2 + b^2 + 2ab \cos (\omega - p)t} \cdot \sin (pt + \phi) \qquad (4\text{–}86)$$

When ω is very close to p, this may be considered as vibrations with circular frequency p and an amplitude varying between $(a + b)$ and $|a - b|$. This phenomenon is usually referred to as *beats*, as shown in Fig. 4–73. The circular frequency of the beats is $(\omega - p)$, which is much smaller than p or ω.

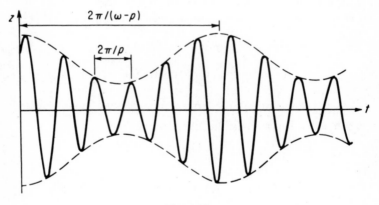

Fig. 4–73

As ω approaches p, the response amplitude $F/M(p^2 - \omega^2)$ in Eq. (4–85), i.e., b in Eq. (4–86), approaches infinity, a condition called *resonance*. See Fig. 4–74.

(b) When $\omega = p$. The differential equation, Eq. (4–84), becomes

$$\ddot{z} + p^2 z = \frac{F}{M} \sin pt$$

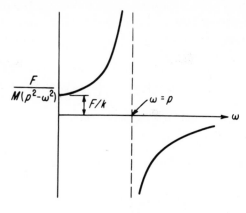

Fig. 4–74

Since the complementary function is $C \cos pt + D \sin pt$, we use for a trial particular integral

$$Z(t) = \gamma t \sin pt + \delta t \cos pt$$

Substituting into the differential equation, we obtain $\gamma = 0$ and $\delta = -F/2Mp$. The general solution is

$$z = C \cos pt + D \sin pt - \frac{F}{2Mp} t \cos pt \qquad (4\text{–}87)$$

where C and D are determined from the initial conditions. Note that the response amplitude $Ft/2Mp$ increases indefinitely with t, under this resonance condition. However, physically such a motion cannot go on indefinitely. The differential equation may become invalid when the amplitude becomes large. The physical system may break down. The effect of damping, even very small, will be felt, as shown in the next example.

Example 4–37. Forced linear vibrations with damping: in Fig. 4–75, a machine of mass M is supported by a system of springs which offer a combined spring constant k and a viscous damping coefficient c. The mass of the springs is small compared with M. Due to some un-balanced rotating parts, there is an effective verti-cal force $F \sin \omega t$ acting on the machine. (This force is the reaction of the forces acting on the

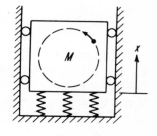

Fig. 4–75

rotating parts.) Find the motion of the machine and the force transmitted to the foundation.

Let x be the displacement of the machine from its position of equilibrium, as shown in Fig. 4–75. At any instant, the upward forces acting on M are $-kx$, $-c\dot{x}$, and $F \sin \omega t$. Thus

$$M\ddot{x} = -kx - c\dot{x} + F \sin \omega t$$

or

$$\ddot{x} + 2n\dot{x} + p^2 x = \frac{F}{M} \sin \omega t \tag{4–88}$$

where $n = c/2M$ and $p = \sqrt{k/M}$. The complementary function depends on the relative values of n and p, as given by Eqs. (4–75) to (4–77). From these equations, it can be seen that in no case are terms like $\sin \gamma t$ and $\cos \gamma t$ (γ being any constant) involved. Thus, we can try for the particular integral

$$X(t) = \alpha \sin \omega t + \beta \cos \omega t$$

Substituting this into Eq. (4–88), we find

$$X(t) = \frac{F}{M[(p^2 - \omega^2)^2 + 4n^2\omega^2]} [(p^2 - \omega^2) \sin \omega t - 2n\omega \cos \omega t]$$

and, according to Eq. (4–67)

$$X(t) = X_0 \sin (\omega t + \phi) \tag{4–89}$$

where

$$X_0 = \frac{F}{k\sqrt{\left[1 - \left(\frac{\omega}{p}\right)^2\right]^2 + \left(2\frac{n}{p}\cdot\frac{\omega}{p}\right)^2}} \quad \text{and} \quad \phi = \tan^{-1}\left(\frac{-2n\omega}{p^2 - \omega^2}\right)$$

With the complementary function from Eqs. (4–75) to (4–77), we have

$$x = X + \begin{cases} e^{-nt}[A \cos (\sqrt{p^2 - n^2}\, t) + B \sin (\sqrt{p^2 - n^2}\, t)] & \text{if } n^2 < p^2 \\ e^{-nt}(c_1 + c_2 t) & \text{if } n^2 = p^2 \\ C_1 \exp[-(n + \sqrt{n^2 - p^2})t] + C_2 \exp[-(n - \sqrt{n^2 - p^2})t] & \text{if } n^2 > p^2 \end{cases}$$
$$\tag{4–90}$$

The particular integral $X(t)$ is of special interest here. In all cases of Eq. (4–90), the complementary function approaches zero with time. Physically, this means that any free oscillation will be damped out with time. Some time after the start, the motion is mainly due to the forcing function, as described by the particular integral $X(t)$, and as shown in Fig. 4–76. The solution $X(t)$ is therefore called the *steady-state solution*, which describes the motion adequately after a period called the *transient period*. The magnitude X_0 of $X(t)$ depends on the values of ω/p and n/p, and there is a phase difference ϕ between the forcing function and the response motion (see Eq. (4–89)). The response magnitude X_0 is plotted in Fig. 4–77. It can be seen that, due to the

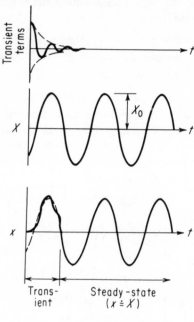

Fig. 4–76

presence of damping, the maximum X_0 for a given n/p is obtained with ω/p less than unity.

To find the force transmitted to the foundation, take the springs as a free body. The springs are under the forces from the machine and the foundation. Since the mass of the springs is negligible, these two forces are practically equal, in accordance with the equation of motion. Since the force from the machine on the springs is equal in magnitude to the force from the springs on

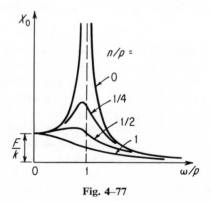

Fig. 4–77

the machine (which is $Mg-kx-c\dot{x}$), we have the force P transmitted to the foundation during steady-state vibrations:

$$P = Mg-kx-c\dot{x} = Mg-kX-c\dot{X}$$
$$= Mg-kX_0\sin{(\omega t+\phi)}-c\omega X_0 \cos{(\omega t+\phi)}$$
$$= Mg-X_0\sqrt{(c\omega)^2+k^2} \sin{(\omega t+\phi+\phi')}$$

This solution consists of two parts: the dead weight Mg, and a dynamic load of magnitude $X_0\sqrt{(c\omega)^2+k^2}$. It is of interest to find the portion of the magnitude F of the applied force transmitted to the foundation. With X_0 from Eq. (4-89),

$$\text{transmissibility} = \frac{X_0\sqrt{(c\omega)^2+k^2}}{F} = \sqrt{\frac{1+\left(2\frac{n}{p}\frac{\omega}{p}\right)^2}{\left[1-\left(\frac{\omega}{p}\right)^2\right]^2+\left(2\frac{n}{p}\frac{\omega}{p}\right)^2}} \quad (4\text{-}91)$$

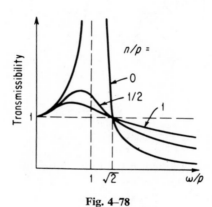

Fig. 4-78

This result is plotted in Fig. 4-78. To reduce the transmission, small values of k should be used, so that $\omega/p > \sqrt{2}$. For $\omega/p > \sqrt{2}$, small value of c should be used.

Example 4-38. An infinitely long uniform beam rests on an elastic foundation with a principal axis of the beam sections vertical. The local reaction from the foundation is assumed to be proportional to the local deformation. Find the elastic curve of the beam under a uniformly distributed load w per unit length over a length $2a$, as shown in Fig. 4-79.

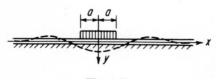

Fig. 4-79

There are two types of forces acting on the beam, namely, the distributed load w, and the reaction ky from the foundation, where k is the modulus of the foundation. In this case, we cannot use the equation $EI(d^2y/dx^2) = \pm M$ directly, because the function $M(x)$ cannot be written immediately. An equation for the elastic curve is to be derived in terms of the forces $f(x)$ on the beam.

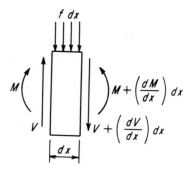

Fig. 4–80

Let f be the downward force per unit length of beam. For equilibrium of an element of beam dx in length, as shown in Fig. 4–80, we have

$$f \, dx + \left(V + \frac{dV}{dx} \, dx \right) - V = 0$$

and

$$M + V \, dx - f \, dx \frac{dx}{2} - \left(M + \frac{dM}{dx} \, dx \right) = 0$$

Therefore

$$\frac{dV}{dx} = -f \tag{4–92}$$

and

$$\frac{dM}{dx} = V \quad \text{or} \quad \frac{d^2M}{dx^2} = -f \tag{4–93}$$

When the loads are in the plane of a principal axis of the sections, and if the deflections are small, Eq. (4–58) is applicable. With the y axis pointing downward,

$$M = -EI \frac{d^2y}{dx^2}$$

Thus

$$\frac{d^2}{dx^2} \left(EI \frac{d^2y}{dx^2} \right) = f(x, y) \tag{4–94}$$

This is the differential equation of the elastic curve in terms of forces f.

For a uniform beam on an elastic foundation supporting a distributed load $w(x)$, we have $f(x, y) = w(x) - ky$. Thus

$$EI\frac{d^4y}{dx^4} + ky = w(x) \tag{4–95}$$

Calling $\beta = \sqrt[4]{k/4EI}$, we have

$$\frac{d^4y}{dx^4} + 4\beta^4 y = \frac{w}{EI}$$

The characteristic equation is $m^4 + 4\beta^4 = 0$, giving $m = \sqrt{2}\beta\sqrt[4]{-1}$. There are four values of $\sqrt[4]{-1}$ which can be found with the aid of Eq. (4–66). Write

$$-1 = \cos(2r+1)\pi + i\sin(2r+1)\pi = e^{i(2r+1)\pi} \tag{4–96}$$

where r is an integer. The four values of $\sqrt[4]{-1}$ are given by $e^{i(2r+1)\pi/4}$, with r taking four different values, say, 0, 1, 2 and 3. Thus $\sqrt[4]{-1} = e^{i\pi/4}$, $e^{i3\pi/4}$, $e^{i5\pi/4}$ and $e^{i7\pi/4}$. Using Eq. (4–66) again, we have

$$e^{i\pi/4} = \cos(\pi/4) + i\sin(\pi/4) = (1+i)/\sqrt{2}, \text{ etc.}$$

Thus, $\sqrt[4]{-1} = (1+i)/\sqrt{2}$, $(-1+i)/\sqrt{2}$, $(-1-i)/\sqrt{2}$ and $(1-i)/\sqrt{2}$, and $m = (1+i)\beta$, $(-1+i)\beta$, $(-1-i)\beta$ and $(1-i)\beta$. With $Y(x)$ as the particular integral of Eq. (4–95), we have

$$\begin{aligned} y &= c_1 e^{(1+i)\beta x} + c_2 e^{(-1+i)\beta x} + c_3 e^{(-1-i)\beta x} + c_4 e^{(1-i)\beta x} + Y(x) \\ &= e^{\beta x}(A\cos\beta x + B\sin\beta x) + e^{-\beta x}(C\cos\beta x + D\sin\beta x) + Y(x) \end{aligned} \tag{4–97}$$

This is the general solution of any uniform beam on an elastic foundation. In using initial or boundary conditions to determine a particular solution, it is well to remember that $M = -EI \cdot d^2y/dx^2$ and $V = -EI \cdot d^3y/dx^3$. Thus, at a hinge where $M = 0$, we have $d^2y/dx^2 = 0$. For convenience of future use, we record here the derivatives of y:

$$\left.\begin{aligned} \frac{dy}{dx} &= \beta e^{\beta x}[(A+B)\cos\beta x + (-A+B)\sin\beta x] \\ &\quad + \beta e^{-\beta x}[(-C+D)\cos\beta x + (-C-D)\sin\beta x] + Y'(x) \\[6pt] \frac{d^2y}{dx^2} &= 2\beta^2 e^{\beta x}(B\cos\beta x - A\sin\beta x) \\ &\quad + 2\beta^2 e^{-\beta x}(-D\cos\beta x + C\sin\beta x) + Y''(x) \\[6pt] \frac{d^3y}{dx^3} &= 2\beta^3 e^{\beta x}[(-A+B)\cos\beta x + (-A-B)\sin\beta x] \\ &\quad + 2\beta^3 e^{-\beta x}[(C+D)\cos\beta x + (-C+D)\sin\beta x] + Y'''(x) \end{aligned}\right\} \tag{4–98}$$

For the particular case of this problem, we have

$$EI\frac{d^4y}{dx^4} + ky = \text{constant } w \qquad \text{(for } 0 \leq x \leq a)$$

$$EI\frac{d^4y}{dx^4} + ky = 0 \qquad \text{(for } x \geq a)$$

(Because of symmetry, we consider only one half of the beam.) With $Y(x)=w/k$ for $0 \leq x \leq a$, and $Y(x)=0$ for $x \geq a$, we have

$$y = e^{\beta x} (A \cos \beta x + B \sin \beta x) + e^{-\beta x} (C \cos \beta x + D \sin \beta x) + \frac{w}{k} \qquad (0 \leq x \leq a)$$

$$y = e^{\beta x} (A' \cos \beta x + B' \sin \beta x) + e^{-\beta x} (C' \cos \beta x + D' \sin \beta x) \qquad (x \geq a)$$

To determine the eight constants, we have the following eight boundary conditions. Because of symmetry, we have $dy/dx=0$ and $d^3y/dx^3=0$ $(V=0)$ at $x=0$; $y=0$ and $dy/dx=0$ at $x=\infty$. At $x=a$, the two equations must yield the same values for y, dy/dx, d^2y/dx^2 (i.e., same M) and d^3y/dx^3 (i.e., same V). For the first two conditions at $x=0$, we have $A+B-C+D=0$ and $-A+B+C+D=0$; i.e., $C=A$ and $D=-B$. Thus

$$y = 2A \cosh \beta x \cos \beta x + 2B \sinh \beta x \sin \beta x + \frac{w}{k} \qquad (0 \leq x \leq a)$$

For the condition $y=0$ or $dy/dx=0$ at $x=\infty$, we have $A'=B'=0$. Thus

$$y = e^{-\beta x} (C' \cos \beta x + D' \sin \beta x) \qquad (x \geq a)$$

The constants A, B, C' and D' are determined from four linear algebraic equations according to the four conditions at $x=a$. It can be shown that

$$y = \frac{w}{k} - \frac{w}{k} e^{-\beta a} (\cos \beta a \cosh \beta x \cos \beta x + \sin \beta a \sinh \beta x \sin \beta x) \qquad (0 \leq x \leq a)$$

$$y = \frac{w}{k} e^{-\beta x} (\sinh \beta a \cos \beta a \cos \beta x + \cosh \beta a \sin \beta a \sin \beta x) \qquad (x \geq a)$$

From this solution, the bending moment $M=-EI \cdot d^2y/dx^2$ and shear $V=-EI \cdot d^3y/dx^3$ can be computed, if desired.

In this solution, y may be negative in some portions of the beam, as indicated in Fig. 4–79. We have assumed that, for negative y, the foundation may develop negative reactions.

Problems

4–72. A smooth straight tube is revolving in a vertical plane about one end at a constant angular speed ω. At the instant when the tube is vertically below the fixed end, a particle is placed into the tube at this end. Find the motion of the particle.

Ans. $\rho = \dfrac{g}{2\omega^2} (\cosh \omega t - \cos \omega t)$

4–73. A block weighing 10 lb is attached to a spring of constant $k=5$ lb/ft, as shown in Fig. 4–81. The coefficient of kinetic friction is $\frac{1}{5}$ and that of static friction is $\frac{1}{4}$. If the block is moved out for a distance of 1.5 ft and then released, find how close the block will come to the wall. Where is the block when it ceases to move? (Hint: different equations are used in motions in

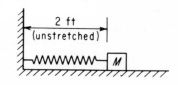

Fig. 4–81

different directions. The block will not start moving unless static friction can
be overcome.   *Ans.* 1.3 ft, 1.9 ft from wall

4–74. A monocycle is travelling at a constant speed v when it goes over a hump on a

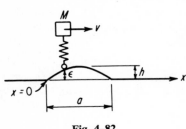

Fig. 4–82

level road: $\epsilon = h \sin \dfrac{\pi x}{a}$ (for $0 < x < a$),
as shown in Fig. 4–82. The monocycle
is represented by a mass M and a spring
with constant k. Damping in the system
cannot be felt during the short duration over the hump. Given $v = \sqrt{k/M}$
$2a/\pi$, find the amplitude of the vertical vibrations of M thus set up. (Hint:
first find conditions at $x = a$.)
                                        Ans. $2\sqrt{2}h/3$

4–75. A measuring instrument on an airplane is supported by a set of springs of
combined constant k and damping coefficient c. The vibration of the airplane
under the instrument is $h \sin \omega t$. Let the magnitude of the steady state
vibration of the instrument be x_0. Show that x_0/h is equal to the right side of
Eq. (4–91).

4–76. A cart of mass M is resting on a smooth floor and is attached to a wall with a
spring of constant k, as shown in Fig. 4–83. During an earthquake, the wall

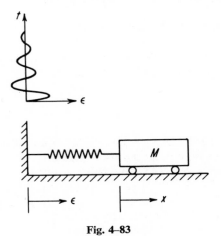

Fig. 4–83

moves horizontally with $\epsilon(t) = he^{-rt} \sin \omega t$, where h, r and ω are known constants. Show that the motion of the cart is

$$x = \frac{\beta r - \alpha \omega}{p} \sin pt - \beta \cos pt + \frac{he^{-rt}}{M} (\alpha \sin \omega t + \beta \cos \omega t)$$

where α and β are functions of r, ω and p. ($p = \sqrt{k/M}$)

4–77. A uniform beam of infinite length rests on an elastic foundation of modulus k. A concentrated load P is applied to the beam. Find the elastic curve of the beam. What is its maximum bending moment? (Hint: shear $V \to \pm P/2$ as $x \to 0$ under P.)

$$\text{Ans. } y = \frac{P\beta}{2k} e^{-\beta x} (\cos \beta x + \sin \beta x); \ P/4\beta$$

4–78. A very long beam rests on an elastic foundation with two ends hinged at unyielding supports, as shown in Fig. 4–84. A distributed load w per unit length is applied to the whole beam. Find the reaction at the hinges. (Hint: the deflection of sections far away from the supports is w/k.)

Fig. 4–84

$$\text{Ans. } R = w/2\beta$$

4–79. If in the previous problem the ends are built-in, find the shear and bending moment at the supports. $\text{Ans. } w/\beta, \ -2\beta^2 EIw/k$

4–80. A beam of length L on an elastic foundation is loaded with a concentrated load P at one end. Show that the deflection at the other end is zero if L and β are such that $\tan \beta L = \tanh \beta L$.

4–81. Find a particular integral for each of the following differential equations. Use more than one method if possible.

(a) $\dfrac{d^2y}{dx^2} - 2 \dfrac{dy}{dx} + 3y = x^2 + \cos x$

(b) $\dfrac{d^2y}{dx^2} + 4y = x^2 \sin 2x$

(c) $\dfrac{d^2y}{dx^2} + y = \csc x$ $\text{Ans. (c) } Y = \sin x \log_e (\sin x) - x \cos x$

4–14. Mechanical and electrical vibrations. Linearization

In previous articles, several examples of linear mechanical vibrations have been presented (see Examples 4–34 to 4–37). In these systems, the general equation is

$$\ddot{x} + 2n\dot{x} + p^2 x = \frac{F}{M} \sin \omega t$$

We will summarize here what has been learned about this equation.
(1) Undamped free vibration:

$$\ddot{x} + p^2 x = 0$$

$$x = A \cos pt + B \sin pt = C \cos (pt - \psi)$$

This represents vibrations with frequency $p/2\pi$, called the *natural frequency* of the system. It depends solely on the properties of the system.

(2) Damped free vibration:

$$\ddot{x} + 2n\dot{x} + p^2 x = 0$$

$$x = \begin{cases} e^{-nt} (A \cos \sqrt{p^2 - n^2}\, t + B \sin \sqrt{p^2 - n^2}\, t) & \text{if } n^2 < p^2 \\ e^{-nt} (c_1 + c_2 t) & \text{if } n^2 = p^2 \\ C_1 \exp\left[-(n + \sqrt{n^2 - p^2})t\right] + C_2 \exp\left[-(n - \sqrt{n^2 - p^2})t\right] & \text{if } n^2 > p^2 \end{cases}$$

In all cases, $x \to 0$ as $t \to \infty$. The motion is finally stopped by the damping force. Only when the damping is light $(n^2 < p^2)$ is the motion oscillatory (see Figs. 4–67 and 4–68).

(3) Forced vibration without damping:

$$\ddot{x} + p^2 x = \frac{F}{M} \sin \omega t$$

$$x = C_1 \cos pt + D_1 \sin pt + \begin{cases} \dfrac{F}{M(p^2 - \omega^2)} \sin \omega t & \text{if } \omega \neq p \\ -\dfrac{F}{2Mp} t \cos pt & \text{if } \omega = p \end{cases}$$

When the frequency of the forcing function is different from the natural frequency of the system, the motion is a combination of two harmonic motions. The result may or may not be periodic. When the two frequencies are very close, there will be beats (see Fig. 4–73). When the two frequencies are the same, the magnitude of vibrations will grow indefinitely, a condition called *resonance*.

(4) Forced vibration with damping:

$$\ddot{x} + 2n\dot{x} + p^2 x = \frac{F}{M} \sin \omega t$$

$$x = \text{transient terms} + \frac{F}{Mp^2 \sqrt{\left[1 - \left(\dfrac{\omega}{p}\right)^2\right]^2 + \left(2 \dfrac{n}{p} \dfrac{\omega}{p}\right)^2}} \sin (\omega t + \phi)$$

where

$$\phi = \tan^{-1} \left(\frac{-2n\omega}{p^2 - \omega^2}\right)$$

After a transient period, the transient terms die out and the motion has the circular frequency of the forcing function (see Fig. 4–76).

These results can be used to study the analogous vibrations in linear electrical circuits. These circuits may consist of elements called resistors, inductors and capacitors (condensers). A resistor offers a resistance to the flow of current through it, such that the drop of voltage across it in the direction of the current is

$$V_R = iR$$

where i = current and R = resistance of the resistor. When V is expressed in volts and i in amperes, R is in ohms. An inductor offers a resistance to any change of the current, such that the voltage drop across it is

$$V_L = L \frac{di}{dt}$$

where L = inductance of the inductor. When V, i and t are in volts, amperes and seconds, respectively, L is in henrys. The voltage drop across a capacitor depends on the charge q in it:

$$V_C = \frac{q}{C}$$

where C = capacitance of the capacitor or condenser. When V and q are expressed in volts and coulombs, the unit of C is the farad.

In studying oscillations in electrical circuits, Kirchhoff's second law is used:

Kirchhoff's law: The algebraic sum of the voltage drops around a closed circuit is zero.

Thus, in Fig. 4–85, with an arbitrary chosen positive direction for the current

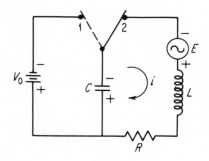

Fig. 4–85

i, the charge q and the electromotive force E, we have by summing up the voltage drops in the direction of the current:

$$L \frac{di}{dt} + Ri + \frac{q}{C} - E = 0$$

But the current i (in amperes, or coulombs per second) is related to q:

$$i = \frac{dq}{dt}$$

Thus, if the imposed $E = E_0 \sin \omega t$, as in an *a-c* circuit,

$$L\ddot{q} + R\dot{q} + \frac{1}{C}q = E_0 \sin \omega t$$

or

$$\ddot{q} + 2n\dot{q} + p^2 q = \frac{E_0}{L} \sin \omega t$$

where $n = R/2L$ and $p = 1/\sqrt{LC}$. Thus, the oscillations in a linear electrical circuit are described by an equation similar to that of linear mechanical vibrations, with L, R, $1/C$ and E_0 analogous to M, c, k and F, respectively (see Example 4–39 and Problem 4–82).

The systems discussed above are linear. This may not always be the case. For example, the restoring force in a mechanical system may not be proportional to the displacement. The voltage drop across an electrical element, such as a vacuum tube, may not be proportional to the current. In general, instead of $2n\dot{x}$ and p^2x, we may have a function $G(x, \dot{x})$. With an arbitrary forcing function $F(t)$, the equation is then

$$\ddot{x} + G(x, \dot{x}) = F(t)$$

Linear cases where $F(t)$ is periodic, though not sinusoidal, will be discussed in Chapter 5. In many cases, the function $G(x, \dot{x})$ can be linearized by expanding it into power series of x and $\dot{x}$, and using the linear terms only. For example, when the displacement θ of the pendulum shown in Fig. 4–57 is small, the restoring force $mg \sin \theta$ is

$$mg \sin \theta = mg \left(\theta - \frac{\theta^3}{3!} + \dots \right) \doteq mg\theta$$

Although the validity of the result thus obtained is limited to small amplitudes, it usually gives very valuable information. For example, the period of a simple pendulum with small amplitudes, as determined from $mL\ddot{\theta} + mg\theta = 0$, is $2\pi\sqrt{L/g}$, which is a good approximation of the periods for large amplitudes (see Example 3–34). Two examples of linearization are given in Examples 4–40 and 4–41. In all cases, the amplitude is considered to be infinitesimal, and all terms of the same order of magnitude are either retained or ignored.

Example 4–39. Given in Fig. 4–85, $E = 0$ and $R = 0$. The condenser is first charged by a battery of voltage V_0 by putting the switch to position 1. Find the current $i(t)$ in the L-C circuit after the switch is moved to position 2.

With the switch at position 1, Kirchhoff's law gives

$$V_0 - \frac{q_0}{C} = 0$$

When the switch is moved to position 2, the charge in the condenser is $q_0 = CV_0$.

With the switch at position 2, Kirchhoff's law gives at any instant

$$L\ddot{q} + \frac{1}{C}q = 0$$

Thus

$$q = A \cos pt + B \sin pt$$

where $p = 1/\sqrt{LC}$, and

$$i = \dot{q} = -Ap \sin pt + Bp \cos pt$$

The constants A and B are determined from the initial conditions $q = q_0$ and $i = 0$ at $t = 0$, on closing the circuit at position 2. (At $t = 0$, i must be zero so that $L \cdot di/dt$ or $L\ddot{q}$ is not infinite.) Thus $A = q_0$, and $B = 0$.

$$i = -q_0 p \sin pt$$

The negative sign in this expression shows that the current, immediately after closing the switch, is opposite to the chosen positive direction indicated in Fig. 4–85. This case is analogous to the case of undamped free mechanical vibrations with the mass initially displaced from its position of equilibrium. The condenser tries to discharge to return to its condition of equilibrium (zero charge), but the change of movement of its charges is resisted by the inductor, just as the change of movement of a mass to its position of equilibrium is resisted by its inertia. (The student can now solve Problem 4–82.)

Example 4–40. A particle M slides on a smooth surface described by $y = ax^2$, as shown in Fig. 4–86. (a) Write the equation of motion of M. (b) By linearizing this equation for cases with $ax \ll 1$, find the frequency of free vibrations with small amplitudes.

(a) The particle is under two forces, namely its weight Mg and the normal reaction N. The equations of motion are

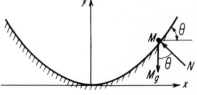

Fig. 4–86

$$M\ddot{x} = -N \sin \theta$$
$$M\ddot{y} = N \cos \theta - Mg$$

Here x, y and θ cannot vary independently, but are related by $y = ax^2$ and $\tan \theta = dy/dx = 2ax$. Thus, we have four equations for four unknown functions, x, y, θ and N. To describe the motion, it is sufficient to find $x(t)$.

To eliminate the variables other than x, proceed as follows. From $y = ax^2$, we have $\dot{y} = 2ax\dot{x}$ and $\ddot{y} = 2a(x\ddot{x} + \dot{x}^2)$. Substituting into the second equation of motion, we have

$$2Ma(x\ddot{x} + \dot{x}^2) + Mg = N \cos \theta$$

Combining with the first equation, we have

$$\frac{M\ddot{x}}{2Ma(x\ddot{x} + \dot{x}^2) + Mg} = \frac{-N \sin \theta}{N \cos \theta} = -\tan \theta = -2ax$$

Simplifying, we have the equation for $x(t)$

$$(1+4a^2x^2)\ddot{x}+(4a^2\dot{x}^2+2ag)x = 0$$

This equation is nonlinear.

(b) When the amplitude is considered to be infinitesimal, $\dot{x}$ must also be infinitesimal, since the period is finite. By similar argument, $\ddot{x}$ is also infinitesimal. Thus, the terms $x^2\ddot{x}$ and $x\dot{x}^2$ are negligible compared to the terms $\ddot{x}$ and x. Consequently, for small amplitudes, the equation becomes linear:

$$\ddot{x}+2agx = 0$$

The natural frequency is therefore $\sqrt{2ag}/2\pi$.

(The student can now solve Problems 4–83 and 4–84.)

Example 4–41. A particle m is travelling steadily in a circular path inside a smooth vertical cone at an elevation h above the apex, as shown in Fig. 4–87.

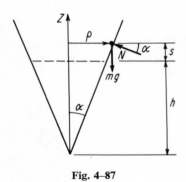

Fig. 4–87

If the particle is slightly disturbed by an impulse along an element of the cone, describe its subsequent motion.

At any instant except during the disturbance, the forces acting on the particle are: its weight mg and the normal reaction N. Using polar-cylindrical coordinates, the equations of motion are

$$m(\ddot{\rho}-\rho\dot{\theta}^2) = -N\cos\alpha$$

$$\frac{m}{\rho}\frac{d}{dt}(\rho^2\dot{\theta}) = 0$$

$$m\ddot{z} = N\sin\alpha - mg$$

With $\rho = z\tan\alpha$, we have four equations for ρ, θ, z and N.

During steady motion at elevation h, we have $\rho = h\tan\alpha$, $\dot{\rho}=0$ and $\ddot{\rho}=0$. From the third equation, $N=mg/\sin\alpha$; and from the first equation, $m(h\tan\alpha)\dot{\theta}^2 = N\cos\alpha = mg/\tan\alpha$, or $\dot{\theta}^2 = g/(h\tan^2\alpha)$. The second equation is satisfied with $\rho^2\dot{\theta}=\sqrt{gh}\,h\tan\alpha$.

During the disturbance, the second equation is still applicable, since there is no force in the θ direction. Thus, the quantity

$$\rho^2\dot{\theta} = \sqrt{gh}\,h\tan\alpha$$

remains throughout the motion, although ρ and θ may vary individually.

The equations of motion for the disturbed particle are nonlinear. To study the effect of a small disturbance, let $s(t)=z-h$, as shown in Fig. 4–87. With

$\theta = \sqrt{gh}\, h \tan \alpha / \rho^2$, $\rho = (h+s) \tan \alpha$, $\ddot{\rho} = \ddot{s} \tan \alpha$, and $\ddot{z} = \ddot{s}$, the first and third equations of motion can be rewritten in terms of s:

$$m\left[\ddot{s} \tan \alpha - \frac{gh^3}{(h+s)^3 \tan \alpha}\right] = -N \cos \alpha$$

$$m\ddot{s} + mg = N \sin \alpha$$

Thus, the equation for $s(t)$ is

$$\frac{m\left[\ddot{s} \tan \alpha - \dfrac{gh^3}{(h+s)^3 \tan \alpha}\right]}{m\ddot{s} + mg} = \frac{-1}{\tan \alpha}$$

Simplifying,

$$\ddot{s} \sec^2 \alpha = -g\left[1 - \left(\frac{h}{h+s}\right)^3\right]$$

This equation is nonlinear, but can be linearized if s is very small compared with h:

$$\left(\frac{h}{h+s}\right)^3 = \left(1 + \frac{s}{h}\right)^{-3} = 1 - 3\frac{s}{h} + \dots$$

Thus

$$\ddot{s} = -g \cos^2 \alpha \left[1 - \left(1 - 3\frac{s}{h} + \dots\right)\right] \doteq -\frac{3g \cos^2 \alpha}{h} s$$

This is a simple harmonic motion about the original path. The circular frequency is $\sqrt{3g/h}\, \cos \alpha$.

Problems

4–82. Resistor R, inductor L and condenser C are in series. At $t=0$, the charge q in the condenser is zero. The condenser C is to be charged by connecting the two ends of the series to an electromotive force E. Find the charge $q(t)$ and the current $i(t)$ for the following three cases: (a) $E=$ constant E_0, (b) $E = E_0 \sin \omega t$, (c) $E = E_0 e^{-\alpha t} \sin \omega t$. Also indicate an analogous case of mechanical vibrations for cases (a) and (b).

4–83. A mass M is in equilibrium, as shown in Fig. 4–88, under tension T_0 in the springs. The spring constant of each is k. Write the equation of motion of M

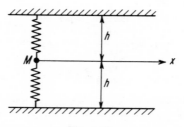

Fig. 4–88

along the x axis. Linearizing your equation for cases of amplitude much less than T_0/k, find the natural frequency of free vibrations of small amplitudes.

$$Ans. \ \frac{1}{\pi} \sqrt{\frac{T_0}{2Mh}}$$

4-84. A spherical body of radius R is floating with $\frac{3}{4}$ of its height in water. Assuming that the buoyant force is equal to the displaced weight of water and neglecting any fluid resistance, write the equation for the vertical motion of the body. By linearizing the equation, find the natural frequency of small oscillations in vertical motion. (Hint: volume of height $h(\leq R)$ above water $= \pi Rh^2 - \pi h^3/3$.)

$$Ans. \ \frac{1}{2\pi} \sqrt{\frac{2g}{3R}}$$

4-85. A rocket of mass m is in orbit around the earth under force $F_\rho = -m\lambda/\rho^2$. The orbit is a circle of radius a. It is hit radially by a meteor. By linearizing the equations of motion for a small departure from the original orbit, show that the rocket will oscillate about the orbit at the frequency $\sqrt{\lambda/a^3}/2\pi$.

4-86. A circular ring of smooth wire rotates about its vertical diameter at a constant angular speed ω, as shown in Fig. 4-89. A bead slides on the wire. Given that

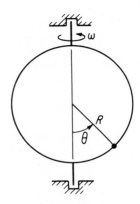

Fig. 4-89

the equations of motion of a particle in polar-spherical coordinates (see Fig. 3-68):

$$\sum F_\rho = ma_\rho = m(\ddot{\rho} - \rho\dot{\theta}^2 - \rho\dot{\phi}^2 \sin^2 \theta)$$

$$\sum F_\theta = ma_\theta = m \left[\frac{1}{\rho} \frac{d}{dt} (\rho^2 \dot{\theta}) - \rho\dot{\phi}^2 \sin\theta \cos\theta \right] \left. \right\} \quad (4.100)$$

$$\sum F_\phi = ma_\phi = \frac{m}{\rho \sin\theta} \frac{d}{dt} (\rho^2 \sin^2 \theta \ \dot{\phi})$$

(a) Show that the bead can stay in a circular path with constant $\theta_0 = \cos^{-1} (g/R\omega^2)$. (b) If the bead is slightly disturbed from this position, show that, with $\theta = \theta_0 + \epsilon (t)$, $\epsilon (t)$ is a simple harmonic motion about the original path, with circular frequency $\sin \theta_0 \sqrt{g/R \cos \theta_0}$. (Hint: for small ϵ, $\sin \theta = \sin \theta_0 + \epsilon \cdot \cos \theta_0$, etc.)

4–15. Characteristic functions of boundary problems

In Art. 4–9, a theorem has been stated giving the conditions for a linear differential equation of the nth order to have the general solution (see Eq. (4–53)).

$$y = c_1 y_1(x) + c_2 y_2(x) + \ldots + c_n y_n(x) + Y(x)$$

which is a complete solution. In the present article, we study the nature of the particular solutions after the c constants have been determined according to n known conditions.

If the n conditions are given at one value of the independent variable (such as $y = a$, $dy/dx = b$, $\ldots$ at $x = x_1$), these conditions are called *initial conditions*. For a particular solution determined according to initial conditions, we have the following theorem, which is a special case of the theorem stated in Art. 4–9:

Theorem: for the linear differential equation

$$a_0(x) \frac{d^n y}{dx^n} + a_1(x) \frac{d^{n-1} y}{dx^{n-1}} + \ldots + a_{n-1}(x) \frac{dy}{dx} + a_n(x) y = f(x)$$

where $a_0(x), \ldots, f(x)$ are continuous and single-valued functions and $a_0(x) \neq 0$ in an interval, there is a unique solution satisfying n initial conditions at $x = x_1$ in this interval.

When the known conditions are given at more than one value of the independent variable (such as $y = a$ at $x = x_1$, and $y = b$ at $x = x_2$, $\ldots$), these conditions are called *boundary conditions*. As suggested in Fig. 4–41, a particular solution determined according to boundary conditions may or may not be unique. First let us consider *homogeneous boundary problems*. In these problems, the differential equation is homogeneous, and each boundary condition is described as y, or its derivatives, or their linear combination, being zero (for instance, $y + 2y'' = 0$ at $x = x_1$).

Take, for example, the homogeneous linear equation with real k

$$\frac{d^2 y}{dx^2} - k^2 y = 0 \tag{4–101}$$

with the boundary conditions $y = 0$ at $x = 0$ and $y = 0$ at $x = a$. This is a homogeneous boundary problem. The general solution is

$$y = c_1 e^{kx} + c_2 e^{-kx}$$

From the homogeneous boundary conditions, we have

$$c_2 = -c_1 \quad \text{and} \quad c_1(e^{ka} - e^{-ka}) = 0$$

The only possible solution is $c_1 = c_2 = 0$, giving $y = 0$.

Next, take the homogeneous equation

$$\frac{d^2y}{dx^2} + k^2y = 0 \tag{4-102}$$

with the same homogeneous boundary conditions. The general solution is

$$y = A \cos kx + B \sin kx \tag{4-103}$$

For the condition $y=0$ at $x=0$, we have $A=0$. For the condition $y=0$ at $x=a$, we have

$$B \sin ka = 0$$

A solution is obtained with $B=0$, giving $y=0$. However, other particular solutions are possible if the parameter k^2 in Eq. (4–102) happens to have one of the values such that $\sin ka=0$, or

$$k_n = \frac{1}{a} \sin^{-1} 0 = \frac{n\pi}{a} \qquad (n = 1, 2, 3, \ldots)$$

With each of these values of k, Eq. (4–103) gives a nontrivial solution

$$y_n = B_n \sin k_n x = B_n \sin \frac{n\pi x}{a} \qquad (n = 1, 2, 3, \ldots) \tag{4-104}$$

These values of k^2 which yield nontrivial solutions of a homogeneous boundary problem are called the *characteristic values* or *eigenvalues* of the problem.

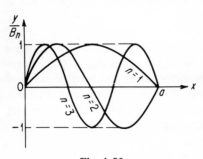

The solutions in Eq. (4–104) are called the *characteristic functions* or *eigenfunctions* of the problem. Several of these solutions are shown in Fig. 4–90. Note that the magnitude of B_n in the solutions is not defined.

These examples demonstrate that, while the homogeneous problem of Eq. (4–101) has only one trivial solution $y=0$, there are, in addition to $y=0$, nontrivial particular solutions of the homogeneous problem of Eq. (4–102).

Fig. 4–90

The essential difference between these two problems that leads to this difference in the solutions is the fact that the general solution, Eq. (4–103), of Eq. (4–102) is oscillatory. With an oscillatory general solution, homogeneous boundary conditions can be satisfied with solutions other than the trivial solution. (The student can now study Examples 4–42 and 4–43, and solve Problems 4–87 to 4–89.)

Next, consider *nonhomogeneous boundary problems.* A problem is said to be nonhomogeneous if either the equation or one or more of the boundary conditions is nonhomogeneous.

Take for example the equation

$$\frac{d^2y}{dx^2} - k^2y = f(x)$$

with the boundary conditions $y=0$ at $x=0$ and $y=b$ at $x=a$. This problem is nonhomogeneous for two reasons: the equation and the condition $y=b$ at $x=a$ are both nonhomogeneous. The general solution is

$$y = c_1e^{kx} + c_2e^{-kx} + Y_1(x)$$

While the associated homogeneous boundary problem with Eq. (4–101) has only a trivial solution $y=0$, it can be verified that, in the present case, there is a finite particular solution.

Next, take the nonhomogeneous problem of

$$\frac{d^2y}{dx^2} + k^2y = f(x)$$

with the same boundary conditions. The general solution is

$$y = A\cos kx + B\sin kx + Y_2(x)$$

From the condition $y=0$ at $x=0$, we have $A=-Y_2(0)$. From the condition $y=b$ at $x=a$, we have

$$B = \frac{b + Y_2(0)\cos ka - Y_2(a)}{\sin ka}$$

The particular solution is therefore

$$y = -Y_2(0)\cos kx + \frac{b + Y_2(0)\cos ka - Y_2(a)}{\sin ka}\sin kx + Y_2(x)$$

When the parameter k^2 is such that $\sin ka \neq 0$, we have one finite particular solution. However, if the parameter k^2 has the characteristic values such that $\sin ka = 0$, $y(x)$ will become infinite. Compare with the associated homogeneous boundary problem of Eq. (4–102), which has $y=0$ as the only solution if $\sin ka \neq 0$, and has characteristic solutions if $\sin ka = 0$.

These examples demonstrate that a nonhomogeneous boundary problem has a unique finite solution if the associated boundary problem has only a trivial solution $y=0$. If the associated homogeneous boundary problem has characteristic solutions, the solution of the nonhomogeneous boundary problem becomes infinite. The physical meaning of this behavior is demonstrated in Examples 4–44 and 4–45.

Example 4–42. In Fig. 4–91 is shown a straight uniform column with hinged ends under an axial load P. Find the elastic curve of the column.

Let $y(x)$ be a position of equilibrium. We have then $M(x)=Py$, and according to Eq. (4–58)

$$\frac{d^2y}{dx^2} + \frac{Py}{EI} = 0$$

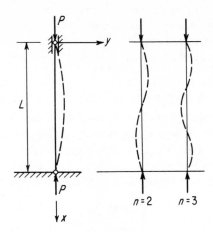

Fig. 4–91

The boundary conditions are $y=0$ at $x=0$ and at $x=L$. This is a homogeneous boundary problem. The general solution is

$$y = A \cos \sqrt{\frac{P}{EI}}\, x + B \sin \sqrt{\frac{P}{EI}}\, x$$

From the condition $y=0$ at $x=0$, we have $A=0$. From the condition $y=0$ at $x=L$, we have

$$B \sin \sqrt{\frac{P}{EI}}\, L = 0$$

One particular solution is obtained with $B=0$, giving $y(x)=0$ as a position of equilibrium. There are other solutions if the axial load P is of such a magnitude that

$$\sin \sqrt{\frac{P}{EI}}\, L = 0 \quad \text{or} \quad \sqrt{\frac{P_n}{EI}} = \frac{n\pi}{L} \qquad (n = 1, 2, 3, \ldots) \qquad (4\text{--}105)$$

For each of these values of P, we have the characteristic solutions

$$y_n = B_n \sin \sqrt{\frac{P_n}{EI}}\, x = B_n \sin \frac{n\pi x}{L} \qquad (n = 1, 2, 3, \ldots)$$

Several such possible positions of equilibrium are shown in Fig. 4–91.

This analysis is only approximate, because Eq. (4–58) is not exact. For this reason, the characteristic solutions thus obtained furnish no information about the magnitude B_n of the deflections. Also, the solution $y(x)=0$ for P slightly different from the values given by Eq. (4–105) does not seem to be realistic. However, this approximate analysis does give an interesting result. According to this analysis, the smallest value P_1 from Eq. (4–105) is the smallest load that can maintain the column in a deflected position. It can be shown, by another approach, that the straight position of equilibrium ($y=0$) is a stable position if $P<P_1$, but is unstable if $P>P_1$. For that reason, the values of P in Eq. (4–105) are called the *critical loads* of the column.

Example 4–43. In Fig. 4–92, a cantilever beam is shown rotating at an angular speed ω. Find the equation of the elastic curve of the beam for small

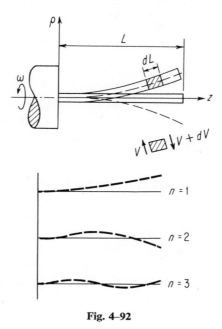

Fig. 4–92

deflections. The weight of the beam is assumed to be negligible compared with the other forces involved.

Let $m=$ mass per unit length of beam. Let $\rho(z)$ be the equation of the deflected beam. Take an element dL in length. Since the net ρ component of the forces acting on this element is $-dV$, as shown in Fig. 4–92, we have, according to the equation of motion, Eq. (4–60),

$$-dV = -m \cdot dL \cdot \omega^2 \rho$$

For small deflections, $dL \rightarrow dz$. Thus

$$\frac{dV}{dz} = m\omega^2\rho$$

(This beam is equivalent to one under a distributed load of $m\omega^2\rho$ per unit length.) According to Eqs. (4–93) and (4–58), $dM/dz = V$ and $d^2\rho/dz^2 = M/EI$. We have the differential equation for $\rho(z)$:

$$EI\frac{d^4\rho}{dz^4} = \frac{d^2M}{dz^2} = \frac{dV}{dz} = m\omega^2\rho$$

or

$$\frac{d^4\rho}{dz^4} - \alpha^4\rho = 0 \qquad (4\text{–}106)$$

where $\alpha^4 = m\omega^2/EI$. The boundary conditions are: $\rho = 0$ and $d\rho/dz = 0$ at $z = 0$, and $d^2\rho/dz^2 = 0$ ($M = 0$) and $d^3\rho/dz^3 = 0$ ($V = 0$) at $z = L$. This is a homogeneous boundary problem.

The general solution is

$$\begin{aligned}\rho &= c_1e^{\alpha z} + c_2e^{-\alpha z} + c_3e^{i\alpha z} + c_4e^{-i\alpha z}\\ &= A\cosh\alpha z + B\sinh\alpha z + C\cos\alpha z + D\sin\alpha z\end{aligned}$$

which involves oscillatory terms. From the two conditions at $z = 0$, we have $A + C = 0$ and $B + D = 0$. With $C = -A$ and $D = -B$, we have

$$\rho = A(\cosh\alpha z - \cos\alpha z) + B(\sinh\alpha z - \sin\alpha z) \qquad (4\text{–}107)$$

From the conditions at $z = L$, we have

$$A(\cosh\alpha L + \cos\alpha L) + B(\sinh\alpha L + \sin\alpha L) = 0 \qquad (4\text{–}108)$$

and

$$A(\sinh\alpha L - \sin\alpha L) + B(\cosh\alpha L + \cos\alpha L) = 0 \qquad (4\text{–}109)$$

One possible solution of these two equations is $A = B = 0$, giving $\rho(z) = 0$ for the position of the rotating beam. However, the boundary conditions in Eqs. (4–108) and (4–109) can also be satisfied with nonzero values of A and B if the parameter α^4 in Eq. (4–106) takes some particular values. Eliminating B from Eqs. (4–108) and (4–109),

$$A(\cosh\alpha L + \cos\alpha L)^2 - A(\sinh\alpha L - \sin\alpha L)(\sinh\alpha L + \sin\alpha L) = 0$$

With $A \neq 0$, $\cosh^2(\alpha L) - \sinh^2(\alpha L) = 1$, etc., this equation can be simplified to

$$1 + \cosh\alpha L \cdot \cos\alpha L = 0 \qquad (4\text{–}110)$$

This equation gives the characteristic values of α^4 in Eq. (4–106) to yield characteristic solutions. Solving Eq. (4–110) for α (by trials, or by finding graphically the intersections of the curves of $\cos\alpha L$ and $-1/\cosh\alpha L$), we have

$$\alpha L = 0.60\pi, 1, 49\pi, 2.50\pi, 3.50\pi, 4.50\pi, \ldots \qquad (4\text{–}111)$$

or, since $\alpha^2 = \omega\sqrt{m/EI}$

$$\omega L^2\sqrt{\frac{m}{EI}} = (0.60\pi)^2, (1.49\pi)^2, \ldots$$

These values of ω to yield characteristic solutions are called the *critical speeds*, at which this approximate analysis indicates a position of the beam other than a straight position.

To find $\rho(z)$ at each of these critical speeds, let α_n ($n=1, 2, 3, \ldots$) denote the successive values of α in Eq. (4–111). With B expressed in terms of A, in accordance with Eqs. (4–108) and (4–109), we have from Eq. (4–107) for each value of α_n

$$\rho_n(z) = A_n \left[(\cosh \alpha_n z - \cos \alpha_n z) - \frac{\cosh \alpha_n L + \cos \alpha_n L}{\sinh \alpha_n L + \sin \alpha_n L} \cdot (\sinh \alpha_n z - \sin \alpha_n z) \right]$$

$$= E_n \left(\frac{\cosh \alpha_n z - \cos \alpha_n z}{\cosh \alpha_n L + \cos \alpha_n L} - \frac{\sinh \alpha_n z - \sin \alpha_n z}{\sinh \alpha_n L + \sin \alpha_n L} \right)$$

Due to the approximation involved in the beam equation used, the magnitude A_n or E_n of the deflection is undetermined. Several of these characteristic solutions are shown in Fig. 4–92.

Example 4–44. In Fig. 4–93 is shown a uniform column with hinged ends under the action of loads P with eccentricity δ. Find the elastic curve.

Let $y(x)$ be the elastic curve of the column. At any section, $M(x)=P(\delta+y)$. According to Eq. (4–58)

$$EI \frac{d^2 y}{dx^2} + Py = -P\delta$$

The boundary conditions are $y=0$ at $x=0$ and at $x=L$. This is a nonhomogeneous boundary problem, because the differential equation is nonhomogeneous. The general solution is

$$y = A \cos \sqrt{\frac{P}{EI}} x + B \sin \sqrt{\frac{P}{EI}} x - \delta$$

From the boundary conditions, we have $A=\delta$ and

$$B = \frac{\delta}{\sin \sqrt{\frac{P}{EI}} L} \left(1 - \cos \sqrt{\frac{P}{EI}} L \right)$$

Thus

$$y = \frac{\delta}{\sin \sqrt{\frac{P}{EI}} L} \left(1 - \cos \sqrt{\frac{P}{EI}} L \right) \sin \sqrt{\frac{P}{EI}} x$$

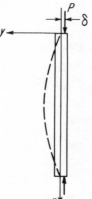

Fig. 4–93

The associated homogeneous boundary problem is given in Example 4–42. When $\sin (\sqrt{P/EI} \cdot L) \neq 0$, the solution of Example 4–42 is the trivial $y=0$, while in the present case, the solution $y(x)$ is not trivial. Physically, this means that, with eccentric load, the column cannot remain in a straight position. When P has the value of one of the critical loads, such that $\sin (\sqrt{P/EI} \cdot L)=0$, Example 4–42 has a nontrivial characteristic solution. In the present case, B, and therefore y, become infinite. Physically, this means that, when an eccentric load reaches a critical value, the column will have very large deflections.

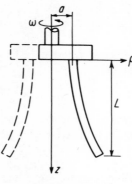

Fig. 4–94

Example 4–45. A cantilever beam is attached to a base rotating at speed ω, as shown in Fig. 4–94. Find the elastic curve of the beam.

For the coordinate system shown in Fig. 4–94, Eq. (4–106) is applicable

$$\frac{d^4\rho}{dz^4} - \alpha^4\rho = 0$$

where $\alpha^4 = m\omega^2/EI$. The boundary conditions in this case are $\rho = a$ and $d\rho/dz = 0$ at $z = 0$, and $d^2\rho/dz^2 = 0$ $(M = 0)$ and $d^3\rho/dz^3 = 0$ $(V = 0)$ at $z = L$. This is a nonhomogeneous boundary problem, because of the condition $\rho = a$ at $z = 0$.

The general solution of the differential equation is

$$\rho = A \cos \alpha z + B \sinh \alpha z + C \cos \alpha z + D \sin \alpha z$$

From the two conditions at $z = 0$, we have $A + C = a$ and $B + D = 0$. Thus

$$\rho = A(\cosh \alpha z - \cos \alpha z) + B(\sinh \alpha z - \sin \alpha z) + a \cos \alpha z$$

From the two conditions at $z = L$, we have

$$A(\cosh \alpha L + \cos \alpha L) + B(\sinh \alpha L + \sin \alpha L) - a \cos \alpha L = 0$$

and

$$A(\sinh \alpha L - \sin \alpha L) + B(\cosh \alpha L + \cos \alpha L) + a \sin \alpha L = 0$$

Solving for A and B, we have

$$A = \frac{a}{2} \cdot \frac{1 + \cos \alpha L \cosh \alpha L + \sin \alpha L \sinh \alpha L}{1 + \cosh \alpha L \cos \alpha L}$$

and

$$B = -\frac{a}{2} \cdot \frac{\cosh \alpha L \sin \alpha L + \sinh \alpha L \cos \alpha L}{1 + \cosh \alpha L \cos \alpha L}$$

The associated homogeneous boundary problem is given in Example 4–43. When $(1 + \cosh \alpha L \cos \alpha L) \neq 0$, the solution of Example 4–43 is the trivial $\rho = 0$, while in the present case $\rho(z)$ is finite. When the speed ω is equal to one of the critical speeds, such as $(1 + \cosh \alpha L \cos \alpha L) = 0$, Example 4–43 has a characteristic solution. In the present case, A and B, and therefore the deflection $\rho(z)$, become infinite, a phenomenon generally referred to as *resonance*.

Problems

4–87. The lower end of a column is clamped, while the upper end is free from restraint, as shown in Fig. 4–95. Find the critical loads and the characteristic solutions of the elastic curve.

$$\text{Ans. } y_n = B_n \sin \frac{(2n-1)\pi x}{2L}$$

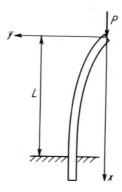

Fig. 4–95

4–88. A beam with clamped ends, as shown in Fig. 4–96, rotates at an angular speed ω. Find the lowest speed ω_1 at which the beam will have a deflected position. The weight of the beam is small compared with other forces involved.

$$\text{Ans. } \left(\frac{4.73}{L}\right)^2 \sqrt{\frac{EI}{m}}$$

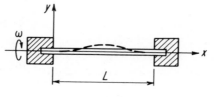

Fig. 4–96

4–89. If the two ends of the beam in the previous problem are hinged to the blocks, find the critical speeds and the characteristic solutions of the elastic curve.

$$\text{Ans. } \omega_n = \left(\frac{n\pi}{L}\right)^2 \sqrt{\frac{EI}{m}}, \ y_n \propto n\pi \sinh \frac{n\pi x}{L} + \sinh n\pi \sin \frac{n\pi x}{L}$$

4–90. A simply supported beam is loaded with axial loads P and a small uniformly distributed load w per unit length, as shown in Fig. 4–97. Find the elastic curve. Under what conditions does the deflection tend to become exceedingly large?

$$\text{Ans. } P_n = \left(\frac{n\pi}{L}\right)^2 EI$$

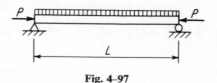

Fig. 4-97

4-16. Simultaneous linear equations with constant coefficients

In previous articles, simultaneous differential equations that can be solved one at a time have been encountered. In the present article, linear equations with constant coefficients that must be solved simultaneously are discussed.

Take two differential equations for $y(x)$ and $z(x)$:

$$\left(A_0 \frac{d^n y}{dx^n} + A_1 \frac{d^{n-1} y}{dx^{n-1}} + \ldots + A_n y\right) + \left(B_0 \frac{d^p z}{dx^p} + B_1 \frac{d^{p-1} z}{dx^{p-1}} + \ldots + B_p z\right) = f_1(x)$$

$$\left(C_0 \frac{d^q y}{dx^q} + C_1 \frac{d^{q-1} y}{dx^{q-1}} + \ldots + C_q y\right) + \left(D_0 \frac{d^m z}{dx^m} + D_1 \frac{d^{m-1} z}{dx^{m-1}} + \ldots + D_m z\right) = f_2(x)$$

For simplicity of presentation, let the linear operations be represented by linear operators L_{11}, L_{12}, etc.; e.g.,

$$L_{11} y = \left(A_0 \frac{d^n}{dx^n} + A_1 \frac{d^{n-1}}{dx^{n-1}} + \ldots + A_n\right) y \equiv A_0 \frac{d^n y}{dx^n} + A_1 \frac{d^{n-1} y}{dx^{n-1}} + \ldots + A_n y$$

The simultaneous equations can then be rewritten as

$$L_{11} y + L_{12} z = f_1(x) \tag{4-112}$$
$$L_{21} y + L_{22} z = f_2(x) \tag{4-113}$$

An equation involving only one dependent variable can be obtained by eliminating the other dependent variable, in a manner very similar to the method of successive elimination in the solution of simultaneous linear algebraic equations. To eliminate z, operate on the first equation with L_{22} and the second equation with L_{12}:

$$L_{22} L_{11} y + L_{22} L_{12} z = L_{22} f_1(x) \tag{4-114}$$
$$L_{12} L_{21} y + L_{12} L_{22} z = L_{12} f_2(x) \tag{4-115}$$

It can be easily verified that $L_{22} L_{12} z = L_{12} L_{22} z$. We have by subtracting one equation from the other

$$(L_{11} L_{22} - L_{12} L_{21}) y = L_{22} f_1(x) - L_{12} f_2(x) \tag{4-116}$$

As the operator $L_{11} L_{22}$ is of the $(m+n)$th order, and $L_{12} L_{21}$ is of the $(p+q)$th order, the order of Eq. (4-116) is equal to the higher of the two.

After the general solution $y(x)$ is found, it can be substituted into Eq. (4-114) or (4-115) to yield a differential equation for $z(x)$. In the general solution of $z(x)$ thus obtained, the number of arbitrary constants may appear to be higher than the order of the differential equation. Actually, these constants are not independent, but must satisfy the other equation of Eqs. (4–114) and (4–115). Examples of finding the general solutions in this manner are shown in Example 4–46.

If in the solution of the simultaneous equations, the variable y is eliminated instead of z from Eqs. (4–114) and (4–115), we obtain a differential equation for $z(x)$:

$$(L_{11}L_{22}-L_{12}L_{21})z = L_{11}f_2(x)-L_{21}f_1(x) \qquad (4\text{–}117)$$

Note that the same operator appears on the left-hand sides of Eqs. (4–116) and (4–117). Thus, the complementary functions of the solutions $y(x)$ and $z(x)$ will involve the same functions. If $y=A_1e^{m_1x}+ \ldots$, we have $z=B_1e^{m_1x}+ \ldots$ While the constants A_1 and B_1, etc., may be different, the same constants $m_1, \ldots$ will appear in both general solutions.

Example 4–46. Two masses of M each are connected with springs, as shown in Fig. 4–98. Neglecting the mass of the springs, find the natural frequencies of undamped free vibrations of the masses.

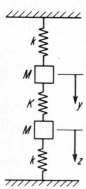

Let the displacements of the masses from their positions of static equilibrium be denoted by $y(t)$ and $z(t)$, as shown in Fig. 4–98. At any y and z, the net force acting on the upper mass is $-ky+K(z-y)$ in the positive direction of y and z. The net force acting on the lower mass is $-K(z-y)-kz$. Thus

$$M\ddot{y} = -ky+K(z-y)$$
$$M\ddot{z} = -K(z-y)-kz$$

which can be rewritten as

$$\left(\frac{d^2}{dt^2}+\frac{k+K}{M}\right)y-\frac{K}{M}z = 0 \qquad (4\text{–}118)$$

$$-\frac{K}{M}y+\left(\frac{d^2}{dt^2}+\frac{k+K}{M}\right)z = 0 \qquad (4\text{–}119)$$

Fig. 4–98

To eliminate z, operate on Eq. (4–118) with $d^2/dt^2+(k+K)/M$ and on Eq. (4–119) with $-K/M$, and then subtract:

$$\left[\left(\frac{d^2}{dt^2}+\frac{k+K}{M}\right)\left(\frac{d^2}{dt^2}+\frac{k+K}{M}\right)-\left(\frac{K}{M}\right)^2\right]y = 0$$

$$\left(\frac{d^4}{dt^4}+2\frac{k+K}{M}\frac{d^2}{dt^2}+\frac{k^2+2kK}{M^2}\right)y = 0$$

The characteristic equation is

$$m^4+2\frac{k+K}{M}m^2+\frac{k^2+2kK}{M^2} = 0$$

It is not difficult to see that there are two negative values of m^2. In many engineering textbooks, $-p^2$ is used for m^2, so that

$$p^4 - 2\frac{k+K}{M}p^2 + \frac{k^2+2kK}{M^2} = 0 \qquad (4\text{-}120)$$

As will be seen later, p is the natural circular frequency of vibrations of the masses. Equation (4-120) is therefore called the *frequency equation*. Let the two positive solutions of p^2 be p_1^2 and p_2^2.

$$p_1^2 = \frac{k+2K}{M} \quad \text{and} \quad p_2^2 = \frac{k}{M}$$

The four solutions of the characteristic equation are therefore $m = \pm ip_1$ and $\pm ip_2$. Thus

$$y(t) = A\cos p_1 t + B\sin p_1 t + C\cos p_2 t + D\sin p_2 t \qquad (4\text{-}121)$$

The general solution for $z(t)$ can be obtained in this case by simply substituting $y(t)$ into Eq. (4-118). However, for the purpose of instruction, we substitute $y(t)$ into Eq. (4-119) instead, to obtain

$$\left(\frac{d^2}{dt^2} + \frac{k+K}{M}\right)z = \frac{K}{M}(A\cos p_1 t + B\sin p_1 t + C\cos p_2 t + D\sin p_2 t)$$

The general solution of this equation is

$$z(t) = E\cos\sqrt{\frac{k+K}{M}}\,t + F\sin\sqrt{\frac{k+K}{M}}\,t - (A\cos p_1 t + B\sin p_1 t)$$
$$+ (C\cos p_2 t + D\sin p_2 t) \qquad (4\text{-}122)$$

In this general solution of $z(t)$, we have six arbitrary constants. These six constants are not independent, but must satisfy Eq. (4-118). Substituting Eqs. (4-121) and (4-122) into Eq. (4-118), we obtain $E=0$ and $F=0$. (That $E=F=0$ can also be seen from the fact that the complementary functions of $y(t)$ and $z(t)$ must involve the same functions.)

$$z(t) = -(A\cos p_1 t + B\sin p_1 t) + (C\cos p_2 t + D\sin p_2 t)$$

Thus, in $y(t)$ and $z(t)$ together, only four arbitrary constants A, B, C and D are involved, which are determined by the initial values y_0, $\dot{y}_0$, z_0 and $\dot{z}_0$ at $t=0$.

It is interesting to note that, if $A=B=0$ (for example, with $y_0=z_0$ and $\dot{y}_0=\dot{z}_0=0$), we have $y(t)=z(t)$. The two masses will move together with a circular frequency $p_2=\sqrt{k/M}$. In this case, the middle spring is inactive. If $C=D=0$ (for example, with $y_0=-z_0$ and $\dot{y}_0=\dot{z}_0=0$), we have $y(t)=-z(t)$. The two masses will move in opposite directions with a higher circular frequency $p_1=\sqrt{(k+2K)/M}$. These two cases represent the two principal modes of vibrations of two masses. In general, these two modes are superposed.

Problems

4–91. Tank A and tank B are connected as shown in Fig. 4–99. At $t=0$, there is in tank A 100 gal of brine with 50 lb of salt in solution; and in tank B, 50 gal of water. Water is then supplied at the rate of $\frac{4}{3}$ gal per min to tank A, and the mixture from tank B is taken out at the same rate. Find the number of pounds of salt left in tank A as a function of t in minutes.

Ans. $\frac{1}{7}\,(250e^{-0.01t}+100e^{-0.08t})$

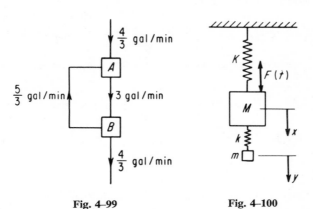

Fig. 4–99   Fig. 4–100

4–92. A mass M is suspended with a spring of constant K, and is acted upon by a periodic force $F(t)=F_0 \sin \omega t$, as shown in Fig. 4–100. There is a small mass m attached to M with a spring of constant k. Find the displacement $x(t)$ of M from its position of static equilibrium in steady-state motion (i.e., the particular integral of $x(t)$, the free vibrations being damped out). Show that, if k and m are so chosen that $\sqrt{k/m}=\omega$, the mass M is stationary. This is the principle of the dynamic vibration absorber.

4–93. Two circuits are coupled with a condenser C_0, as shown in Fig. 4–101. Knowing that $q_1=q_2=q_0=0$ at $t=0$ on closing the switch, find $i_1\,(t)$ and $i_2\,(t)$. (Hint: since $dq_0=(i_1-i_2)dt=d(q_1-q_2)$, and $q_0=q_0=q_2=0$ at $t=0$, we have $q_0=q_1-q_2$ at all time.)

Ans. $\dfrac{E}{2L}\left(\dfrac{\sin p_1 t}{p_1} \pm \dfrac{\sin p_2 t}{p_2}\right)$,   where $p_1^2=\dfrac{1}{LC}$, $p_2^2=\dfrac{1}{L}\left(\dfrac{1}{C}+\dfrac{2}{C_0}\right)$

4–94. Two circuits are coupled magnetically as shown in Fig. 4–102. According to Kirchhoff's law,

$$L\frac{di_1}{dt}+M\frac{di_2}{dt}+Ri_1 = E$$

$$L\frac{di_2}{dt}+M\frac{di_1}{dt}+Ri_2 = 0$$

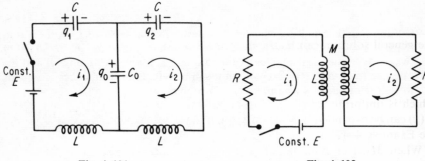

Fig. 4–101   Fig. 4–102

where M is called the *mutual inductance coefficient*. Show that, with $i_1 = i_2 = 0$ at $t = 0$ when the switch is closed,

$$i_1(t) = \frac{E}{R}(1 - e^{-at}\cosh bt)$$

$$i_2(t) = -\frac{EL}{RM}e^{-at}\sinh bt$$

where $a = RL/(L^2 - M^2)$ and $b = RM/(L^2 - M^2)$.

4–17. Homogeneous linear equations with variable coefficients

As stated in Art. 4–9, the general solution of a homogeneous linear equation, with constant or variable coefficients, is given by Eq. (4–52). In this article, methods of obtaining the general solution are presented. These methods are applicable to linear equations with constant as well as variable coefficients. However, as a simpler method is available for equations with constant coefficients (see Art. 4–12), these methods are used mainly for equations with variable coefficients.

In general, there is no general method of solving equations with variable coefficients of order higher than the first. A method which sometimes yields a solution is to assume a series solution:

$$y = a_0 + a_1 x + a_2 x^2 + \ldots = \sum_{n=0}^{\infty} a_n x^n$$

However, this method works only when the (unknown) general solution can be expanded into a Maclaurin series (i.e., Taylor series about $x = 0$). If this is not the case, other forms of solution must be assumed. Various forms of solution are presented below for second-order linear equations, as these equations represent one of the most important classes of equations in engineering and physics. The aim is to find the general solution $y = c_1 y_1(x) + c_2 y_2(x)$. The theorems involved will be stated without proof.

For the equation

$$\frac{d^2y}{dx^2} + M(x)\frac{dy}{dx} + N(x)y = 0 \qquad (4\text{–}123)$$

the general solution can be found by assuming

$$y = \sum_{n=0}^{\infty} a_n x^n \qquad (4\text{–}124)$$

which is uniformly convergent in an interval $-R < x < R$ if both $M(x)$ and $N(x)$ can be expanded in Maclaurin series in the same interval. As an example, see Example 4–47.

When $M(x)$ or $N(x)$ becomes infinite at $x=0$, and therefore cannot be expanded in a Maclaurin series, an assumed solution in the form of Eq. (4–124) will not lead to a solution. If, however, $xM(x)$ and $x^2N(x)$ can be expanded in Maclaurin series, a solution can be obtained with

$$y = \sum_{n=0}^{\infty} a_n x^{n+\alpha} \qquad (4\text{–}125)$$

where α is a constant to be determined. Sometimes two values of α are found which lead to the general solution with $y_1(x) = \sum_{n=0}^{\infty} a_n x^{n+\alpha_1}$ and

$y_2(x) = \sum_{n=0}^{\infty} b_n x^{n+\alpha_2}$ (see Example 4–48). When $\alpha_1 = \alpha_2$, or α_2 is greater than α_1 by an integer, we will find that Eq. (4–125) does not always lead to a general solution. In such a case, use Eq. (4–125) with α_1, the smaller of the two, to obtain y with one or two arbitrary constants. In the former case, let

$$y_2 = y_1 \log_e x + \sum_{n=0}^{\infty} b_n x^{n+\alpha_1} \qquad (4\text{–}126)$$

As an example, see Example 4–49.

If $xM(x)$ or $x^2N(x)$ cannot be expanded in a Maclaurin series, Eq. (4–125) may lead to one solution $y_1(x)$ or none at all. If $y_1(x)$ can be obtained in this way, $y_2(x)$ can be obtained by the method of reduction of order, which will be presented in the following article.

In the discussion above, solutions in the form of power series of x are used. When $M(x)$ and $N(x)$ are finite and can be expanded about x_0, it is sometimes desirable to use power series of $(x-x_0)$. By using a new variable $z = x - x_0$, the differential equation can be transformed into an equation for $y(z)$, with a power series of z as its solution.

Some equations with variable coefficients can be reduced to one with constant coefficients and solved by the method in Art. 4–12. A well known example is *Euler's* or *Cauchy's linear equation*

$$a_0 x^n \frac{d^n y}{dx^n} + a_1 x^{n-1} \frac{d^{n-1}y}{dx^{n-1}} + \ldots + a_{n-1}x\frac{dy}{dx} + a_n y = f(x) \qquad (4\text{–}127)$$

which can be reduced to an equation with constant coefficients by changing the independent variable to z, with $x = e^z$.

Example 4-47. Find a power series solution of *Legendre's equation*

$$(1-x^2)\frac{d^2y}{dx^2} - 2x\frac{dy}{dx} + k(k+1)y = 0 \tag{4-128}$$

where $k = $ constant. This equation occurs frequently when polar-spherical coordinates are used in analysis.

Legendre's equation can be rewritten as

$$\frac{d^2y}{dx^2} - \frac{2x}{1-x^2}\frac{dy}{dx} + \frac{k(k+1)}{1-x^2}y = 0$$

As both coefficients can be expanded in Maclaurin series in the interval $-1 < x < 1$, a general solution can be obtained for this interval with Eq. (4-124):

$$y = b_0 + b_1 x + b_2 x^2 + \ldots = \sum_{n=0}^{\infty} b_n x^n$$

Then

$$2x\frac{dy}{dx} = 2x\sum_{n=0}^{\infty} nb_n x^{n-1} = \sum_{n=0}^{\infty} 2nb_n x^n$$

$$(1-x^2)\frac{d^2y}{dx^2} = (1-x^2)\sum_{n=0}^{\infty} n(n-1)b_n x^{n-2}$$

$$= \sum_{n=0}^{\infty} n(n-1)b_n x^{n-2} - \sum_{n=0}^{\infty} n(n-1)b_n x^n$$

To determine the coefficients b_n, we substitute these series into the differential equation.

In collecting terms, it is more convenient to have the general term of each series in x^n. In the first series of the last expression, the first two terms (for $n = 0$ and 1) are zero. With $r = n-2$, we have

$$\sum_{n=0}^{\infty} n(n-1)b_n x^{n-2} = \sum_{n=2}^{\infty} n(n-1)b_n x^{n-2} = \sum_{r=0}^{\infty} (r+2)(r+1)b_{r+2} x^r$$

Since r is merely a dummy variable, the value of the series is not changed by replacing r with n. Thus

$$\sum_{n=0}^{\infty} n(n-1)b_n x^{n-2} = \sum_{n=0}^{\infty} (n+2)(n+1)b_{n+2} x^n$$

Substituting these series into the differential equation, we have

$$\sum_{n=0}^{\infty}(n+2)(n+1)b_{n+2}x^n - \sum_{n=0}^{\infty}n(n-1)b_nx^n - \sum_{n=0}^{\infty}2nb_nx^n + \sum_{n=0}^{\infty}k(k+1)b_nx^n = 0$$

$$\sum_{n=0}^{\infty}\{(n+2)(n+1)b_{n+2} - [n(n-1)+2n-k(k+1)]b_n\}x^n = 0$$

Since this series equals zero at all values of x in $-1 < x < 1$, the coefficient of each term x^n must be zero. Thus, for any $n(=0, 1, 2, \ldots)$

$$(n+2)(n+1)b_{n+2} - [n(n-1)+2n-k(k+1)]b_n = 0$$

$$b_{n+2} = \frac{n^2+n-k(k+1)}{(n+2)(n+1)}b_n$$

This is a relation among the coefficients and is called a *recursion relation*. Thus

$$b_2 = -\frac{k(k+1)}{2}b_0$$

$$b_4 = \frac{6-k(k+1)}{4\cdot 3}b_2 = \frac{-[6-k(k+1)]k(k+1)}{4!}b_0 = \frac{k(k-2)(k+1)(k+3)}{4!}b_0$$

$\cdot\quad\cdot\quad\cdot\quad\cdot\quad\cdot\quad\cdot\quad\cdot\quad\cdot\quad\cdot\quad\cdot\quad\cdot\quad\cdot$

$$b_3 = \frac{2-k(k+1)}{3!}b_1 = \frac{-(k-1)(k+2)}{3!}b_1$$

$$b_5 = \frac{12-k(k+1)}{5\cdot 4}b_3 = \frac{(k-1)(k-3)(k+2)(k+4)}{5!}b_1$$

$\cdot\quad\cdot\quad\cdot\quad\cdot\quad\cdot\quad\cdot\quad\cdot\quad\cdot\quad\cdot\quad\cdot\quad\cdot\quad\cdot$

$$y = \sum_{n=0}^{\infty}b_nx^n = b_0\left[1-\frac{k(k+1)}{2!}x^2+\frac{k(k-2)(k+1)(k+3)}{4!}x^4 - \cdots\right]$$

$$+b_1\left[x-\frac{(k-1)(k+2)}{3!}x^3+\frac{(k-1)(k-3)(k+2)(k+4)}{5!}x^5 - \cdots\right]$$

This is the general solution, since it involves two arbitrary constants, b_0 and b_1, and the two series are linearly independent.

Example 4–48. Find a series solution of *Bessel's equation*

$$x^2\frac{d^2y}{dx^2}+x\frac{dy}{dx}+(x^2-k^2)y = 0 \tag{4–129}$$

where $k=$constant. This equation occurs frequently when polar-cylindrical coordinates are used in analysis.

Bessel's equation can be rewritten as

$$\frac{d^2y}{dx^2}+\frac{1}{x}\frac{dy}{dx}+\left(1-\frac{k^2}{x^2}\right)y = 0$$

Comparing with Eq. (4–123), we have $M(x)=1/x$ and $N(x)=1-(k^2/x^2)$. While $M(x)$ and $N(x)$ become infinite at $x=0$, $xM(x)$ and $x^2N(x)$ can be expanded in Maclaurin series. For a general solution, use Eq. (4–125):

$$y = \sum_{n=0}^{\infty} b_n x^{n+\alpha}$$

Then

$$x\frac{dy}{dx} = x\sum_{n=0}^{\infty} (n+\alpha)b_n x^{n+\alpha-1} = x^\alpha \sum_{n=0}^{\infty} (n+\alpha)b_n x^n$$

$$x^2\frac{d^2y}{dx^2} = x^2 \sum_{n=0}^{\infty} (n+\alpha)(n+\alpha-1)b_n x^{n+\alpha-2} = x^\alpha \sum_{n=0}^{\infty} (n+\alpha)(n+\alpha-1)b_n x^n$$

and

$$(x^2-k^2)y = x^\alpha \sum_{n=0}^{\infty} b_n x^{n+2} - x^\alpha \sum_{n=0}^{\infty} k^2 b_n x^n$$

Since the first series in the last expression can be rewritten as

$$\sum_{n=0}^{\infty} b_n x^{n+2} = \sum_{r=2}^{\infty} b_{r-2} x^r = \sum_{n=2}^{\infty} b_{n-2} x^n$$

we have, upon substituting these series into the differential equation,

$$x^\alpha \left\{ \sum_{n=0}^{\infty} [(n+\alpha)(n+\alpha-1)+(n+\alpha)-k^2]b_n x^n + \sum_{n=2}^{\infty} b_{n-2} x^n \right\} = 0$$

$$x^\alpha \left\{ \sum_{n=0}^{\infty} [(n+\alpha)^2-k^2]b_n x^n + \sum_{n=2}^{\infty} b_{n-2} x^n \right\} = 0$$

As x^α does not vanish, we have

$$\sum_{n=0}^{\infty} [(n+\alpha)^2-k^2]b_n x^n + \sum_{n=2}^{\infty} b_{n-2} x^n = 0$$

$$(\alpha^2-k^2)b_0 + [(1+\alpha)^2-k^2]b_1 x + \sum_{n=2}^{\infty} \left\{ [(n+\alpha)^2-k^2]b_n + b_{n-2} \right\} x_n = 0 \quad (4\text{–}130)$$

As this equation is applicable for various values of x, all the coefficients must be zero. The equation obtained by setting the coefficient of the term of the lowest order to zero is known as the *indicial equation*. In this case, the indicial equation is

$$\alpha^2-k^2 = 0$$

from which we determine the constant $\alpha = \pm k$. If $k=0$, the two values of α are equal. If k is an integer, the two values of α differ by an integer. As will be seen, in both these cases, only one solution $y_1(x)$ is obtained. When k is neither zero nor an integer, we obtain two solutions $y_1(x)$ and $y_2(x)$, and therefore the general solution, as follows:

With $\alpha = \pm k$, Eq. (4–130) is satisfied with an arbitrary value of b_0, $b_1 = 0$ and

$$b_n = -\frac{1}{(n+\alpha)^2 - k^2} b_{n-2} \qquad (n \geq 2)$$

Since $b_1 = 0$, we have $b_3 = b_5 = \ldots = 0$.

One solution $y_1(x)$ is obtained with $\alpha = k$:

$$b_n = -\frac{1}{n(2k+n)} b_{n-2} \qquad (n \geq 2)$$

$$b_2 = -\frac{1}{2(2k+2)} b_0$$

$$b_4 = -\frac{1}{4(2k+4)} b_2 = \frac{1}{2 \cdot 4(2k+2)(2k+4)} b_0$$

. . . .

$$y_1(x) = \sum_{n=0}^{\infty} b_n x^{n+\alpha} = b_0 x^k \left[1 - \frac{x^2}{2(2k+2)} + \frac{x^4}{2 \cdot 4(2k+2)(2k+4)} - \cdots \right]$$

The other solution $y_2(x)$ is obtained with $\alpha = -k$. In a similar manner, we obtain

$$y_2(x) = b_0 x^{-k} \left[1 + \frac{x^2}{2(2k-2)} + \frac{x^4}{2 \cdot 4(2k-2)(2k-4)} + \cdots \right]$$

If $k=0$, these two solutions become identical. If k is a positive integer, $y_2(x)$ becomes infinite. If k is a negative integer, $y_1(x)$ becomes infinite. When k is neither zero nor an integer, we have the general solution $y = c_1 y_1(x) + c_2 y_2(x)$.

As Bessel's equation is encountered very often in practical analysis, the series $y_1(x)$ and $y_2(x)$ have been computed and tabulated with b_0 taking the particular value $b_0 = 1/2^k \Gamma(k+1)$, and can be found in Jahnke and Emde's *Tables of Functions*. (Here, the *Gamma function* $\Gamma(k+1)$ is the definite integral $\int_0^\infty x^k e^{-x}\, dx$. It can be shown that, when k is a positive integer, $\Gamma(k+1) = k!$ Values of the Gamma function can also be found in Jahnke and Emde's tables.) The series $y_1(x)$ becomes what is called the *Bessel function* of the first kind of order k:

$$J_k(x) = \frac{x^k}{2^k \Gamma(k+1)} - \frac{x^{k+2}}{2^{k+2} \Gamma(k+2)} + \frac{x^{k+4}}{2^{k+4} 2! \Gamma(k+3)} - \cdots$$

$$= \sum_{s=0}^{\infty} \frac{(-1)^s}{s! \Gamma(k+s+1)} \left(\frac{x}{2}\right)^{k+2s} \qquad (4\text{–}131)$$

(Note: for $s=0$, $s! = 0! = \Gamma(1) = 1$.)

It can be seen that

$$y_2(x) = \sum_{s=0}^{\infty} \frac{(-1)^s}{s! \Gamma(s-k+1)} \left(\frac{x}{2}\right)^{2s-k} = J_{-k}(x)$$

Thus, the general solution of Bessel's equation is

$$y = c_1 J_k(x) + c_2 J_{-k}(x) \qquad (k \neq 0 \text{ or an integer})$$

Example 4–49. Find the general solution of the equation

$$z^2 \frac{d^2 y}{dz^2} + z \frac{dy}{dz} + p^2 z^2 y = 0$$

Also find the particular solution for the following boundary conditions: $dy/dz = 0$ at $z = 0$, and $y = 0$ at $z = L$.

This equation can be reduced to a Bessel's equation by changing the independent variable to $x = pz$. With

$$\frac{dy}{dz} = \frac{dy}{dx} \cdot \frac{1}{dz/dx} = p \frac{dy}{dx}$$

$$\frac{d^2 y}{dz^2} = \frac{d}{dx}\left(\frac{dy}{dz}\right) \cdot \frac{1}{dz/dx} = \frac{d}{dx}\left(p \frac{dy}{dx}\right) \cdot p = p^2 \frac{d^2 y}{dx^2}$$

we have

$$x^2 \frac{d^2 y}{dx^2} + x \frac{dy}{dx} + x^2 y = 0$$

This is Bessel's equation of zero order, with $k = 0$ in Eq. (4–129).

In the previous example, we have obtained two solutions $y_1(x)$ and $y_2(x)$ for Bessel's equation. However, when $k = 0$, y_1 is the same as y_2. Thus, we have only one series solution $J_0(x)$ (see Eq. (4–131)):

$$J_0(x) = \sum_{s=0}^{\infty} \frac{(-1)^s}{(s!)^2} \left(\frac{x}{2}\right)^{2s} = 1 - \frac{x^2}{2^2} + \frac{x^4}{2^2 4^2} - \frac{x^6}{2^2 4^2 6^2} + \cdots$$

We must look for another solution which is linearly independent of $J_0(x)$.

In the previous example, by assuming that $y = \sum_{n=0}^{\infty} b_n x^{n+\alpha}$, we find α_1 and $\alpha_2 = \mp k (= 0$ in this case). According to Eq. (4–126), we assume for the second solution

$$y = J_0(x) \log_e x + \sum_{n=0}^{\infty} b_n x^n$$

Then

$$\frac{dy}{dx} = J_0' \log_e x + \frac{J_0}{x} + \sum_{n=0}^{\infty} n b_n x^{n-1}$$

$$\frac{d^2 y}{dx^2} = J_0'' \log_e x + \frac{2J_0'}{x} - \frac{J_0}{x^2} + \sum_{n=0}^{\infty} n(n-1) b_n x^{n-2}$$

Substituting into the differential equation

$$(x^2 J_0'' + x J_0' + x^2 J_0) \log_e x + 2x J_0' + \sum_{n=0}^{\infty} n^2 b_n x^n + \sum_{n=0}^{\infty} b_n x^{n+2} = 0$$

Since $J_0(x)$ is a solution of the differential equation, the value in the parentheses is zero. The value $J_0'(x)$ is

$$\frac{d}{dx} J_0(x) = \frac{d}{dx} \sum_{n=0}^{\infty} \frac{(-1)^n}{(n!)^2} \left(\frac{x}{2}\right)^{2n} = \sum_{n=0}^{\infty} (-1)^n \frac{n}{(n!)^2} \left(\frac{x}{2}\right)^{2n-1}$$

Thus

$$\sum_{n=1}^{\infty} (-1)^n \frac{2n}{2^{2n-1}(n!)^2} x^{2n} + \sum_{n=0}^{\infty} n^2 b_n x^n + \sum_{n=0}^{\infty} b_n x^{n+2} = 0$$

The first series contains only even powers of x. In collecting terms, it is convenient to separate the odd and even terms of the two other series in terms of x^{2n+1} and x^{2n}, respectively:

$$\sum_{n=0}^{\infty} n^2 b_n x^n = (b_1 x + 3^2 b_3 x^3 + \ldots) + (2^2 b_2 x^2 + 4^2 b_4 x^4 + \ldots)$$

$$= \sum_{n=0}^{\infty} (2n+1)^2 b_{2n+1} x^{2n+1} + \sum_{n=1}^{\infty} (2n)^2 b_{2n} x^{2n}$$

$$\sum_{n=0}^{\infty} b_n x^{n+2} = (b_1 x^3 + b_3 x^5 + \ldots) + (b_0 x^2 + b_2 x^4 + \ldots)$$

$$= \sum_{n=1}^{\infty} b_{2n-1} x^{2n+1} + \sum_{n=1}^{\infty} b_{2n-2} x^{2n}$$

Thus

$$b_1 x + \sum_{n=1}^{\infty} [(2n+1)^2 b_{2n+1} + b_{2n-1}] x^{2n+1}$$

$$+ \sum_{n=1}^{\infty} \left[(-1)^n \frac{2n}{2^{2n-1}(n!)^2} + (2n)^2 b_{2n} + b_{2n-2} \right] x^{2n} = 0$$

Since the coefficients of all powers of x have to be zero, we have $b_1 = 0$ and $b_{2n+1} = -b_{2n-1}/(2n+1)^2$. Thus $b_1 = b_3 = b_5 = \ldots = 0$. For the coefficients of even powers of x, we have the recursion relation

$$b_{2n} = -\frac{b_{2n-2}}{(2n)^2} - (-1)^n \frac{1}{2^{2n}n(n!)^2} \qquad (n = 1, 2, 3, \ldots)$$

All coefficients are thus expressed in terms of b_0, which is arbitrary. We have thus obtained a second solution.

This solution, with b_0 taking a particular value, becomes

$$Y_0(x) = \frac{2}{\pi} \left[J_0(x) \left(\log_e \frac{x}{2} + \gamma\right) + \left(\frac{x}{2}\right)^2 - \left(1 + \frac{1}{2}\right) \frac{(x/2)^4}{(2!)^2} \right.$$
$$\left. + \left(1 + \frac{1}{2} + \frac{1}{3}\right) \frac{(x/2)^6}{(3!)^2} - \ldots \right] \qquad (4\text{-}132)$$

which is called the *Bessel function* of zero order of the second kind. Here, γ is known as *Euler's constant* and is equal to 0.577216. Thus, the general solution of Bessel's equation of zero order is

$$y = c_1 J_0(x) + c_2 Y_0(x)$$

The Bessel functions of zero order are plotted in Fig. 4–103. These functions are oscillatory with decreasing amplitude.

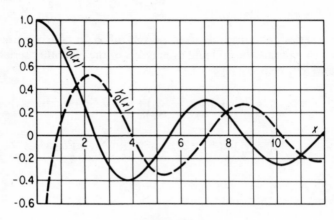

Fig. 4–103

For the homogeneous boundary problem with $dy/dz=0$ at $z=0$ and $y=0$ at $z=L$, we have characteristic functions as solutions. Since

$$y = c_1 J_0(pz) + c_2 Y_0(pz)$$

and $dy/dz=0$ at $z=0$, c_2 must be zero. The second boundary condition requires

$$c_1 J_0(pL) = 0$$

One possible solution is $c_1=0$, giving the trivial solution $y=0$. However, it can be shown that $J_0(x)=0$ at $x=2.405$, 5.520, 8.654, 11.792, 14.931, ... (just as $\cos x=0$ at $x=\pi/2$, $3\pi/2$ ...). If the parameter p^2 in the given differential equation is such that pL is equal to one of these values, we have the boundary conditions satisfied without specifying c_1.

Problems

4-95. Find the series solution of $(d^2y/dx^2)+y=0$, and show that your answer is $y=A\cos x+B\sin x$.

4-96. Find the general solution of $(1-xy)y'-y=0$ as a power series of x.

Ans. $y=C\left[1+x+\frac{1}{2}(1+C)x^2+\ldots\right]$

4–97. A hanging chain in steady rotation about the vertical z axis is shown in Fig. 4–104 with angular speed ω. The weight per unit length of chain is mg.

(a) By using the approximation $ds = dz$ for cases with very small deflections, show that the equation $\rho(z)$ of the chain is given by

$$z^2 \frac{d^2\rho}{dz^2} + z \frac{d\rho}{dz} + \frac{\omega^2 z}{g}\rho = 0$$

(b) Show that, with $y = 2\omega\sqrt{z/g}$, this equation can be reduced to a Bessel's equation

$$y^2 \frac{d^2\rho}{dy^2} + y \frac{d\rho}{dy} + y^2\rho = 0$$

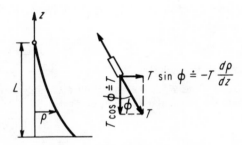

Fig. 4–104

(c) Show that the boundary conditions $\rho \neq \infty$ at $z = 0$ and $\rho = 0$ at $z = L$ are satisfied by $\rho(z) = cJ_0(2\omega\sqrt{z/g})$ if ω is such that $2\omega\sqrt{L/g}$ is equal to one of the following values: 2.405, 5.520, 8.654, 11.792, 14.931, ... (Hint: see Fig. 4–103.)

4–98. A bucket is suspended in the rain by a string of length L from a fixed point. The mass of the bucket is very small, so that the total mass of the bucket and content can be considered to be proportional to time t since the beginning of the rain. If the bucket is released from rest from a small value of θ_0 at $t = 0$, show that the angle $\theta(t)$ between the string and the vertical is

$$\theta = \theta_0 J_0\left(\sqrt{\frac{g}{L}}\, t\right)$$

4–99. Solve the following differential equations:

(a) $\dfrac{d^2y}{dx^2} + 2x^2 y = 0$ *Ans.* $y = c_1\left(1 - \dfrac{x^4}{6} + \dfrac{x^8}{168} - \cdots\right) + c_2\left(x - \dfrac{x^5}{10} + \dfrac{x^9}{360} - \cdots\right)$

(b) $x(1-x)\dfrac{d^2y}{dx^2} - 2\dfrac{dy}{dx} + 2y = 0$ *Ans.* $y = c_1(1 + x + x^2) + c_2 \displaystyle\sum_{n=3}^{\infty} x^n$

(c) $\dfrac{d^2y}{dx^2} + \dfrac{1}{x}\dfrac{dy}{dx} - 4y = 0$ *Ans.* $y = (c_1 + c_2\log_e x)\displaystyle\sum_{n=0}^{\infty}\dfrac{x^{2n}}{(n!)^2} - c_2(x^2 + \tfrac{3}{8}x^4 + \cdots)$

4-100. The cross-section of a thin cooling fin is shown in Fig. 4–105. The loss of heat from the surface per unit width over a short distance dx is $\beta(T-T_r)dx$, where β is a constant of proportionality, T is the temperature of the fin, and T_r is the constant room temperature.

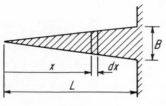

(a) Show that the differential equation for $T(x)$ is

$$x\frac{d^2T}{dx^2}+\frac{dT}{dx}-K(T-T_r)=0$$

Fig. 4–105

where $K=\beta L/Bk$, and $k=$ thermal conductivity of the fin.

(b) The general solution of this equation is of the form

$$T-T_r = c_1 \sum_{n=0}^{\infty} a_n x^{n+\alpha}+c_2\left[\log_e x \sum_{n=0}^{\infty} a_n x^{n+\alpha}+\sum_{n=0}^{\infty} b_n x^{n+\alpha}\right]$$

Find the first series in this solution.

(c) Given the temperature T_1 at the base, and assuming that there is no flow across the tip, find the particular solution of $T(x)$.

$$Ans.\ \frac{T-T_r}{T_1-T_r}=\sum_{n=0}^{\infty}\frac{(Kx)^n}{(n!)^2}\bigg/\sum_{n=0}^{\infty}\frac{(KL)^n}{(n!)^2}$$

4-101. Solve the equation

$$x^3\frac{d^3y}{dx^3}+3x^2\frac{d^2y}{dx^2}+2x\frac{dy}{dx}=0$$

$$Ans.\ y=c_1+c_2\log_e\sin x+c_3\log_e\cos x$$

4-18. Nonhomogeneous linear equations with variable coefficients

Three methods of solution of nonhomogeneous linear equations with variable coefficients are presented in this article. As the solution of the associated homogeneous equation has been discussed in the previous article, it is sufficient in this article to find a particular integral in the general solution.

(a) Method of reduction of order.

When a nonzero particular solution of the associated homogeneous equation is known, a linear ordinary differential equation can be reduced to an equation of one order lower. This method is particularly useful for a second-order equation, since the resulting equation is of the first order, which can be integrated by using Eq. (4–13).

Take the equation

$$a_0(x)\frac{d^2y}{dx^2}+a_1(x)\frac{dy}{dx}+a_2(x)y=f(x)$$

Let $y_1(x)$ be a particular solution of the associated homogeneous equation. For the general solution, assume

$$y = vy_1 \tag{4–133}$$

where v is a function of x to be determined. Substituting this y and its derivatives into the differential equation, we have

$$a_0 y_1 v'' + 2a_0 y_1' v' + a_1 y_1 v' + v(a_0 y_1'' + a_1 y_1' + a_2 y_1) = f(x)$$

Since y_1 is a solution of the associated homogeneous equation, the value in the parentheses is zero. Thus

$$a_0 y_1 \frac{dv'}{dx} + (2a_0 y_1' + a_1 y_1) v' = f(x)$$

which can be integrated by using Eq. (4–13) to yield v' or dv/dx. The general solution is obtained by integrating for v and substituting v into Eq. (4–133).

This method is also found useful in finding the general solution of second-order homogeneous equations and equations with constant coefficients. Theoretically, any nonzero particular solution of the (associated) homogeneous second-order linear equation will lead to the general solution. However, the integration involved may sometimes be very complicated, and this method may not lead to a practical solution. For an example of solution by this method, see Example 4–50.

(b) Method of variation of parameters.

When the complementary function of a linear equation is known, theoretically it is always possible to find a particular integral by this method. Take the equation

$$a_0(x) \frac{d^n y}{dx^n} + a_1(x) \frac{d^{n-1} y}{dx^{n-1}} + \dots + a_n(x) y = f(x) \tag{4–134}$$

Let $y_1(x)$, $y_2(x)$, ... $y_n(x)$ be n known linearly independent solutions of the associated homogeneous equation. For a particular integral, we assume

$$Y(x) = u_1 y_1 + u_2 y_2 + \dots + u_n y_n \tag{4–135}$$

where u_1, u_2, ... u_n are functions of x to be determined. Since there are n such functions to satisfy only one condition, namely, Eq. (4–134), to find a particular integral we can impose $(n-1)$ more conditions when convenient. Differentiating $Y(x)$, we get

$$Y' = (u_1 y_1' + u_2 y_2' + \dots + u_n y_n') + (y_1 u_1' + y_2 u_2' + \dots + y_n u_n')$$

We impose the first condition

$$y_1 u_1' + y_2 u_2' + \dots + y_n u_n' = 0 \tag{4–136}$$

Differentiating Y', we obtain

$$Y'' = (u_1 y_1'' + u_2 y_2'' + \ldots + u_n y_n'') + (y_1' u_1' + y_2' u_2' + \ldots + y_n' u_n')$$

We impose the second condition

$$y_1' u_1' + y_2' u_2' + \ldots + y_n' u_n' = 0 \tag{4-137}$$

After differentiating $(n-1)$ times, and imposing the $(n-1)$th condition

$$\frac{d^{n-2} y_1}{dx^{n-2}} u_1' + \frac{d^{n-2} y_2}{dx^{n-2}} u_2' + \ldots + \frac{d^{n-2} y_n}{dx^{n-2}} u_n' = 0 \tag{4-138}$$

we have

$$\frac{d^{n-1} Y}{dx^{n-1}} = u_1 \frac{d^{n-1} y_1}{dx^{n-1}} + u_2 \frac{d^{n-1} y_2}{dx^{n-1}} + \ldots + u_n \frac{d^{n-1} y_n}{dx^{n-1}} = \sum_{s=1}^{n} u_s \frac{d^{n-1} y_s}{dx^{n-1}}$$

Differentiating to obtain the nth derivative

$$\frac{d^n Y}{dx^n} = \sum_{s=1}^{n} u_s \frac{d^n y_s}{dx^n} + \sum_{s=1}^{n} \frac{d^{n-1} y_s}{dx^{n-1}} u_s'$$

Substituting these n derivatives of Y into Eq. (4–134), we have

$$\sum_{s=1}^{n} u_s \left[a_0 \frac{d^n y_s}{dx^n} + a_1 \frac{d^{n-1} y_s}{dx^{n-1}} + \ldots + a_n y_s \right] + \sum_{s=1}^{n} \frac{d^{n-1} y_s}{dx^{n-1}} u_s' = f(x)$$

Since each y_s $(s=1, 2, \ldots n)$ is a solution of the associated homogeneous equation, the value of the first summation is zero. Thus, Eq. (4–134) is satisfied with the second summation equal to $f(x)$:

$$\frac{d^{n-1} y_1}{dx^{n-1}} u_1' + \frac{d^{n-1} y_2}{dx^{n-1}} u_2' + \ldots + \frac{d^{n-1} y_n}{dx^{n-1}} u_n' = f(x) \tag{4-139}$$

There are $(n-1)$ equations similar to Eqs. (4–136) to (4–138). With Eq. (4–139), there are n algebraic equations in which the n unknowns are u_s' $(s=1, 2, \ldots n)$. After these values are determined, their integrals are substituted into Eq. (4–135) to give a particular integral $Y(x)$. For an example of finding a particular integral by this method, see Example 4–51.

(c) Series solutions.

A particular integral for a linear equation can sometimes be obtained by assuming

$$Y = \sum_{n=0}^{\infty} b_n x^{n+m}$$

When this assumption does not lead to a particular integral, other forms for Y must be assumed. For suggestions, consult more advanced textbooks on ordinary differential equations. For an example of finding a particular integral by means of series, see Example 4–52.

Example 4–50. Given that x^2 is a particular solution of the associated homogeneous equation of the following equation:

$$x^2 \frac{d^2y}{dx^2} + x \frac{dy}{dx} - 4y = x + x^3$$

find the general solution of this equation.

As suggested by Eq. (4–133), we assume $y = vx^2$. Substituting this y and its derivatives into the differential equation, we have

$$x^4 v'' + 5x^3 v' = x + x^3$$

This is a first order linear equation of v'. In accordance with Eq. (4–13), we multiply each term with x to obtain

$$\frac{d}{dx}(x^5 v') = x^2 + x^4$$

Thus

$$\frac{dv}{dx} = \frac{1}{3x^2} + \frac{1}{5} + \frac{C}{x^5}$$

$$v = -\frac{1}{3x} + \frac{x}{5} + \frac{c_1}{x^4} + c_2$$

Thus the general solution

$$y = vx^2 = \frac{c_1}{x^2} + c_2 x^2 - \frac{x}{3} + \frac{x^3}{5}$$

Example 4–51. Given that $(c_1/x^2) + c_2 x^2$ is the complementary function in the general solution of the equation

$$x^2 \frac{d^2y}{dx^2} + \frac{dy}{dx} - 4y = x + x^3$$

find the particular integral by the method of variation of parameters.

In accordance with Eq. (4–135), we assume a particular integral

$$Y(x) = \frac{u_1}{x^2} + x^2 u_2$$

Here, the two functions u_1 and u_2 must satisfy one condition, i.e., satisfying the differential equation. We can impose one more condition. Differentiating,

$$Y' = -\frac{2u_1}{x^3} + 2xu_2 + \left(\frac{u_1'}{x^2} + x^2 u_2'\right)$$

We impose the condition

$$\frac{u_1'}{x^2} + x^2 u_2' = 0 \qquad (4\text{–}140)$$

Differentiating again,

$$Y'' = \frac{6u_1}{x^4} + 2u_2 - \frac{2u_1'}{x^3} + 2xu_2'$$

Substituting Y and its derivatives into the differential equation, we have

$$-\frac{2u_1'}{x}+2x^3u_2' = x+x^3 \qquad (4\text{--}141)$$

From Eqs. (4–140) and (4–141), we obtain

$$u_1' = -\frac{x^2(1+x^2)}{4} \quad \text{and} \quad u_2' = \frac{1+x^2}{4x^2}$$

Integrating,

$$u_1 = -\frac{x^3}{12}-\frac{x^5}{20} \quad \text{and} \quad u_2 = -\frac{1}{4x}+\frac{x}{4}$$

Thus

$$Y = \frac{u_1}{x^2}+x^2u_2 = -\frac{x}{3}+\frac{x^3}{5}$$

Example 4–52. Using series, find a particular integral for the equation

$$x^2\frac{d^2y}{dx^2}+x\frac{dy}{dx}+x^2y = \frac{2}{x}+\sin x$$

Assume a particular integral for each term on the right-hand side

$$Y = \sum_{n=0}^{\infty} b_n x^{n+m}$$

where m is to be determined. With

$$xY' = x\sum_{n=0}^{\infty}(n+m)\,b_nx^{n+m-1} = \sum_{n=0}^{\infty}(n+m)\,b_nx^{n+m}$$

$$x^2Y'' = x^2\sum_{n=0}^{\infty}(n+m)\,(n+m-1)\,b_nx^{n+m-2} = \sum_{n=0}^{\infty}(n+m)\,(n+m-1)\,b_nx^{n+m}$$

$$x^2Y = \sum_{n=0}^{\infty}b_nx^{n+m+2} = b_0x^{m+2}+b_1x^{m+3}+\;\ldots\; = \sum_{n=2}^{\infty}b_{n-2}x^{n+m}$$

the left-hand side of the equation becomes

$$b_0m^2x^m+b_1(1+m)^2x^{m+1}+\sum_{n=2}^{\infty}[b_n(n+m)^2+b_{n-2}]x^{n+m}$$

(a) For the term $2/x$:

$$b_0m^2x^m+b_1(1+m)^2x^{m+1}+\sum_{n=2}^{\infty}[b_n(n+m)^2+b_{n-2}]x^{n+m} = 2x^{-1}$$

Equating the terms of the lowest power on both sides, $b_0m^2x^m=2x^{-1}$, we have $m = -1$, and $b_0 m^2 = 2$ or $b_0 = 2$. Since the coefficients for all other powers of x must be zero, we have $b_1 = 0$, and

$$b_n = -\frac{b_{n-2}}{(n+m)^2} = -\frac{b_{n-2}}{(n-1)^2} \qquad (n = 2, 3, 4, \ldots)$$

Since $b_1 = 0$, we have from this recursion relation $b_1 = b_3 = b_5 = \ldots = 0$. For even values of n, we have

$$b_2 = -\frac{b_0}{1^2} = -2$$

$$b_4 = -\frac{b_2}{3^2} = \frac{2}{3^2}$$

$$b_6 = -\frac{b_4}{5^2} = -\frac{2}{3^2 5^2}$$

· · · · · ·

Thus, for the term $2/x$,

$$Y_1 = \sum_{n=0}^{\infty} b_n x^{n-1} = 2\left(\frac{1}{x} - x + \frac{x^3}{3^2} - \frac{x^5}{3^2 5^2} + \frac{x^7}{3^2 5^2 7^2} - \cdots\right)$$

(b) For the term $\sin x$: with $\sin x$ expressed as a series, the equation becomes

$$b_0 m^2 x^m + b_1 (1+m)^2 x^{m+1} + \sum_{n=2}^{\infty} [b_n(n+m)^2 + b_{n-2}] x^{n+m} = x - \frac{x^3}{3!} + \frac{x^5}{5!} - \cdots$$

Equating the terms of the lowest power on both sides, we have in this case $m = 1$, and $b_0 m^2 = 1$ or $b_0 = 1$. Equating terms of like powers on both sides, we have $4b_1 x^2 = 0$ or $b_1 = 0$, and

$$[b_2(2+1)^2 + b_0]x^3 = -\frac{x^3}{3!} \quad \text{or} \quad b_2 = \frac{1}{3^2}\left(-\frac{1}{3!} - 1\right) = -\frac{7}{54}$$

$$[b_3(3+1)^2 + b_1]x^4 = 0 \quad \text{or} \quad b_3 = 0$$

$$[b_4(4+1)^2 + b_2]x^5 = \frac{x^5}{5!} \quad \text{or} \quad b_4 = \frac{1}{5^2}\left[\frac{1}{5!} - \frac{1}{3^2}\left(-\frac{1}{3!} - 1\right)\right] = \frac{149}{27,000}$$

· · · · · · · · · ·

Thus, for the term $\sin x$:

$$Y_2 = \sum_{n=0}^{\infty} b_n x^{n+1} = x - \frac{7x^3}{54} + \frac{149x^5}{27,000} - \cdots$$

The complementary function of the solution has been shown to consist of the Bessel functions of zero order of the first and second kind (see Example 4–49). Due to the linearity of the equation, the two particular integrals can be superposed. Thus, the general solution of the equation is

$$y(x) = c_1 J_0(x) + c_2 Y_0(x) + 2\left(\frac{1}{x} - x + \frac{x^3}{3^2} - \frac{x^5}{3^2 5^2} + \cdots\right) + \left(x - \frac{7x^3}{54} + \frac{149x^5}{27,000} - \cdots\right)$$

Problems

4-102. The use of the method of order reduction is not limited to equations with variable coefficients. Using this method, show that the general solution of $(d^2y/dx^2) + y = \sec x$ is $y = c_1 \cos x + c_2 \sin x + x \sin x + \cos x \log_e (\cos x)$.

4-103. The use of the method of variation of parameters is not limited to non-homogeneous equations with variable coefficients. Using this method, find a particular integral for the differential equation in the previous problem.

4-104. The complementary function of the equation

$$(1 - x^2) \frac{d^2y}{dx^2} - 2x\frac{dy}{dx} + 2y = x$$

has been found in Example 4–47 with $k = 1$ in Eq. (4–128). Find a particular integral in the form of a series.

Ans. $Y(x) = \frac{1}{6} x^3 + \frac{1}{12} x^5 + \frac{1}{18} x^7 + \frac{1}{24} x^9 + \cdots$

CHAPTER 5

FOURIER SERIES

5–1. Expansion in trigonometric series

In Art. 1–12, Taylor's expansion of a function in a power series has been introduced. Under suitable conditions, this series converges to the function as more and more terms are taken into account. We have encountered many cases where Taylor's expansion is useful. In this article, the expansion of an arbitrary function in a series of sines and cosines is presented. Such an expansion is called a *Fourier series*, after its founder.

It is common knowledge that to pass three points in the x–y plane, one can use a function with three coefficients, such as $y = c_0 + c_1 x + c_2 x^2$, or $y = c_0 + c_1 \sin x + c_2 \cos x$. When there are more points, one uses a function with more coefficients. In our discussion of trigonometric series, the question is whether an infinite series of sines and cosines can always fit an arbitrary function (at an infinite number of points). The answer to this question is given by Fourier's theorem, which states the sufficient condition for expansion in such a series.

Theorem: if a single-valued function $f(x)$ has at most a finite number of finite discontinuities and a finite number of maxima and minima in the interval $[h, h+2\pi]$, then in this interval, $f(x)$ can be expanded as

$$f(x) = \frac{a_0}{2} + \sum_{n=1}^{\infty} (a_n \cos nx + b_n \sin nx) \qquad (5\text{–}1)$$

where

$$a_n = \frac{1}{\pi} \int_{h}^{h+2\pi} f(x) \cos nx \, dx$$

$$b_n = \frac{1}{\pi} \int_{h}^{h+2\pi} f(x) \sin nx \, dx$$

At a discontinuity, this series converges to the mean of the two limits of the function there.

Under these specified conditions, generally known as the *Dirichlet conditions*, discontinuous functions can be expanded in Fourier series. (The student will recall that it is impossible to expand a function in a Taylor's series across a discontinuity.) However, Fourier series cannot be applied to a function which becomes infinite. The requirement that the function have at most a finite number of maxima and minima excludes application to functions such as $G(x)$ in Fig. 1–15, with $x=0$ in the interval.

Since a uniformly convergent series can be integrated term by term, a convergent Fourier series can be so integrated. However, the series resulting from term by term differentiation of a Fourier series may be divergent. Such series must be tested for uniform convergence before use.

The coefficients a_n and b_n of the series can be so simply determined, as shown above with Eq. (5–1), because of a property of the sines and cosines called orthogonality. In general, a set of continuous functions $\theta_1(x)$, $\theta_2(x)$, ... is said to be *orthogonal* with respect to an interval $[a, b]$ if

$$\left. \begin{aligned} \int_a^b \theta_m(x)\theta_n(x)\,dx &= 0 \quad \text{if } m \neq n \\ &= \text{nonzero constant} \quad \text{if } m = n \end{aligned} \right\} \tag{5-2}$$

For the set of sines and cosines (cos x, cos $2x$, ... sin x, sin $2x$, ...) we can easily verify that

$$\left. \begin{aligned} \int_h^{h+2\pi} \sin mx \cos nx\,dx &= 0 \\ \int_h^{h+2\pi} \cos mx \cos nx\,dx &= 0 \\ \int_h^{h+2\pi} \sin mx \sin nx\,dx &= 0 \end{aligned} \right\} \quad \text{if } m \neq n \tag{5-3}$$

and

$$\left. \begin{aligned} \int_h^{h+2\pi} \sin mx \sin nx\,dx &= \pi \\ \int_h^{h+2\pi} \cos mx \cos nx\,dx &= \pi \end{aligned} \right\} \quad \text{if } m = n \neq 0 \tag{5-4}$$

For example, with

$$\cos mx \cos nx = \frac{1}{2}\cos (m+n)x + \frac{1}{2}\cos (m-n)x$$

$$\int_h^{h+2\pi} \cos mx \cos nx\,dx = \frac{1}{2}\left[\frac{\sin (m+n)x}{m+n} + \frac{\sin (m-n)x}{m-n}\right]\Big|_h^{h+2\pi}$$

$$= 0 \quad \text{if } m-n \neq 0 \text{ (since } m+n \neq 0)$$

If $m=n\neq0$,

$$\int_h^{h+2\pi} \cos mx \cos nx\,dx = \int_h^{h+2\pi} \cos^2 mx\,dx = \pi$$

As can be seen from Eqs. (5–3) and (5–4), the sines and cosines together form a set of orthogonal functions with respect to an interval of 2π. Now, to determine a coefficient a_m in Eq. (5–1), multiply both sides of the equation by $\cos mx$ and integrate over an interval of 2π. Because of Eq. (5–3), the only contributing term on the right-hand side of Eq. (5–1) is $\cos mx$ with $n=m$. Thus

$$\int_h^{h+2\pi} f(x) \cos mx \, dx = a_m \int_h^{h+2\pi} \cos mx \cos mx \, dx = a_m \pi$$

Since m is only a dummy variable and can be changed to n, we have

$$a_n = \frac{1}{\pi} \int_h^{h+2\pi} f(x) \cos nx \, dx$$

Similarly, by multiplying both sides of Eq. (5–1) by $\sin mx$ and integrating over an interval of 2π, we have

$$b_n = \frac{1}{\pi} \int_h^{h+2\pi} f(x) \sin nx \, dx$$

In particular, with $n=0$, the first term in the Fourier series is

$$\frac{a_0}{2} = \frac{1}{2\pi} \int_h^{h+2\pi} f(x) \, dx$$

which is the mean value of $f(x)$ in the interval of 2π. For an example of expanding a function in a Fourier series, see Example 5–1.

The series in Eq. (5–1) is periodic, with a fundamental period of 2π. Sometimes it is desirable to expand a function $f(x)$ with a period of $2L$. This can be accomplished by calling $z=\pi x/L$. Corresponding to an interval of $2L$ of x, z varies through a range of 2π. Call $f(x)=f(zL/\pi)=F(z)$ and expand $F(z)$ into a Fourier series with a fundamental period of 2π:

$$F(z) = \frac{a_0}{2} + \sum_{n=1}^{\infty} (a_n \cos nz + b_n \sin nz)$$

where

$$a_n = \frac{1}{\pi} \int_h^{h+2\pi} F(z) \cos nz \, dz$$

$$b_n = \frac{1}{\pi} \int_h^{h+2\pi} F(z) \sin nz \, dz$$

For an expansion in the interval $[s, s+2L]$ of x, we note that $F(z)=f(x)$, $h=\pi s/L$, and $dz=(\pi/L) \, dx$. Thus

$$f(x) = \frac{a_0}{2} + \sum_{n=1}^{\infty} \left(a_n \cos \frac{n\pi x}{L} + b_n \sin \frac{n\pi x}{L} \right) \qquad (5\text{–}5)$$

where

$$a_n = \frac{1}{L} \int_s^{s+2L} f(x) \cos \frac{n\pi x}{L} \, dx$$

$$b_n = \frac{1}{L} \int_s^{s+2L} f(x) \sin \frac{n\pi x}{L} \, dx$$

For an example of expanding a function by using Eq. (5–5), see Example 5–2.

As a Fourier expansion is periodic, it is often a more suitable expansion than Taylor's expansion, if the function $f(x)$ is actually periodic. For example,

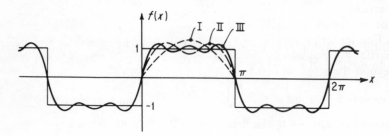

Fig. 5–1

take the periodic function $f(x)$ shown in Fig. 5–1. It is shown in Example 5–1 that the Fourier expansion is

$$f(x) = \frac{4}{\pi} \left(\sin x + \frac{\sin 3x}{3} + \frac{\sin 5x}{5} + \ldots \right) \qquad (5\text{–}6)$$

Three terms of this series will give a fair representation of $f(x)$ over the whole range of x, as shown in Fig. 5–1, where the numbers I, II, and III indicate the number of terms of the series included in plotting the curves. In contrast, it requires a large number of terms of a power series to represent any periodic function over a relatively wide range.

The use of Fourier series is not limited to periodic functions. If the expansion of $f(x)$ is to be used only in a limited interval of x, a Fourier expansion for this interval can be used even when $f(x)$ is not periodic. In fact, by assuming various forms for $f(x)$ outside this interval, one can obtain several expansions, all valid for the given interval (see Example 5–2). The most frequently assumed forms of $f(x)$ are: (a) $f(x)$ as an even function, with $f(-x) = f(x)$, as illustrated in Fig. 5–2(a); and (b) $f(x)$ as an odd function, with $f(-x) = -f(x)$, as illustrated in Fig. 5–2(b). It can easily be proved that, in the former case, the coefficients b_n in Eqs. (5–1) and (5–5) are equal to zero, while in the latter case the coefficients a_n are equal to zero. Thus, by assuming $f(x)$ to be an even function, we have a cosine series; and by assuming $f(x)$ to be an odd function, we have a sine series.

Fourier series yield useful information of sums of infinite series of numbers. For example, take Eq. (5–6). Since given $f(\pi/2)=1$ (see Fig. 5–1), we have from the Fourier series

$$1 = \frac{4}{\pi}\left(1-\frac{1}{3}+\frac{1}{5}-\cdots\right)$$

or

$$\sum_{s=0}^{\infty}\frac{(-1)^s}{2s+1} = \frac{\pi}{4}$$

The student will find several similar results in Problems 5–5 and 5–6 following this article.

For examples of application of Fourier series, see Examples 5–3 and 5–4. Fourier series are often used in the solution of boundary-value problems of partial differential equations. However, the discussion of these equations is beyond the scope of this book.

Example 5–1. Find a Fourier expansion of the function shown in Fig. 5–1:

$$f(x) = 1 \quad (\text{for } 0 < x < \pi)$$
$$= -1 \quad (\text{for } \pi < x < 2\pi)$$

The given function satisfies the Dirichlet conditions and is periodic, with a period of 2π. It can therefore be expanded in a Fourier series by using Eq. (5–1) with $h=0$:

$$a_n = \frac{1}{\pi}\int_0^{2\pi} f(x)\cos nx\,dx = \frac{1}{\pi}\left[\int_0^{\pi}\cos nx\,dx + \int_{\pi}^{2\pi}-\cos nx\,dx\right] = 0$$

$$b_n = \frac{1}{\pi}\int_0^{2\pi} f(x)\sin nx\,dx = \frac{1}{\pi}\left[\int_0^{\pi}\sin nx\,dx + \int_{\pi}^{2\pi}-\sin nx\,dx\right]$$

$$= \frac{1}{n\pi}(-\cos n\pi + \cos 0 + \cos 2n\pi - \cos n\pi) = \frac{2}{n\pi}(1-\cos n\pi)$$

$$f(x) = \sum_{n=1}^{\infty} b_n \sin nx = \sum_{n=1}^{\infty}\frac{2}{n\pi}(1-\cos n\pi)\sin nx$$

$$= \frac{4}{\pi}\left(\sin x + \frac{\sin 3x}{3} + \frac{\sin 5x}{5} + \cdots\right)$$

The plot of this series is shown in Fig. 5–1, where the numbers I, II, and III indicate the number of terms included. At the discontinuities at $x=0$, π, 2π, etc., the value of the series is zero, which is the mean of 1 and -1, the two limits of $f(x)$ as these discontinuities are approached.

Example 5–2. Given $f(x)=x$ in the interval $0<x<L$, find several Fourier series describing this function in this interval.

We can assume various forms for $f(x)$ outside the interval $0<x<L$.

Since the expansion will be periodic, all these assumed forms should be periodic.

(a) Let $f(x)$ be an even function with $f(-x) = f(x)$, i.e., symmetrical about the f axis, as shown in Fig. 5–2(a). Thus

$$f(x) = -x \qquad \text{(for } -L < x < 0\text{)}$$
$$= x \qquad \text{(for } 0 < x < L\text{)}$$

with a period of $2L$. Using Eq. (5–5) with $s = -L$,

$$a_n = \frac{1}{L} \int_{-L}^{L} f(x) \cos \frac{n\pi x}{L} \, dx = \frac{1}{L} \int_{-L}^{0} -x \cos \frac{n\pi x}{L} \, dx + \frac{1}{L} \int_{0}^{L} x \cos \frac{n\pi x}{L} \, dx$$

$$= \frac{2L}{(n\pi)^2} (\cos n\pi - 1)$$

$$b_n = \frac{1}{L} \int_{-L}^{L} f(x) \sin \frac{n\pi x}{L} \, dx = 0$$

It is easier to compute a_0 independently:

$$a_0 = \frac{1}{L} \int_{-L}^{L} f(x) \, dx = \frac{1}{L} \left[\int_{-L}^{0} -x \, dx + \int_{0}^{L} x \, dx \right] = L$$

Thus

$$f(x) = \frac{a_0}{2} + \sum_{n=1}^{\infty} \left(a_n \cos \frac{n\pi x}{L} + b_n \sin \frac{n\pi x}{L} \right)$$

$$= \frac{L}{2} + \frac{2L}{\pi^2} \sum_{n=1}^{\infty} \frac{\cos n\pi - 1}{n^2} \cos \frac{n\pi x}{L}$$

$$= \frac{L}{2} - \frac{4L}{\pi^2} \left(\cos \frac{\pi x}{L} + \frac{1}{3^2} \cos \frac{3\pi x}{L} + \frac{1}{5^2} \cos \frac{5\pi x}{L} + \ldots \right)$$

(b) Let $f(x)$ be an odd function with $f(-x) = -f(x)$, as shown in Fig. 5–2(b). Then $f(x) = x$ for $-L < x < L$.

$$a_n = \frac{1}{L} \int_{-L}^{L} x \cos \frac{n\pi x}{L} \, dx = 0$$

$$b_n = \frac{1}{L} \int_{-L}^{L} x \sin \frac{n\pi x}{L} \, dx = -\frac{2L}{n\pi} \cos n\pi$$

Thus

$$f(x) = -\frac{2L}{\pi} \sum_{n=1}^{\infty} \frac{\cos n\pi}{n} \sin \frac{n\pi x}{L}$$

$$= \frac{2L}{\pi} \left(\sin \frac{\pi x}{L} - \frac{1}{2} \sin \frac{2\pi x}{L} + \frac{1}{3} \sin \frac{3\pi x}{L} - \ldots \right)$$

Note that the expansion of an even function contains no sine terms, while that of an odd function contains no cosine terms. Other forms can be

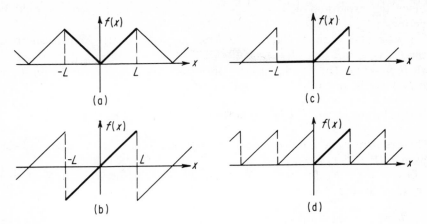

Fig. 5–2

assumed for $f(x)$, such as those shown in Figs. 5–2(c) and (d). In the latter cases, both sines and cosines will be present in the expansions. In all these cases, the expansions describe the given $f(x)$ in the interval $0 < x < L$.

Example 5–3. A mass m is suspended by a spring of constant k, as shown in Fig. 5–3. An oscillatory force $F(t)$ acts upon m with a period T, as shown. Find the steady-state motion of m, the free vibrations having been damped out by a very small damping force.

Let $x(t)$ be the displacement of m from its position of static equilibrium. With damping neglected, the equation of motion is

$$m\frac{d^2x}{dt^2} + kx = F(t)$$

The given function $F(t)$, being an odd function, can be expanded into a sine series.

$$m\frac{d^2x}{dt^2} + kx = F(t) = b_1 \sin \omega_1 t + b_2 \sin \omega_2 t + \ldots$$

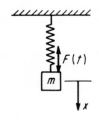
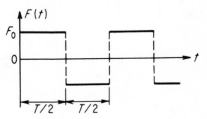

Fig. 5–3

For each $b \sin \omega t$, the particular integral for steady motion is, according to Eq. (4–85),

$$x(t) = \frac{b}{m(p^2 - \omega^2)} \sin \omega t$$

where $p^2 = k/m$. Due to the linearity of the differential equation, the response to $F(t)$ can be obtained by superposition:

$$x(t) = \frac{1}{m}\left(\frac{b_1}{p^2 - \omega_1^2} \sin \omega_1 t + \frac{b_2}{p^2 - \omega_2^2} \sin \omega_2 t + \ldots\right)$$

The problem is thus reduced to finding b_n and ω_n in the expansion of the given $F(t)$.

Given $F(t) = F_0$ for $0 < t < T/2$, and $F(t) = -F_0$ for $T/2 < t < T$. Using Eq. (5–5) with $T/2 = L$ and $s = 0$,

$$b_n = \frac{2}{T} \int_0^T F(t) \sin \frac{2n\pi t}{T}\, dt$$

$$= \frac{2}{T}\left(\int_0^{T/2} F_0 \sin \frac{2n\pi t}{T}\, dt + \int_{T/2}^T -F_0 \sin \frac{2n\pi t}{T}\, dt\right) = 2F_0 \frac{1 - \cos n\pi}{n\pi}$$

Obviously $a_n = 0$, as $F(t)$ is an odd function. Thus calling $\omega_n = 2n\pi/T$, we have $\omega_n = n\omega_1$, and

$$F(t) = \sum_{n=1}^{\infty} b_n \sin \frac{2n\pi t}{T} = \frac{4F_0}{\pi}\left(\sin \omega_1 t + \frac{1}{3}\sin \omega_3 t + \frac{1}{5}\sin \omega_5 t + \ldots\right)$$

$$= \frac{4F_0}{\pi}\left(\sin \omega_1 t + \frac{1}{3}\sin 3\omega_1 t + \frac{1}{5}\sin 5\omega_1 t + \ldots\right), \quad \left(\omega_1 = \frac{2\pi}{T}\right)$$

Therefore, the steady-state motion of m is

$$x(t) = \frac{4F_0}{\pi k}\left(\frac{p^2}{p^2 - \omega_1^2}\sin \omega_1 t + \frac{p^2}{p^2 - 9\omega_1^2} \cdot \frac{1}{3}\sin 3\omega_1 t + \ldots\right)$$

Note that the response to the various harmonics may be different in phase and in amplification. For example, suppose $\omega_1 = p/2$. We have then $p^2/(p^2 - \omega_1^2) = \frac{4}{3}$ and $p^2/(p^2 - 9\omega_1^2) = -\frac{4}{5}$. This difference in value indicates that the amplification is different for the fundamental mode and the higher harmonic. The difference in sign shows that the response to the higher harmonic differs in phase by $180°$ from the response to the fundamental mode.

Example 5–4. Given the load per unit length $f(x)$ on a simply supported uniform beam of span L, as shown in Fig. 5–4:

$$f(x) = kx \quad \text{(for } 0 < x < L/2)$$
$$= 0 \quad \text{(for } L/2 < x < L)$$

Find the elastic curve of the beam.

This problem can be solved by the method presented in Art. 4–10, where separate analytical expressions for $f(x)$ are used for different portions of the beam. In this example, we use one expression of $f(x)$ for the whole beam by using Fourier expansion.

According to Eq. (4–94), we have for the uniform beam

$$EI\frac{d^4y}{dx^4} = -\frac{d^2M}{dx^2} = -\frac{dV}{dx} = f(x)$$

As $f(x)$ is defined only in the interval $0 < x < L$, we can, if we prefer, expand the function into a sine or cosine series. The choice varies with the problem.

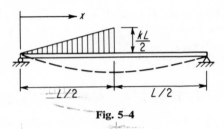

Fig. 5–4

In this case, the elastic curve $y(x)$ is expected to be a sine series with a fundamental period of $2L$ (see Fig. 5–4). Since the fourth derivative of a sine series is also a sine series, we want a sine series of period $2L$ for $f(x)$. In fact, by using such a series for $f(x)$, the sine series $y(x)$ will satisfy all boundary conditions, which are $y = 0$ and $d^2y/dx^2 = 0$ ($M = 0$) at $x = 0$ and at $x = L$. With

$$EI\frac{d^4y}{dx^4} = f(x) = \sum_{n=1}^{\infty} b_n \sin\frac{n\pi x}{L}$$

we have

$$EI\frac{d^2y}{dx^2} = \sum_{n=1}^{\infty} -b_n\left(\frac{L}{n\pi}\right)^2 \sin\frac{n\pi x}{L} + C_1 x + C_2$$

$$EIy = \sum_{n=1}^{\infty} b_n\left(\frac{L}{n\pi}\right)^4 \sin\frac{n\pi x}{L} + C_1\frac{x^3}{6} + C_2\frac{x^2}{2} + C_3 x + C_4$$

To satisfy the four boundary conditions, we have $C_1 = C_2 = C_3 = C_4 = 0$. Thus, the problem is reduced to finding b_n of the sine series of $f(x)$ with a period of $2L$.

To obtain this sine series, let $f(x)$ be an odd function, as shown in Fig. 5–5. According to Eq. (5–5),

$$b_n = \frac{1}{L}\int_{-L}^{L} f(x)\sin\frac{n\pi x}{L}\,dx = \frac{1}{L}\int_{-L/2}^{L/2} kx\sin\frac{n\pi x}{L}\,dx$$

$$= \frac{2kL}{(n\pi)^2}\sin\frac{n\pi}{2} - \frac{kL}{n\pi}\cos\frac{n\pi}{2}$$

Thus

$$EIy = k\left(\frac{L}{\pi}\right)^5 \sum_{n=1}^{\infty} \left(\frac{2}{\pi} \cdot \frac{1}{n^6} \sin \frac{n\pi}{2} - \frac{1}{n^5} \cos \frac{n\pi}{2}\right) \sin \frac{n\pi x}{L}$$

$$= k\left(\frac{L}{\pi}\right)^5 \left(\frac{2}{\pi} \sin \frac{\pi x}{L} + \frac{1}{32} \sin \frac{2\pi x}{L} - \frac{2}{729\pi} \sin \frac{3\pi x}{L} - \frac{1}{1024} \sin \frac{4\pi x}{L} + \ldots\right)$$

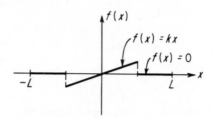

Fig. 5-5

Two terms of this series will give results of sufficient accuracy for practical purposes.

Problems

5-1. A periodic function is shown in Fig. 5-6. Find its Fourier expansion.

Ans. $\frac{8}{\pi^2} (\cos x + \frac{1}{9} \cos 3x + \frac{1}{25} \cos 5x + \ldots)$

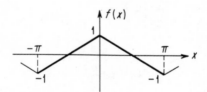

Fig. 5-6

5-2. Expand $f(x) = x^2$ in a Fourier series for the interval $(-\pi, \pi)$. Sketch the expansion, not $f(x)$, for $-\pi < x < 3\pi$.

Ans. $x^2 = \frac{\pi^2}{3} + 4 \sum_{n=1}^{\infty} (-1)^n \frac{\cos nx}{n^2}$

5-3. Show that the Fourier expansion of $f(x) = e^x$ for the interval $(0, 2\pi)$ is

$$e^x = \frac{e^{2\pi} - 1}{\pi}\left(\frac{1}{2} + \sum_{n=1}^{\infty} \frac{\cos nx}{1+n^2} - \sum_{n=1}^{\infty} \frac{n \sin nx}{1+n^2}\right)$$

Without computation, tell the value to which the series converges at $x = 2\pi$ or at $x = 0$.

5-4. Show that, for $-\pi < x < \pi$,

$$\cos kx = \frac{\sin k\pi}{k\pi} + \frac{2k \sin k\pi}{\pi} \sum_{n=1}^{\infty} (-1)^n \frac{\cos nx}{k^2 - n^2}$$

where k is a constant.

5-5. Show that the function $f(x)$ shown in Fig. 5-7 can be expressed as

$$f(x) = \frac{\pi}{4} - \frac{2}{\pi} \left(\cos x + \frac{\cos 3x}{3^2} + \frac{\cos 5x}{5^2} + \ldots \right) + \left(\sin x - \frac{\sin 2x}{2} + \frac{\sin 3x}{3} - \ldots \right)$$

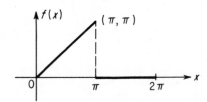

Fig. 5-7

From this series, derive the following:

$$\sum_{s=0}^{\infty} \frac{1}{(2s+1)^2} = \frac{\pi^2}{8} \quad \text{and} \quad \sum_{s=0}^{\infty} \frac{(-1)^s}{2s+1} = \frac{\pi}{4}$$

5-6. From the result of Problem 5-2, derive the following:

$$\sum_{n=1}^{\infty} \frac{1}{n^2} = \frac{\pi^2}{6} \quad \text{and} \quad \sum_{n=1}^{\infty} \frac{(-1)^{n-1}}{n^2} = \frac{\pi^2}{12}$$

From the result of Problem 5-4, derive

$$\sum_{n=1}^{\infty} \frac{1}{n^2 - k^2} = \frac{1}{2k} \left(\frac{1}{k} - \pi \cot k\pi \right)$$

Also, from the result of Problem 5-3, derive

$$\sum_{n=1}^{\infty} \frac{1}{1+n^2} = \frac{\pi}{2} \cdot \frac{e^{2\pi}+1}{e^{2\pi}-1} - \frac{1}{2}$$

and

$$\sum_{n=1}^{\infty} \frac{(-1)^n}{1+n^2} = \frac{\pi e^{\pi}}{e^{2\pi}-1} - \frac{1}{2}$$

5-7. In Fig. 5-8 is shown a mass m suspended from an oscillating ceiling with a spring of constant k. The motion of the ceiling is described by $z(t)$, as shown. Neglecting the small damping force in the equation of motion, find a series solution of the steady-state motion of the mass. If the disturbance is such

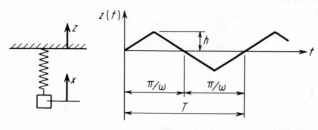

Fig. 5–8

that $\omega^2 = 8.5\ k/m$, sketch $x(t)$ using two terms of the series solution. (Hint: first show that

$$z(t) = \frac{8h}{\pi^2}\left(\sin \omega t - \frac{1}{9} \sin 3\omega t + \frac{1}{25} \sin 5\omega t - \ldots \right)$$

5–8. In the circuit shown in Fig. 5–9, the periodic output of the generator is $E(t) = E_0 \sin \omega t$ for $0 < t < \pi/\omega$, and $E(t) = 0$ for $\pi/\omega < t < 2\pi/\omega$. Find the steady-state current $i(t)$ in the circuit.

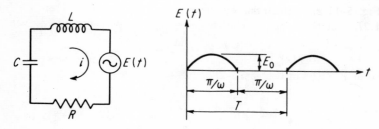

Fig. 5–9

5–9. Find the elastic curve of the beam shown in Fig. 5–4 when it is supported by an elastic foundation of modulus k, in addition to the two unyielding supports at the two ends.

5–10. Express the elastic curve of a cantilever beam in terms of the coefficients of a Fourier expansion of the loads given as $f(x)$. (Hint: As shown in Fig. 5–10,

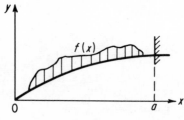

Fig. 5–10

$y(x)$ is expected to be a sine series with a fundamental period of $4a$, although, by itself, such a series does not satisfy all the boundary conditions.)

5–11. The speed $v(t)$ of a mass m is described by its Fourier expansion

$$v(t) = \frac{a_0}{2} + \sum_{n=1}^{\infty} \left(a_n \cos \frac{2n\pi t}{T} + b_n \sin \frac{2n\pi t}{T} \right)$$

Find $\dfrac{1}{T} \displaystyle\int_0^T \tfrac{1}{2}mv^2 \, dt$, the mean kinetic energy during an interval T.

5–2. Harmonic analysis—Numerical methods

The representation of a given function with an infinite Fourier series has been discussed in the previous article. A periodic function has been seen to be composed of a fundamental mode and harmonics of shorter periods. For this reason, the process of determination of the Fourier coefficients is called *harmonic analysis*. Sometimes the periodic function is known only by several discrete values, and is to be represented by a finite series of sines and cosines. The determination of the coefficients in this finite series is the subject matter of this article.

In Fig. 5–11 are shown the known values of a periodic function $f(x)$ of period $2L$. Let there be $2k$ known values in the period, spaced evenly at

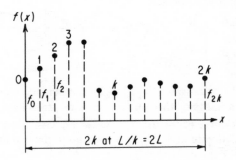

Fig. 5–11

$\varDelta x = L/k$. The function being periodic, f_0 is equal to f_{2k}. To pass a curve through all the $2k$ points in the period, one can assume a finite series of sines and cosines with $2k$ coefficients:

$$f(x) \doteq \frac{A_0}{2} + \sum_{n=1}^{k} A_n \cos \frac{n\pi x}{L} + \sum_{n=1}^{k-1} B_n \sin \frac{n\pi x}{L}$$

By substituting the $2k$ known values of $f(x)$ into this equation, one at a time, $2k$ algebraic equations can be written from which the $2k$ unknown coefficients A_n and B_n can be determined. (Note that only $(k-1)$ sine terms are used because, with $n=k$, the term $B_k \sin (k\pi x/L)$ is equal to zero for all values of x which are multiples of $\Delta x = L/k$. The coefficient B_k therefore cannot be determined from these algebraic equations.) The process of determining the $2k$ coefficients by solving simultaneous algebraic equations may seem tedious, but can be reduced to a routine in practice. In following this procedure, it is convenient to use a multiple of four for $2k$. A popular number of points used in a period is $12(k=6)$. In this case, all the sines and cosines involved take one of the following absolute values: 0, 1/2, $\sqrt{3}/2$, 1.

Next, suppose that it is desired to use a finite series with $(2r+1)$ terms, where $(2r+1) < 2k$, while making full use of all $2k$ known points in the period:

$$f(x) \doteq S(x) = \frac{A_0}{2} + \sum_{n=1}^{r} \left(A_n \cos \frac{n\pi x}{L} + B_n \sin \frac{n\pi x}{L} \right)$$

Obviously, we cannot pass all $2k$ arbitrary points with an expression with less than $2k$ coefficients. To determine A_n and B_n, we do not require the series to pass any of the points but, following Gauss, we do require the mean square error to be minimum. For ease of presentation, let $f(x)$ be completely known $(2k \to \infty)$. Our requirement is then

$$\frac{1}{2L} \int_0^{2L} [f(x) - S(x)]^2 \, dx$$

to be minimum. This integral is a function of the $(2r+1)$ coefficients in $S(x)$. To minimize this integral, we set

$$\frac{\partial}{\partial A_n} \int_0^{2L} [f(x) - S(x)]^2 \, dx = 0 \quad (n = 0, 1, 2, \ldots, r)$$

$$\frac{\partial}{\partial B_n} \int_0^{2L} [f(x) - S(x)]^2 \, dx = 0 \quad (n = 1, 2, \ldots, r)$$

From these $(2r+1)$ equations, the $(2r+1)$ coefficients are determined. Because of the orthogonality of the sines and cosines, (see Eqs. (5–3) and (5–4)), these equations can be reduced to

$$\left. \begin{aligned} A_n &= \frac{1}{L} \int_0^{2L} f(x) \cos \frac{n\pi x}{L} \, dx \quad (n = 0, 1, 2, \ldots, r) \\ B_n &= \frac{1}{L} \int_0^{2L} f(x) \sin \frac{n\pi x}{L} \, dx \quad (n = 1, 2, \ldots, r) \end{aligned} \right\} \quad (5\text{–}8)$$

For example, since the limits of integration are constants,

$$\frac{\partial}{\partial A_n} \int_0^{2L} [f(x) - S(x)]^2 \, dx = \int_0^{2L} \frac{\partial}{\partial A_n} [f(x) - S(x)]^2 \, dx$$

$$= 2 \int_0^{2L} [f(x) - S(x)] \left(-\cos \frac{n\pi x}{L} \right) dx = 0$$

Substituting in the series $S(x)$ and using Eqs. (5–3) and (5–4),

$$\int_0^{2L} f(x) \cos \frac{n\pi x}{L} \, dx = \int_0^{2L} A_n \cos^2 \left(\frac{n\pi x}{L} \right) dx = A_n L$$

Hence the first of Eqs. (5–8). Note that for given $f(x)$ the coefficients in Eq. (5–8) for the finite series in Eq. (5–7) are the same as those in Eq. (5–5) for the infinite series. This throws a new light on Fourier series: each of these coefficients is determined once and for all, and is independent of the number of terms used in the series.

Returning to the problem of numerical determination of the coefficients of the finite series in Eq. (5–7), we note that A_n and B_n in Eq. (5–8) are equal to twice the mean value of $f(x) \cos (n\pi x/L)$ and $f(x) \sin (n\pi x/L)$, respectively. With $2k$ known values of $f(x)$ evenly spaced in the period of $2L$, we have the following approximate values for A_n and B_n: with f_i indicating the ith value at $x = i\Delta x = iL/k$,

$$\left.\begin{aligned} A_n &\doteq \frac{1}{k} \sum_{i=1}^{2k} f_i \cos \frac{n\pi i}{k} \\ B_n &\doteq \frac{1}{k} \sum_{i=1}^{2k} f_i \sin \frac{n\pi i}{k} \end{aligned}\right\} \tag{5–9}$$

For an example of computing the coefficients by using Eq. (5–9), see Example 5–5.

Example 5–5. In Fig. 5–12 are shown eight evenly spaced values of a periodic function $f(x)$ with a period of 2π. Compute the five coefficients of the finite Fourier series

$$f(x) \doteq \frac{A_0}{2} + \sum_{n=1}^{2} (A_n \cos nx + B_n \sin nx)$$

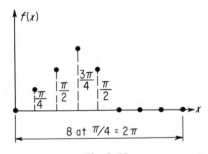

Fig. 5–12

Here $2k = 8$. The computation according to Eq. (5–9) is shown in Tables 5–1 and 5–2, which are self-explanatory. Thus

$$f(x) \doteq \frac{\pi}{4} - \frac{\pi}{8} \left(1 + \frac{1}{\sqrt{2}}\right) \cos x + \frac{\pi}{4} \left(\frac{1}{\sqrt{2}} + \frac{1}{2}\right) \sin x - \frac{\pi}{8} \sin 2x$$

TABLE 5–1

i	$\dfrac{i\pi}{k}$	$n=0$ $f(x)$	$n=1$ $\cos\dfrac{i\pi}{k}$	$f\cos\dfrac{i\pi}{k}$	$n=2$ $\cos\dfrac{2i\pi}{k}$	$f\cos\dfrac{2i\pi}{k}$
1	$\dfrac{\pi}{4}$	$\dfrac{\pi}{4}$	$\dfrac{1}{\sqrt{2}}$	$\dfrac{\pi}{4\sqrt{2}}$	0	0
2	$\dfrac{\pi}{2}$	$\dfrac{\pi}{2}$	0	0	-1	$\dfrac{-\pi}{2}$
3	$\dfrac{3\pi}{4}$	$\dfrac{3\pi}{4}$	$\dfrac{-1}{\sqrt{2}}$	$\dfrac{-3\pi}{4\sqrt{2}}$	0	0
4	π	$\dfrac{\pi}{2}$	-1	$\dfrac{-\pi}{2}$	1	$\dfrac{\pi}{2}$
5	$\dfrac{5\pi}{4}$	0	$\dfrac{-1}{\sqrt{2}}$	0	0	0
6	$\dfrac{3\pi}{2}$	0	0	0	-1	0
7	$\dfrac{7\pi}{4}$	0	$\dfrac{1}{\sqrt{2}}$	0	0	0
8	2π	0	1	0	1	0
		$\Sigma = 2\pi$	$\Sigma = -\dfrac{\pi}{2}\left(1+\dfrac{1}{\sqrt{2}}\right)$		$\Sigma = 0$	
		$A_0 = \dfrac{\pi}{2}$	$A_1 = -\dfrac{\pi}{8}\left(1+\dfrac{1}{\sqrt{2}}\right)$		$A_2 = 0$	

TABLE 5–2

i	$\dfrac{i\pi}{k}$	$f(x)$	$n = 1$		$n = 2$	
			$\sin\dfrac{i\pi}{k}$	$f\sin\dfrac{i\pi}{k}$	$\sin\dfrac{2i\pi}{k}$	$f\sin\dfrac{2i\pi}{k}$
1	$\dfrac{\pi}{4}$	$\dfrac{\pi}{4}$	$\dfrac{1}{\sqrt{2}}$	$\dfrac{\pi}{4\sqrt{2}}$	1	$\dfrac{\pi}{4}$
2	$\dfrac{\pi}{2}$	$\dfrac{\pi}{2}$	1	$\dfrac{\pi}{2}$	0	0
3	$\dfrac{3\pi}{4}$	$\dfrac{3\pi}{4}$	$\dfrac{1}{\sqrt{2}}$	$\dfrac{3\pi}{4\sqrt{2}}$	-1	$\dfrac{-3\pi}{4}$
4	π	$\dfrac{\pi}{2}$	0	0	0	0
5	$\dfrac{5\pi}{4}$	0	$\dfrac{-1}{\sqrt{2}}$	0	1	0
6	$\dfrac{3\pi}{2}$	0	-1	0	0	0
7	$\dfrac{7\pi}{4}$	0	$\dfrac{-1}{\sqrt{2}}$	0	-1	0
8	2π	0	0	0	0	0

$$\Sigma = \pi\left(\frac{1}{\sqrt{2}}+\frac{1}{2}\right) \qquad\qquad \Sigma = \frac{-\pi}{2}$$

$$B_1 = \frac{\pi}{4}\left(\frac{1}{\sqrt{2}}+\frac{1}{2}\right) \qquad\qquad B_2 = \frac{-\pi}{8}$$

Three more Fourier coefficients can be computed from the given data in a similar manner, if desired. It can be shown that

$$A_3 = -\frac{\pi}{8}\left(1-\frac{1}{\sqrt{2}}\right), \quad A_4 = 0, \quad \text{and} \quad B_3 = \frac{\pi}{4}\left(\frac{1}{\sqrt{2}}-\frac{1}{2}\right)$$

In this example, it happens that the same values for these eight coefficients are obtained from the eight given values of $f(x)$ by solving eight simultaneous algebraic equations, as suggested at the beginning of Art. 5–2.

The given values of $f(x)$ in Fig. 5–12 have been taken from Fig. 5–7. It is interesting to compare the coefficients A_n and B_n determined from a finite number of discrete values with the coefficients a_n and b_n (from Problem 5–5) determined with complete knowledge of $f(x)$:

$$A_0 = \pi/4, \quad A_1 = -0.67, \ A_2 = 0, \ A_3 = -0.12, \ A_4 = 0$$
$$a_0 = \pi/4, \quad a_1 = -0.64, \ a_2 = 0, \ a_3 = -0.07, \ a_4 = 0$$

$$B_1 = 0.95, \ B_2 = -0.39, \ B_3 = 0.16$$
$$b_1 = 1, \quad b_2 = -0.5, \quad b_3 = 0.33$$

Problem

5–12. In operating a scale model of a tidal estuary, it is desired to similate the tidal fluctuation of the surface elevation $f(t)$ of the sea by using three displacement plungers in simple harmonic motion. To design these plungers, it is necessary to determine the coefficients in the series

$$f(t) = \frac{A_0}{2} + \sum_{n=1}^{2} A_n \cos\frac{2n\pi t}{T} + B_1 \sin\frac{2\pi t}{T}$$

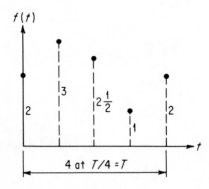

Fig. 5–13

Given four evenly spaced values of $f(t)$ in the period T, as shown in Fig. 5–13, find the coefficients in the series by the two methods presented in Art. 5–2.

INDEX

INDEX